Muyu Zhao
Lizhu Song
Xiaobao Fan

The Boundary Theory of Phase Diagrams and Its Application

Rules for Phase Diagram Construction with Phase Regions and Their Boundaries

Muyu Zhao
Lizhu Song
Xiaobao Fan

The Boundary Theory of Phase Diagrams and Its Application

Rules for Phase Diagram Construction with Phase Regions and Their Boundaries

With 72 figures

Science Press
Beijing

Springer

Authors
Muyu Zhao
College of Chemistry
Jilin University
Changchun, 130012, China
Email: muyuzhao1929@yahoo.com.cn

Lizhu Song
College of Chemistry
Jilin University
Changchun, 130012, China
Email: slz@jlu.edu.cn

Xiaobao Fan
Tekna Plasma Systems, Inc.
Sherbrooke, Canada
Email: xiaobao.fan@tekna.com

ISBN 978-7-03-024458-1
Science Press Beijing

ISBN 978-3-642-02939-4 e-ISBN 978-3-642-02940-0
Springer Dordrecht Heidelberg London New York

Library of Congress Control Number: 2009930027

Cover design: Frido Steinen-Broo, EStudio Calamar, Spain

Printed on acid-free paper

Springer is a part of Springer Science+Business Media (www.springer.com)

Preface

The phase diagram is one of the most extensively used disciplines in the Applied Sciences. They are relevant to different areas both in science and engineering, as well as to the various branches of the national economy. In many scientific and technical specialties, such as physics, chemistry, geology, materials science and technology, chemical engineering, *etc,* it is easy to find its application that strongly shows the importance of phase diagram in the science and technology today.

In the early stages of development, phase diagrams were mainly obtained from experimental measurements. With the increasing number of the system components as well as the severe demands placed on experimental materials requiring corrosion-resistant, heat-resistant, *etc,* the experimental methods were no longer able to meet these requirements, especially with respect to generating multi-component phase diagrams. The theoretical calculation of phase diagram has now become the principal method for obtaining the desired phase diagrams. This route has been especially favored by the rapid advance of research and development in computer science and technology that induced the "art" of phase diagram calculation to a new level. Under these circumstances, the continuing research on the theory of phase diagrams has recently and naturally becomes the topic of great and lasting interest, to both applied scientists and engineers alike.

Research on the theory of phase diagrams may be divided into two categories. The first category involves the research needed to study the necessary conditions that all phase diagrams must satisfy. For instance, abstracting the physical concepts from concrete phase diagrams such as the specific number of phases, the number of independent components, the degrees of freedom, *etc;* and then establishing the relationship between these parameters belong the first category work, though, that can not be used to construct a specific phase diagram, they are strict and absolute and give an universal principle in evaluating a particular phase diagram obtained from experiments. Any phase diagram violating this relationship must be incorrect. The second category of theory concerns the sufficient conditions for a concrete phase diagram; they study the quantitative relation of the thermodynamic properties of each component in specific phase equilibrium with temperature, pressure and composition, *etc.* Based on this quantitative relation, a complete and specific phase diagram can be constructed. This particular topic has attracted many scientists and researchers devoting their efforts in this subject over recent years. The combination of these two category theories has constituted a whole theory of phase diagram.

The great thermodynamic and statistical physicist Josiah Willard Gibbs, was the founder of the theory of the first category. The "phase rule" derived by him is a typical classic work in this aspect. After Gibbs, many scientists, for example, Palatnik and Landau, and various other scholars engaged in the research undertaken by this circle, achieved some success. The great scientist and the founder of solid state chemistry, Carl Wagner, was the pioneer of the theory for the second category. Early in those years, in which the computer was becoming developed, he had pointed to the importance of studying the relation between the phase diagrams and the materials thermodynamic properties. The relation existing between the phase boundaries and the corresponding thermodynamic properties, as deduced by him, are still extensively applied today. Other scientists, for example, Hildebrand, Mitering, Richardson, *et al.*, have also made important contributions. The CALPHAD technology has played a great role for promoting the calculation of phase diagrams. It is worthy mentioning that the Chinese scholars have also made some significant contribution in both of these two category works that shouldn't be ignored.

Through his deep level research over several decades, Professor Muyu Zhao has made a significant contribution to the research on the theory of phase diagrams. For the theory of the first category, he has systematically deduced new ideas, derived a series of new relation, constructed a whole and unique systematic theory, and applied it to real phase diagrams, obtaining good results in the process. In addition to this considerable task, he has also undertaken many pioneering works, involving both experimental and theoretical research on high pressure phase diagrams.

In his book *The Boundary Theory of Phase Diagrams and Its Application*, Professor Muyu Zhao has collected the results of his research over several decades, and presented them systematically and completely, as his substantial theoretical works. Besides this work on the theory of the first category, as mentioned above, this book also contains the contents and related works on the second category. We sincerely hope that the publication of this book will bring some new energy to the phase diagram research.

Kuo-Chih Chou

Professor, University of Science and Technology Beijing
Member of Chinese Academy of Sciences

Beijing, 18 January 2008

Comment

There are two main rules governing the construction and interpretation of phase diagrams, the phase rule by Gibbs and the contact rule by Palatnik and Landau. Many years ago professor Muyu Zhao was intrigued by the fact that both rules need special instructions when applied to mixed phase diagrams, *i.e.*, diagrams with both potential and molar axes. This has caused much confusion for generations of students of materials science and has forced teachers to invent explanations that can be criticized by observant students. It is evident that there is a considerable need for better understanding of these difficulties. The reason of the difficulties is that the phase rule is strictly valid for diagrams with only potential axes and the contact rule for diagrams with only molar axes. In practice, it is more common to use a mixture of axes, *e.g.* the temperature-mole fraction diagrams, which is the type the students are first confronted with.

Professor Zhao has devoted many years of interest and energy to resolve these difficulties and he is to be congratulated finally to be able to present his results in a monograph that will give a wider audience a chance to get a coherent picture of his work.

Dr. Mats Hillert

Emeritus Professor at
Dept. of Materials Science and Engineering
KTH (Royal Institute of Technology)
SE-10044, Stockholm, Sweden

Stockholm, 16 March 2008

Introduction

Phase diagrams are among the most extensively used guides in materials science and engineering, and constitute the basic roadmap for alloy designers.

In its simple form, phase diagram consists of phase regions and their boundaries. The aim of the present text is to discuss the problem of how the phase regions and their boundaries compose a phase diagram.

We have studied the relationship among neighboring phase regions and their boundaries for nearly thirty years. Over this time, a few new concepts have been introduced, and, by application of the relevant thermodynamic principles, a systematic boundary theory of phase diagrams has been worked out. In this approach, all the relationships among the neighboring phase regions and their boundaries, for both simple and more complex, multicomponent phase diagrams, of all types, can be satisfactorily explained by reference to the so called "The boundary theory".

In this book, we contribute the most volume to discuss the isobaric T-x_i phase diagrams. However, with the generalized boundary theory for the p-T-x_i multicomponent phase diagram, this theory is easily to apply in p-T phase diagrams and those diagrams with only mole fraction axes. In the p-T-x_i multicomponent phase diagram, if we keep the pressure and temperature constant, or keep the compositions invariable, it will be the "pure" mole fraction-mole fraction, or potential P-T axes phase diagram. We have discussed these problems in Chapter 3, section 3.6 and Chapter 9, sections 9.2 and 9.3.

Moreover, we have found that there is a lot of application for the boundary theory, and thus we have written a substantial chapter to discuss the important application. In that chapter, the use of the boundary theory of phase diagrams in some specific roles, *e.g.* calculation, determination, assessment and comprehension of phase diagrams, is discussed. Based on the boundary theory, we have designed a new method for the determination of the multicomponent isothermal sections (see Chapter 7, section 7.5).

Professors at several universities in China have taught the boundary theory and its application, in those courses concerned with the phase diagram theory and its practice. One of these professors has told the author of this book: "The students are interested in this theory and, $\cdots$ via its application in some representative examples, are able to learn much from it."

Thus, in this book, we have specially concentrated on and discussed the following 6 points:

1. We discriminate the conception of "phase point" and "system point" in phase diagrams, and find the "phase boundary", besides the "boundary" in common sense, is a real entity within the phase diagrams (see Chapter 2, subsection 2.2.8). Based on this concept and on other thermodynamic principles, we may proceed to construct a boundary theory of phase diagrams.

2. There is a certain relationship between the dimension of phase boundary and the number of total different phases in neighboring phase regions. A theorem describes this relationship. We clearly demonstrate that the "theorem of the corresponding relationship" (TCR) is indeed a fully independent theorem, and is not a variation of the phase rule (see Chapter 2, section 2.4).

3. Two equations of the relation among the dimensions of the phase boundary and the dimensions of the boundary are derived. This is the "boundary theory", the very core of this monograph, which explains well the different types of phase transitions within phase diagram. Thence, the rule of how the phase regions compose a phase diagram has been expounded (see Chapter 2, section 2.6).

4. We have compared the differences between the Palatnik-Landau's "contact rule" for the phase regions, and the "boundary theory" in details (see Chapter 3, section 3.6) and conclusions of the added value of the boundary theory can be appreciated.

5. Gupta's overlapping ZPF (Zero Phase Fraction) lines method for the construction of multicomponent isothermal sections, with limited information, is a very important method and widely applied in phase diagram calculation. The boundary theory, on the other hand, provides an alternative under the same circumstance (see Chapter 5, sections 5.3 and 5.4). To determine experimentally isothermal multicomponent sections, the boundary theory may be more useful (see Chapter 5, section 5.5). Based on the boundary theory, we have designed a new method to determine isothermal multicomponent sections (see Chapter 7, section 7.5).

6. A more general boundary theory of the multi-component p-T-x_i phase diagrams is described in Chapter 8. Applying this theory, we have worked out a thermodynamic method for calculating the multicomponent, high-pressure phase diagrams. We have been able to calculate high-pressure phase diagrams not only for binary, but also ternary alloys. The high pressure (up to several GPa) phase diagrams of the Cd-Pb-Sn and Cd-Sn-Zn systems are calculated, and verified by reference to the experimentally derived phase diagrams. These calculated high-pressure binary and ternary alloy phase diagrams agree well with the experimentally derived ones (see Chapters 8, 9, 10 and 11).

When we finally finished this book and could communicate our readers with our research results, we would like to offer our sincere thanks to all the graduate students who involved in this work: Drs Weiya Zhou, Ping Xiao, and Zezhong Fu, they did most of the calculations and/or determination of phase diagrams relevant to the boundary theory. We offer our sincere thanks to Professor Zhongyi Shen (Institute of Physics, Beijing, Chinese Academy of Sciences), for his cooperation in the high-pressure phase diagram experiments; to Professor Guanghui Rao (Institute of Physics, Beijing, Chinese Academy of Sciences), for helping me to prepare a manuscript in the early time, to Mr. Hai Huang (Science Press, Beijing), for helping us to publish this work.

Our special gratitude goes to Professor Mats Hillert (Royal Institute of Technology in Stockholm, Sweden) for his attention to and recognition of this work, and discussion with us on boundary theory over a long time; to Dr. Patrice E. A. Turchi (LLNL, Livermore, USA) for his appreciation of our work and valuable advices; and to Dr. Peter G. Lanigan (Researcher and writer, University of Sherbrooke, Canada), who gave his kind help and encouragement as a veteran industrial researcher in chemistry and metallurgy, particularly for his patient proof-reading and "text polishing" over the whole book.

Acknowledgements: This work was supported by the National Natural Science Foundation of China.

Muyu Zhao

College of Chemistry, Jilin University
Changchun, China
e-mail: muyuzhao1929@yahoo.com.cn

Contents

Part One

The Phase Rule, Its Deduction and Application

Chapter 1

The Phase Rule, Its Deduction and Application

1.1 Why do We Discuss the Phase Rule at First

The Gibbs phase rule is now a long established principle of Chemistry, very well known by all physical chemists and materials scientists. So, why do we still need to write a chapter to discuss this classic, fundamental law of Chemical science, at the outset of this treatise?

Textbooks, as published for the explanation of physical chemistry and the use of phase diagrams, usually present only a simple method for the "deduction" of the phase rule. However, the original "rule" as deduced by Gibbs himself, is both strict and well thought-out, indeed students can learn much from his method. The Gibbs-Roozebooms method, though simple, is, nevertheless, full of wisdom. The deduction of the phase rule under the circumstance, involving particular chemical reactions, by application of the mathematical method of Gibbs free energy minimization, is today, only presented in a few monographs. By means of this method however, both the phase rule, and the law of mass action used for the chemical equilibrium, are successfully deduced. This is indeed a very interesting circumstance.

When applying the phase rule, an important and difficult problem to treat is the determination of the number of independent components involved. Generally, ordinary Physical Chemistry texts only present Jouguet's method for the deduction of this number and do not discuss either the strengths and or the shortcomings, of this method. Here, we present another useful approach, *i.e.* that of the Brinkley's method and these two methods will be shortly compared in detail.

The application of the phase rule is generally not a very easy task, so here we will also address some brief remarks to the resolution of this problem.

Usually, we apply the phase rule and then discuss the differences between the phase rule predictions and our theory, as set out in detail in Chapter 2. Therefore, at first, a special introductory chapter is now provided, being devoted to a discussion of the phase rule.

1.2 Different Methods for Deducing the Phase Rule: The Method of Gibbs Himself, Gibbs-Roozeboom's Method and the Method of Gibbs Free Energy Minimization

The phase rule is the most important principle concerning the phase equilibrium. In 1875–1878, the now famous physicist J. Willard Gibbs established the phase rule. Because his work was published in the rather obscure *Transactions of the Connecticut Academy*, and the phase rule itself, was embedded in an abstruse mathematical feature, this rule did not initially attract much attention in scientific circles until Roozeboom "stripped off" its abstract mathematical disguise, and exposed its physical meanings, thereafter using it to analyze some concrete heterogeneous equilibria. Nowadays, the importance of the phase rule is very widely recognized. Thus, it is used not only to summarize vast and diverse equilibrium regularities, but it is also used in the study of unknown systems, acting as an effectual guidance tool.

Although it is now more than a century that has passed since the phase rule was established, and there have been a large number of books expounding its qualities, there is yet still a necessity for studying the precise understanding and application of the phase rule.

The phase rule itself can be deduced in different ways. Even though the same result is achieved from these different approaches, they do not, by any means, amount to mere repetition. The different deduction routes help us to penetrate the phase rule from different viewpoints, and, at the same time, to both widen and enliven our philosophical thoughts as well.

1.2.1 The deduction of the phase rule in the circumstances without chemical reaction

1.2.1.1 Gibbs' method [Gibbs, 1950]

Gibbs studied a closed system and assumed that entropy S and volume V of the system were kept constant, the equilibrium condition of the system would be: the internal energy U of the system must be at a minimum.

Supposing that there is a closed system, and that each component is distributed in every phase and is mobile among these phases. U, V, S, p, T and M are the internal energy, volume, entropy, pressure, temperature and the total molar number of the entire system, respectively. M_i and x_i are the mole number and mole fraction of i-th component in the system. u_j, v_j, s_j, p_j, t_j and m_j are the internal energy, volume, entropy, pressure, temperature and mole number of the j-th phase of the system, respectively. m_{ij}, x_{ij} and μ_{ij} are the mole number, mole fraction and chemical potential of i-th component in the j-th phase. N is the number of components and ϕ is the number of phases existing in the system. In these circumstances, one then has the following straightforward relationship

$$x_i = M_i/M \quad (i = 1, 2, \cdots, N) \tag{1-1}$$

$$x_{ij} = m_{ij}/m_j \quad (i = 1, 2, \cdots, N; j = 1, 2, \cdots, \phi) \tag{1-2}$$

$$\sum_i x_i = 1, \quad \sum_i x_{ij} = 1 \quad (j = 1, 2, \cdots, \phi) \tag{1-3}$$

$$\sum_i m_{ij} = m_j \quad (i = 1, 2, \cdots, N) \tag{1-4}$$

$$\sum_j m_{ij} = M_i \quad (j = 1, 2, \cdots, \phi) \tag{1-4a}$$

$$\sum_j m_j = M \quad (j = 1, 2, \cdots, \phi) \tag{1-5}$$

According to thermodynamic principles, the internal energy of each phase, u_j, is a function of the entropy, volume and all of the mole numbers of the j-th phase.

$$u_j = u_j(s_j, v_j, m_{1j}, m_{2j}, \cdots, m_{Nj}) \tag{1-6}$$

The total differential of u_j can be represented as follows:

$$du_j = \left(\frac{\partial u_j}{\partial s_j}\right)_{v_j, m_{ij}} ds_j + \left(\frac{\partial u_j}{\partial v_j}\right)_{s_j, m_{ij}} dv_j + \sum_i \left(\frac{\partial u_j}{\partial m_{ij}}\right)_{s_j, v_j} dm_{ij}, \quad (j = 1, 2, \cdots, \phi) \tag{1-7}$$

or

$$du_j = t_j ds_j - p_j dv_j + \sum_i \mu_{ij} dm_{ij}, \quad (j = 1, 2, \cdots, \phi) \tag{1-8}$$

Where:

$$t_j = \left(\frac{\partial u_j}{\partial s_j}\right)_{v_j, m_{ij}}, \quad (j = 1, 2, \cdots, \phi) \tag{1-9}$$

$$p_j = -\left(\frac{\partial u_j}{\partial v_j}\right)_{s_j, m_{ij}}, \quad (j = 1, 2, \cdots, \phi) \tag{1-10}$$

$$\mu_{i,j} = \frac{\partial u_j}{\partial m_{i,j}}, \quad (i = 1, 2, \cdots, N; j = 1, 2, \cdots, \phi) \tag{1-11}$$

If the values of s, v and M_i of the system are kept constant, *i.e.*,

$$\delta S = \delta s_1 + \delta s_2 + \cdots + \delta s_\phi = 0 \tag{1-12}$$

$$\delta V = \delta v_1 + \delta v_2 + \cdots + \delta v_\phi = 0 \tag{1-13}$$

$$\delta M_i = \delta m_{i1} + \delta m_{i2} + \cdots + \delta m_{i\phi} = 0 \quad (i = 1, 2, \cdots, N) \tag{1-14}$$

Then equilibrium condition of the system will be:

$$\delta U = \delta u_1 + \delta u_2 + \cdots + \delta u_\phi \geqslant 0 \tag{1-15}$$

Substituting eq.(1-8) into eq. (1-15), it follows that:

$$\delta U = \sum_{j=1}^{\phi}(t_j \delta s_j + p_j \delta v_j) + \sum_{j=1}^{\phi}\sum_{i=1}^{N} \mu_{ij}\delta m_{ij} \geqslant 0 \tag{1-16}$$

Expressing the variations, $\delta m_{ij}, \delta s_{ij}$ and δv_{ij}, of the q-th phase by the corresponding variations of the other phases, and in making use of eqs. (1-12)–(1-14), one has:

$$\delta s_q = -\sum_{j=1}^{\phi}{}' \delta s_j \tag{1-17}$$

$$\delta v_q = -\sum_{j=1}^{\phi}{}' \delta v_j \tag{1-18}$$

$$\delta m_{iq} = -\sum_{j=1}^{\phi}{}' \delta m_{ij} \tag{1-19}$$

The symbol $\sum'$ denotes the summation over all j's except $j = q$. Substituting the eqs.(1-17)–(1-19) into eq.(1-16), each item of eq.(1-16) can be written in the following form:

$$\begin{aligned}\sum_{j=1}^{\phi} t_i \delta s_j &= \sum_{j=1}^{\phi}{}' t_j \delta s_j + t_q \delta s_q \\ &= \sum_{j=1}^{\phi}{}' t_j \delta s_j - t_q \sum_{j=1}^{\phi}{}' \delta s_j \\ &= \sum_{j=1}^{\phi}{}' (t_j - t_q)\delta s_j\end{aligned}$$

Then eq.(1-16) may be written as:

$$dU = \sum_{j=1}^{\phi}{}'(t_j - t_q)\delta s_j - \sum_{j=1}^{\phi}{}'(p_j - p_q)\delta v_j + \sum_{i=1}^{N}\sum_{j=1}^{\phi}{}'(\mu_{ij} - \mu_{iq})\delta m_{ij} \geqslant 0 \tag{1-20}$$

All the variations remaining in eq.(1-20): $\delta s_1, \delta s_2, \cdots, \delta s_{q-1}, \delta s_{q+1}, \cdots, \delta s_\phi$; δv_1, $\delta v_2, \cdots, \delta v_{q-1}, \delta v_{q+1}, \cdots, \delta v_\phi$; $\delta m_{i1}, \delta m_{i2}, \cdots, \delta m_{i(q-1)}, \delta m_{i(q+1)}, \cdots, \delta m_{i\phi}$, $(i = 1, 2, \cdots, N)$ are completely independent of each other and may take positive, negative or zero values. It is easy to demonstrate that the coefficients of all the variations entering into the inequality (1-20) must be rigorously equal to zero; for if some of these coefficients had non-zero values, we could give the variations with positive coefficients negative values and the variations with negative coefficients positive values (since the variations are completely arbitrary). Then, the left-hand side of the inequality (1-20) would be negative. This is a violation of the equilibrium condition. Therefore, if the values of all the variations entering into the inequality (1-20) are completely independent, then all the coefficients must be equal to zero. This means that the left-hand side of the inequality (1-20) is rigorously equal to zero, and the following additional conditions, of necessity, must be satisfied:

$$\begin{aligned} p_j &= p_q, \quad (j = 1, 2, \cdots, q-1, q+1, \cdots, \phi) \\ t_j &= t_q, \quad (j = 1, 2, \cdots, q-1, q+1, \cdots, \phi) \\ \mu_{ij} &= \mu_{iq}, \quad (j = 1, 2, \cdots, q-1, q+1, \cdots, \phi) \end{aligned}$$

Thus, we arrive at the Gibbs' phase equilibrium relation:

$$t_1 = t_2 = \cdots = t_\phi = T \tag{1-21}$$

$$p_1 = p_2 = \cdots = p_\phi = p \tag{1-22}$$

$$\mu_{i1} = \mu_{i2} = \cdots = \mu_{i\phi} = \mu_i, \quad (i = 1, 2, \cdots, N) \tag{1-23}$$

From these relations, the phase rule may be derived. Thus, for the system considered, there are $(N\phi+2)$ parameters: T, p and $N\phi$ concentration parameters. In accordance with eq. (1-23), there are $N(\phi-1)$ phase equilibrium conditions, and ϕ normalization conditions:

$$\sum_i x_{ij} = 1 \quad (j = 1, 2, \cdots, \phi) \tag{1-3}$$

There are $N(\phi+1)+\phi$ equilibrium conditions in total. Therefore, the number of degrees of freedom for the system must be:

$$f = N\phi + 2 - [N(\phi-1) + \phi] = N - \phi + 2 \tag{1-24}$$

This is the well known phase rule.

In the above derivation, it is assumed that each component exists in each and every phase of the system. In fact, this assumption is unnecessary. Even though some components are absent from some phases, the phase rule still holds. For example, the k-th component is absent from the l-th phase, *i.e.* $m_{kl} = 0$, and let the appearance of this k-th component in the l-th phase not be excluded. Then, the variation, δm_{kl}, can not have a negative value, for the mole number of the k-th component in the l-th phase can not be less than zero. In this case, it can not follow from eq. (1-20) that the chemical potential μ_{kl} of the k-th component in the l-th phase should necessarily be equal to the chemical potentials, $\mu_{k1}, \mu_{k2}, \cdots, \mu_{k(l-1)}, \mu_{k(l+1)}, \cdots, \mu_{k\phi}$, of the k-th component in other phase. However, eq.(1-20) does require that μ_{kl} should not be less than the other μ_{kj}. If $\mu_{kl} < \mu_{kj} (j \neq l)$, the k-th component would automatically transit from the j-th phase into the l-th phase, in order to decrease the total energy of the system, therefore, the condition

$$\mu_{kl} > \mu_{kj}, \quad (j = 1, 2, \cdots, l-1, l+1, \cdots, \phi) \tag{1-25}$$

is required to describe the fact that the k-th component is absent from the l-th phase, while its appearance is not excluded. (Note: $\delta m_{kl} \geqslant 0$, and can not be a negative variation, eq.(1-25) is consistent with eq.(1-16) or eq.(1-20))

The physical meaning of eq. (1-25) is that the work that must be performed to introduce k-th component into l-th phase is no less than those to introduce it into other phases, so that the k-th component existing in other phases can not automatically shift to the l-th phase. This is the reason that there is no k-th component in the l-th phase. The situation, *i.e.* that some components are absent from some phases, does not warrant the denial of the relevant chemical potential. However, this chemical potential no longer participates in the eq. (1-23), thereby decreasing by one the total number of the equilibrium relation. That is to say, if a component is absent in any phase, the numbers of the concentration parameters, and the equilibrium conditions, will be decreased simultaneously by one. Therefore, the expression (1-24) of the phase rule is still valid.

The above deduction of the phase rule is the original version advanced by J. Willard Gibbs himself; it is both rigorous and full of wisdom!

1.2.1.2 Gibbs-Roozeboom's method

Let us select temperature T, pressure p and the chemical potentials of all components as the parameters. Under the circumstance of phase equilibria, the chemical potentials of an independent component in the different phases are the same. If there are N components in the system, there must be N different chemical potentials to describe them respectively. The number of all the independent parameters is $N+2$. There exists one equation of state concerning the $(N+2)$ parameters in every phase: $F_j(T, p, \mu_1, \mu_2, \cdots, \mu_N) = 0 (j = 1, 2, \cdots, \phi)$, and there are ϕ state equations in all. Thereafter, the number of degrees of freedom of the equilibrium system is:

$$f = N + 2 - \phi \tag{1-26}$$

Laconic as the method is, the physical meanings of every term in the phase rule are expressed very distinctly. N refers the number of the chemical potentials of the independent components, 2 are temperature and pressure of the system, $N+2$ is the number of the independent parameters of the system, ϕ is the number of state equations, so the number of degrees of freedom is $(N+2-\phi)$. It is really admirable that the phase rule, as used so widely, can be derived in such a brief way, in addition to each term having its own, distinct physical meaning. This derivation provides us with enlightenment that one must have a profound and distinct grasp of the nature of a matter such that one may well know the inherent relationship and thence reveal the relative laws of relationship so readily.

1.2.2 The determination of the phase rule involving the circumstances of chemical reactions, the method of the Gibbs free energy minimization

If there are phase transitions and chemical reactions simultaneously existing in a multicomponent heterogeneous system, the equilibrium of the system can only be achieved when conditions of both the phase equilibrium and the chemical equilibrium are satisfied. At the constant T and p, the Gibbs free energy of the system must be at a minimum.

Based on the principle of Gibbs free energy minimization, the conditions for phase equilibrium and chemical equilibrium can both be deduced simultaneously. In other words, one may obtain the results of the application, of the phase rule and the law of mass action, on the chemical reactions at the same time. Unfortunately, the deduction is rather long, although quite interesting.

1.2.2.1 The chemical formulas for both the independent components and the derived components and the relation existing between them

Let us first discuss some important concepts. Suppose that there are N components in the system, they may be as molecules or as ions, *i.e.* various chemical species. Let A_i be their formula, $i=1,2,\cdots,N$. They are distributed over some ϕ phases. In the state of constant T and p, the system may achieve both phase equilibrium and chemical equilibrium. Thence, by assuming that there are r' possible chemical reactions, including both the dependent and independent ones, among the N components, all of the chemical reactions can be written as follows:

$$\sum_{i=1}^{N} \nu_{ji} A_i = 0, \quad (j=1,2,\cdots,r') \tag{1-27}$$

Or in the matrix form:

$$\begin{bmatrix} \nu_{1,1} & \cdots & \nu_{1,i} & \cdots & \nu_{1,N} \\ \vdots & & \vdots & & \vdots \\ \nu_{j,1} & \cdots & \nu_{j,i} & \cdots & \nu_{j,N} \\ \vdots & & \vdots & & \vdots \\ \nu_{r',1} & \cdots & \nu_{r',i} & \cdots & \nu_{r',N} \end{bmatrix} \begin{bmatrix} A_1 \\ \vdots \\ A_i \\ \vdots \\ A_N \end{bmatrix} = 0 \tag{1-28}$$

where ν_{ji} is the stoichiometric coefficient of component A_i in the j-th chemical reaction. For example, the j-th chemical reaction in the system is:

$$1 \times \mathrm{C} + 1 \times \mathrm{CO_2} - 2 \times \mathrm{CO} = 0$$

so $\nu_{j,\mathrm{CO}} = -2$. Some of the r' reactions are independent, while others are dependent. In accordance with mathematical principles, if the rank of the matrix be composed of ν_{ji}, is r, the number of independent reactions is r, *i.e.* there are only r independent reactions among the r' reactions mentioned above. All of the $r' - r$ remaining reactions can be derived as a linear combinations of the r independent reactions. Because there are r independent reactions among the N components, r independent equilibrium chemical conditions are required to describe them. Therefore, only the $(N - r)$ concentrations of the components are independent variables. The number of the independent components is thus:

$$C = N - r \tag{1-29}$$

Dividing the N components into two groups, i.e., those that are independent components, having the chemical formulas of $A_c, c = 1, 2, \cdots, C$, while the others consist of the derived components, whose chemical formulas are $A_k, k = C+1, C+2, \cdots, C+r = N, r$ in all. While it is sure that A_k can be written as a linear combinations of the $A_c, i.e.$ components, A_k may be obtained from the mutual reactions of the components, A_c.

$$\sum \nu_{kc} A_c = A_k \tag{1-30}$$

In recalling the example mentioned above, there is an independent reaction taking place among the C, CO and CO_2 components in the system. Let C and CO_2 be the independent components, then the derived component, CO, may be written as:

$$\frac{1}{2}\mathrm{C} + \frac{1}{2}\mathrm{CO_2} = \mathrm{CO} \tag{1-31}$$

Further, suppose that M elements constitute the N components, and the element symbols are referred to by $E_e, e = 1, 2, \cdots, M$, then the chemical formula for any component can be written as a linear combinations of the elemental symbols

$$A_c = \sum_{e=1}^{M} a_{ce} \times E_e, \quad (C = 1, 2, \cdots, C) \tag{1-32}$$

$$A_k = \sum_{e=1}^{M} a_{ke} \times E_e, \quad (k = C+1, C+2, \cdots, N) \tag{1-33}$$

a_{ce}, a_{ke} are the stoichiometric coefficient of E_e, constituting A_c and A_k respectively. The above system can be rewritten as:

$$A_c \quad \mathrm{C} = 1 \times \mathrm{C} + 0 \times \mathrm{O} \tag{1-34}$$

$$\mathrm{CO_2} = 1 \times \mathrm{C} + 2 \times \mathrm{O} \tag{1-35}$$

$$A_k \quad \mathrm{CO} = 1 \times \mathrm{C} + 1 \times \mathrm{O} \tag{1-36}$$

All a_{ke} can thus be expressed through the linear combinations of a_{ce} :

$$a_{ke} = \sum_{e=1}^{M} \nu_{kc} \times a_{ce} \tag{1-37}$$

According to eq. (1-31) above, CO is formed by C and CO_2. Atoms C and O of the molecule CO come from C and CO_2 respectively. The coefficients of atoms C and O in CO are also from those coefficients of the atoms of C and CO_2 in eq. (1-31).

$$a_{\mathrm{CO,C}} = \nu_{\mathrm{CO,C}} \times a_{\mathrm{C,C}} + \nu_{\mathrm{CO,CO_2}} \times a_{\mathrm{CO_2,C}} = \frac{1}{2} \times 1 + \frac{1}{2} \times 1 = 1$$

$$a_{\mathrm{CO,O}} = \nu_{\mathrm{CO,C}} \times a_{\mathrm{C,O}} + \nu_{\mathrm{CO,CO_2}} \times a_{\mathrm{CO_2,O}} = \frac{1}{2} \times 0 + \frac{1}{2} \times 2 = 1$$

$$\mathrm{CO} = a_{\mathrm{CO,C}} \times \mathrm{C} + a_{\mathrm{CO,O}} \times \mathrm{O} = 1 \times \mathrm{C} + 1 \times \mathrm{O}$$

These are the chemical formulas for both the independent components and for the derived components, and for the relation between them.

1.2.2.2 The derivation of the conditions of chemical equilibria and phase equilibria [Van Zeggeren and Story, 1970; Zemansky, 1968]

Let m_{cj}, m_{kj}, μ_{cj} and μ_{kj} be the mole numbers and the chemical potentials of the independent component A_c, and the derived component A_k, in the j-th phase respectively. The Gibbs free energy of the system can then be written as:

$$G = \sum_j \sum_c m_{cj} \times \mu_{cj} + \sum_j \sum_k m_{kj} \times \mu_{kj} \tag{1-38}$$

Each element in the system follows the conservation of mass condition:

$$\sum_j \sum_c m_{cj} \times a_{ce} + \sum_j \sum_k m_{kj} \times a_{ke} - M_e = 0 \quad (e = 1, 2, \cdots, M) \tag{1-39}$$

M_e is the total mole number of the element e in the system, which may also be called the element abundance, $e = 1, 2, \cdots, M$. In a closed system, and, irrespective of whatever chemical reactions and phase transitions that may occur, the total mole number of each element in the system is invariant.

At constant p and T, the equilibrium condition of the system is that where the Gibbs free energy of the system is at its minimum, presupposing that constrained conditions, eqs.(1-39), are satisfied. The usual method employed to solve such questions is the Lagrange's uncertain factor method. Let the function L be

$$L = G - \sum_e \lambda_e \times \left[\sum_j \sum_c m_{cj} \times a_{ce} + \sum_j \sum_k m_{kj} \times a_{kj} - M_e\right] \tag{1-40}$$

This corresponds to multiplying every equation of the eqs. (1-39) by the factor λ_e, then adding the Gibbs free energy of the system, G. The variables in function L are m_{cj} and m_{kj}. To satisfy the constrained conditions (1-39), and the minimization of G, let

$$\frac{\partial L}{\partial m_{cj}} = 0 \tag{1-41}$$

$$\frac{\partial L}{\partial m_{kj}} = 0 \tag{1-42}$$

If $\dfrac{\partial L}{\partial m_{cj}} = 0$

$$\mu_{cj} - \sum_e \lambda_e \times a_{ce} = 0, \quad (c = 1, 2, \cdots, C; j = 1, 2, \cdots, \phi) \tag{1-43}$$

If $\dfrac{\partial L}{\partial m_{kj}} = 0$

$$\mu_{kj} - \sum_e \lambda_e \times a_{ke} = 0, \quad (k = C+1, C+2, \cdots, N; j = 1, 2, \cdots, \phi) \tag{1-44}$$

In substituting (1-37) into (1-44), the substitution gives rise to

$$\mu_{kj} - \sum_e \lambda_e \times \left[\sum_c \nu_{kc} \times a_{ce}\right] = \mu_{kj} - \sum_c \nu_{kc} \times \sum_e [\lambda_e \times a_{ce}] = 0 \tag{1-45}$$

Similarly, in substituting (1-43) into (1-45), one also gives rise to

$$\mu_{kj} - \sum_c \nu_{kc} \times \mu_{cj} = 0, \quad (k = C+1, \cdots, N; j = 1, 2, \cdots, \phi) \tag{1-46}$$

Let us now consider the meanings of eqs. (1-43), (1-44) and (1-46). In eq. (1-43), λ_e and a_{ce} are all constants, as is $\sum\limits_e \lambda_e \times a_{ce}$. This means that μ_{cj} in any phase is the same constant, *i.e.*

$$\mu_{c1} = \mu_{c2} = \cdots = \mu_{c\phi} = \mu_c \quad (c = 1, 2, \cdots, C) \tag{1-47}$$

In the similar way, $\sum_e \lambda_e \times a_{ke}$ in eq. (1-44) is also constant, then

$$\mu_{k1} = \mu_{k2} = \cdots = \mu_{k\phi} = \mu_k, \quad (k = C+1, C+2, \cdots, N) \tag{1-48}$$

All of these eqs.(1-47) and (1-48), are the phase equilibrium conditions. The μ_k parameter, however, is not independent, and can be obtained through a linear combination of μ_c, in accordance with eqs. (1-46), (1-47) and (1-48). Hence

$$\mu_k = \sum_c \nu_{kc}\mu_c, \quad (k = C+1, \cdots, N) \tag{1-49}$$

Eq. (1-49) is just the condition for the chemical equilibrium conditions. By inserting the following equation into eq. (1-49)

$$\mu_i = \mu_i^0 + RT\ln p_i \tag{1-50}$$

$$\mu_i = \mu_i^* + RT\ln x_i \tag{1-51}$$

(μ_i^0 and μ_i^* are the chemical potentials in their standard states), one will achieve the mass action law:

$$p_k^{-1}\prod_c p_c^{\nu_{kc}} = K_{pk} \tag{1-52}$$

$$x_k^{-1}\prod_c x_c^{\nu_{kc}} = K_{ck} \tag{1-53}$$

In eq. (1-49), $k = C+1, \cdots, N$, there are $N-C = r$ chemical equilibrium conditions.

Finally, the phase rule can be deduced as follows. Because the independent parameters are restricted by the phase equilibrium conditions, the chemical potential of each component in all phases must be equal to each other, as presented in eqs. (1-47) and (1-48). There are C different μ_c and $(N-C)$ different μ_k. In taking the temperature and pressure into account, the total number of independent parameters is $(N+2)$ in all. There are r chemical equilibrium conditions in eq. (1-49) and ϕ state equations for all the phases. Therefore, the number of degrees of freedom, *i.e.* the number of the remaining parameters that can be varied independently is

$$f = N + 2 - r - \phi = (N - r) - \phi + 2 = C - \phi + 2 \tag{1-54}$$

$C = N - r$, is the number of the independent components. This is just the phase rule in the particular circumstance with chemical reactions. If there are other independent constraining conditions, regarding the concentrations of these components $\left(\text{condition } \sum x_{ij} = 1 \text{ is exclusive}\right)$, *e.g.*, Z such conditions, the number of degrees of freedom of the system will accordingly be decreased by Z.

$$f = (N - r - Z) - \phi + 2 \tag{1-55}$$

$$C = N - r - Z \tag{1-56}$$

Eq.(1-55) is the general expression of the phase rule, and eq. (1-56) is the formula for the determination of the number of independent components by the Jouguet's method. The basic principle of eq. (1-56) is that: if some equilibrium conditions (r) correspond to the independent chemical reactions among the N components, and other constraining conditions (Z) for concentrations are then added in, the number of independent components correspondingly decreases, as presented in eq. (1-56). Item $C = (N - r - Z)$ is usually described as the number of independent components.

Suppose there are other parameters besides T, p and μ_i affecting the system, such as the electric field, surface tension, *etc.*, the number of which is K, then the number of degrees of freedom will accordingly increase by K. In this case, the phase rule should be rewritten as

$$f = (N - r - Z) + 2 - \phi + K \tag{1-57}$$

The process used to derive the phase rule, as presented above, is somewhat complicated, but it also includes those circumstance involving chemical reactions. Moreover, the physical meaning in the process and the items of eq. (1-57) are all lucid, because the derivation is drawn from the universal principle of Gibbs free energy minimization.

The number of independent components is the minimum number of chemical species that can present all of the compositions in the phases of an equilibrium system. The number of degrees of freedom of the equilibrium system is the number of parameters (*e.g.* T, p and concentration) that can be varied freely within limits, without either inducing the formation of new phases or the disappearance of the original phases. Once the independent parameters, the number of which equals f are fixed, the equilibrium state of the system is established. Some "concrete" examples will be given hereinafter.

1.3 Determination of the Number of Independent Components by Brinkley's Method

1.3.1 Brinkley's method

When applying the phase rule, one may well feel confused about the determination of the number of independent components. Usually, eq.(1-56), *i.e.* Jouguet's method, is used for this purpose. While this method is of universal application, many difficulties are still encountered when applying it. In particular, a system for which its original compositions are known only, but its final equilibrium state is less well known, it is then difficult to determine either the N or the r parameters. Because of interactions among the chemical species, such as chemical reactions, ionizations and associations, *etc.*, the actual species probably existing in the equilibrium state may be a great many and are usually not the same as the original species. Even the existing forms of some components are ambiguous. In this case, the determination of N is rather difficult. Moreover, if N is larger, the number of chemical reactions among all possible components will increase dramatically. To actually write out the "menu" of possible chemical reactions existing in the system is not a "cushy" job, while to select the independent ones from all possible reactions, is also not an easy task. For example, $AlCl_3$ dissolves in water, it ionizes, hydrolyses and is partially re-deposited in the form of $Al(OH)_3$. Such a system is really quite complicated (see subsection 3.4). Therefore it is a somewhat strenuous task to deal with the problem regarding the number of independent components, by the Jouguet's method. We will later introduce a more convenient method to deal with the number of independent components, existing especially in a high-temperature complex system.

Although this method was suggested by Brinkley in early 1946 [Brinkley, 1946], it did not initially attract much attention for the original formula was not perfect. Now that this method has been improved, it is widely used. The revised Brinkley's formula is as follows [van Zeggeren *et al*, 1970]:

$$C = M + r^* - Z \tag{1-58}$$

M is the number of elements in the system, Z is the number of other restrictive conditions placed upon the component concentrations, these being the same as those used in the Jouguet's method. Because of some kinetic restrictive conditions, some of the originally independent chemical reactions are interrupted, the number of which is r^*. For example, at room temperature, and without a catalyst, there is no reaction between the H_2 and O_2 in a system composed of H_2, O_2 and H_2O, *i.e.* the reaction (1-59) does not occur:

$$H_2 + \frac{1}{2}O_2 = H_2O \tag{1-59}$$

So $r^* = 1$.

The principle on which Brinkley's method relies is: chemical components are composed of elemental atoms with various chemical stoichiometric coefficients. Brinkley's method tries to determine the relation among the stoichiometric coefficients of the elemental atoms, constituting the various components to determine the number of independent components. In a closed system, M elements comprise N components. As presented above, the chemical formula of the i-th component A_i (i=1, 2, $\cdots$, N) may be written as

$$\sum_e a_{i,e} \times E_e = A_i \tag{1-32}$$

E_e is the symbol of e-th element, $e = 1, 2, \cdots, M$. $a_{i,e}$ is the number of atoms of E_e in the chemical formula A_i. Take a matrix to represent the chemical formulas of all the components:

$$\begin{bmatrix} a_{1,1} & \cdots & a_{1,e} & \cdots & a_{1,M} \\ \vdots & & \vdots & & \vdots \\ a_{i,1} & \cdots & a_{i,e} & \cdots & a_{i,M} \\ \vdots & & \vdots & & \vdots \\ a_{M,1} & \cdots & a_{M,e} & \cdots & a_{M,M} \\ \vdots & & \vdots & & \vdots \\ a_{N,1} & \cdots & a_{N,e} & \cdots & a_{N,M} \end{bmatrix} \begin{bmatrix} E_1 \\ \vdots \\ E_e \\ \vdots \\ E_M \end{bmatrix} = \begin{bmatrix} A_1 \\ \vdots \\ A_i \\ \vdots \\ A_M \\ \vdots \\ A_N \end{bmatrix} \tag{1-60}$$

If the rank of the matrix $\{a_{ie}\}$ is C, the number of independent components is C. Brinkley pointed out that if $N \geqslant M, C \leqslant M$. If $N \leqslant M$, $C \leqslant N$. That is, $C \leqslant$ min $\{N, M\}$. A more detailed description is set out below.

Initially, we discuss the case of $N \geqslant M$. In general, this is true, especially in the more complex systems. If no two or more elements among the M elements form only one atomic group of invariant composition, and all N components constituted by M elements can react with each other, the rank of the above matrix $\{a_{ie}\}$ is M (M is the number of columns, and the number of columns $M <$ the number of rows N), *i.e.* there are M formulas that are independent of one another among N chemical formulas. None of the M chemical formulas can be represented by a linear combination of other formulas among these M formulas, while any one of the $N-M$ remainder chemical formulas can be represented by those of M formulas.

Randomly choosing $A_c(c = 1, 2, \cdots, M)$ different components from $A_i(i = 1, 2, \cdots, N)$, the rule of the selection is that any elements present must appear at least once in the M formulas. In deleting the terms of $i > M$, representing the respective components in eq.(1-60), it follows that

$$\begin{bmatrix} a_{1,1} & \cdots & a_{1,e} & \cdots & a_{1,M} \\ \vdots & & \vdots & & \vdots \\ a_{c,1} & \cdots & a_{c,e} & \cdots & a_{c,M} \\ \vdots & & \vdots & & \vdots \\ a_{M,1} & \cdots & a_{M,e} & \cdots & a_{M,M} \end{bmatrix} \begin{bmatrix} E_1 \\ \vdots \\ E_e \\ \vdots \\ E_M \end{bmatrix} = \begin{bmatrix} A_1 \\ \vdots \\ A_c \\ \vdots \\ A_M \end{bmatrix} \tag{1-61}$$

in which all of the elements a_{ce} are constant. This equation represents A_c by a_{ce} and E_e. The number of A_c's $(c = 1, 2, \cdots, M)$ we have chosen is equal to the number of E_e's $(e = 1, 2, \cdots, M)$. Thus, the matrix a_{ce} is a square matrix. E_e can be solved inversely from a_{ce} and A_c.

$$[a_{c,e}] \cdot [E_e] = [A_c]$$

$$[a_{i,e}]^{-1}[a_{i,e}] \cdot [E_e] = E[E_e] = [a_{i,e}]^{-1}[A_i]$$

$$[E_e] = [a_{i,e}]^{-1}[A_i]$$

where $[a_{ce}]^{-1}$ is the converse matrix of $[a_{ce}]$, E is a unit matrix.

In chemical terms, it is in-reverse to represent the atoms of $E_e(e = 1, 2, \cdots, M)$ by chemical formulas $A_c(c = 1, 2, \cdots, M)$ and $a_{ce}(c = 1, 2, \cdots, M)$. All of the chemical formulas of remainder component $A_k(k = M+1, M+2, \cdots, N)$ can be represented by $a_{ke}(k = M+1, M+2, \cdots, N)$ and E_e. Thus A_k may be represented indirectly by a_{ke} and $[a_{ce}]^{-1}$, that is to say, the A_c's $(c = 1, 2, \cdots, M)$ are independent, while the A_k' s $(k = M+1, M+2, \cdots, N)$ are derivative.

The chemical formulas of the derived components may be represented by those of the independent components. Still considering the system of C, CO_2 and CO as an example, one has

$$\begin{bmatrix} 1 & 0 \\ 1 & 2 \\ 1 & 1 \end{bmatrix} \begin{bmatrix} \mathrm{C} \\ \\ \mathrm{O} \end{bmatrix} = \begin{bmatrix} \mathrm{C} \\ \mathrm{CO_2} \\ \mathrm{CO} \end{bmatrix}$$

By solving the matrix

$$\begin{bmatrix} 1 & 0 \\ 1 & 2 \end{bmatrix} \begin{bmatrix} \mathrm{C} \\ \mathrm{O} \end{bmatrix} = \begin{bmatrix} \mathrm{C} \\ \mathrm{CO_2} \end{bmatrix}$$

Atoms of elements C and O can be represented by C (simple substance) and CO_2, *i.e.*

$$1 \times \mathrm{C(simple\ substance)} + 0 \times \mathrm{CO_2} = \mathrm{C(element)}$$
$$-\frac{1}{2} \times \mathrm{C(simple\ substance)} + \frac{1}{2} \times \mathrm{CO_2} = \mathrm{O(element)}$$

Thus the derivative component CO can be represented through atoms C and O by the independent components C (graphite) and CO_2

$$\begin{aligned} \mathrm{CO} &= 1 \times \mathrm{C(atom)} + 1 \times \mathrm{O(atom)} \\ &= 1 \times [1 \times \mathrm{C(simple\ substance)} + 0 \times \mathrm{CO_2})] + \\ &\quad 1 \times \left[-\frac{1}{2} \times \mathrm{C(simple\ substance)} + \frac{1}{2} \times \mathrm{CO_2}\right] \\ &= \frac{1}{2}\mathrm{C(simple\ substance)} + \frac{1}{2}\mathrm{CO_2} \end{aligned}$$

The independent components are C and CO_2, the derived component is CO. The number of the independent components and the number of the elements are equal, *i.e.*

$$C = M \tag{1-62}$$

Certainly, the premise $Z = 0$ is needed, as well as $r^* = 0$, which means N components may react with each other, in principle.

If there are some kinetic restrictions that inhibit one or more components from participating in the chemical reactions, assuming the number of such independent reactions which do not occur due to kinetic restrictions be r^*, there must actually be r^* more components, being also independent, besides the M independent components. Although the chemical formulas of these r^* components may be represented formally by linear combinations of the chemical formulas of other components, *i.e.* any one of the r^* components may be obtained through a chemical reaction, joined by other components, it is in fact impossible for the reactions, corresponding to these linear combinations, to actually occur. Therefore, the number of independent components should increase by r^*. If there are also Z independent restrictive conditions on the component concentrations, the number of the independent components should also decrease by Z. Finally, $C = M + r^* - Z$, this is eq. (1-58).

In general, especially in high-temperature systems where existing gases, participate in the complicated chemical reactions, $Z = r^* = 0$ usually applies, so that $C = M$. In this case, neither N, the number of components, nor r, the number of independent chemical reactions, necessarily need to be determined. The number of elements M will give the number C directly. The number of M is easy to determine, provided that the initial conditions of the system are given. People may appreciate the convenience of the Brinkley's method on such occasions.

The M independent components of the system should be chosen in this way, such that any one of the M elements will appear in those chemical formulas of the independent components, at least once. The reason for doing so is very understandable, and we have already discussed it when analyzing eq. (1-61).

When the $N \leqslant M$, Brinkley's method fails, we have to use Jouguet's method to count C. Fortunately, in these cases, N and r are usually small and easy to deal with.

1.3.2 The relation between the Brinkley's method and the Jouguet's methods [Zhao *et al.*, 1992]

Formally, the expressions given by Brinkley, and by Jouguet, seem to be quite different:

$$C = N - Z - r \tag{1-56}$$

$$C = M + r^* - Z \tag{1-58}$$

However, when $N > M$, *i.e.* when Brinkley's method is found to be valid, these two expressions can be derived from each other. Since both expressions can correctly resolve the same question from the two different points of view, they certainly do both reach the same goal but by taking different routes.

According to the Brinkley's method, when $Z = r^* = 0$, then $C = M$. There are M independent components, and $N - M$ derived components as well, in the system. All of the chemical formulas of the derived components may be represented by linear combinations of the M independent components. Each linear combination corresponds to an independent chemical reaction; the number of these reactions is $N - M$. If some kinetic restrictions inhibit r^* independent chemical reactions, the number of independent chemical reactions that actually occur is

$$r = N - M - r^* \tag{1-63}$$

i.e.

$$M + r^* = N - r \tag{1-64}$$

if $r^* \neq 0, Z \neq 0$, in accordance with Brinkley's formula and eq.(1-64) we have

$$\begin{aligned} C &= M + r^* - Z \\ &= N - r - Z \end{aligned}$$

Inversely, according to Jouguet's formula and eq. (1-64), we may also obtain

$$C = M + r^* - Z \qquad \text{Q.E.D.}$$

It is shown that Brinkley's formula and Jouguet's formula are equivalent when $N > M$.

If $N < M$, the rank of matrix $\{a_{ie}\}$ is related only to N, thus Jouguet's formula is the unique alternative.

1.3.3 The strengths and shortcomings of both the Brinkley's method and the Jouguet's method [Zhao *et al*, 1992]

The biggest value of the Jouguet's method lies in its universality. A weakness is its tediousness in use, as well as its fallibility, while applying it to complicated equilibrium systems.

The main shortcoming of the Brinkley's method is that it is only valid when $N > M$. Its superiority lies in the point that it is both convenient and concise in use. Its wide application range, especially in high-temperature systems, makes the Brinkley's method more recommendable than the Jouguet's method. Later, we will set out several examples to illustrate these points further.

Brinkley's method is conveniently able be used to treat systems of high-temperature, complex, chemical equilibrium. In this case, one usually has the conditions that $Z = r^* = 0$, so $C = M$. Thus, we have to decide neither N nor r, and the number of independent components C can be derived directly from the number of elements in the system, for example, in taking a system comprised of three elements, *e.g.* C, H and O, and five components: C, CO, CO_2, H_2 and H_2O. According to the principle for selecting the independent components, we choose CO, CO_2 and H_2 as these independent components among the five initial components. In these cases, the elements C, H and O appear in the three selected chemical formulas, at least once.

Besides the M independent components, there are the $N-M$ derived components also. The chemical formulas of any one "derived" component can be faithfully represented by a linear combination of the chemical formulas of the M independent components. For the system being considered, we have

$$\mathrm{C} = 2\mathrm{CO} - \mathrm{CO_2}$$

$$\mathrm{H_2O} = \mathrm{H_2} + \mathrm{CO_2} - \mathrm{CO}$$

Each combination corresponds to an independent chemical reaction. Thus, it is very easy to obtain, not only the number of the "independent" chemical reactions, but also the chemical equations for these reactions. Finally, we wish to emphasize that, if there are other independent restrictive conditions on the component concentrations, and independent reactions occur in the system, then:

$$C = M + r^* - Z$$

The number of actual independent chemical reactions, r, is still determined by

$$r = N - M - r^*$$

This equation has nothing to do with Z, whether Z is equal to zero or not. Because restrictive conditions on the concentrations influence only the extent of the process of chemical reaction, it does not however influence its basic occurrence.

1.3.4 Examples

1. Consider a system containing C_2H_6, C_2H_4, C_2H_2, H_2 and graphite. The contained elements are C and H only. At high temperature, these components can react with each other. If the quantities of these five components are arbitrary, $Z = r^* = 0$, then it is easy to derive that:

$$C = M = 2$$

If Jouguet's method is used in this example, one has, first of all, to write down all of the possible reactions that can occur amongst the five components,

$$\mathrm{C_2H_2} = 2\mathrm{C} + \mathrm{H_2} \tag{1-65}$$

$$\mathrm{C_2H_4} = 2\mathrm{C} + 2\mathrm{H_2} \tag{1-66}$$

$$\mathrm{C_2H_6} = 2\mathrm{C} + 3\mathrm{H_2} \tag{1-67}$$

$$C_2H_6 = C_2H_4 + H_2 \tag{1-68}$$

$$C_2H_4 = C_2H_2 + H_2 \tag{1-69}$$

$$C_2H_6 = C_2H_2 + 2H_2 \tag{1-70}$$

Then, using the method of linear combination or, by determining the rank of the matrix considering the stoichiometric coefficients of the components of those chemical reactions, one can find $r = 3$. For example, let us choose eqs. (1-65)–(1-67) to be the independent reactions, eqs.(1-68)–(1-70) can be derived from them. For $N = 5, r = 3$, and $Z = 0$, Jouguet's formula yields C=5 − 3 − 0=2. The results from both of these methods are the same. But the Brinkley's method is much simpler.

2. The reduction of $SiCl_4$ by H_2 is an important process for the manufacture of semiconductor materials. At 1500K, there are six major species present: Si (solid), H_2, HCl, $SiCl_2$, $SiCl_4$ and $SiHCl_3$. They are all capable of reacting with one another. Some possible reactions can be written down, according to Jouguet's method:

$$SiCl_4 + 2H_2 = Si(s) + 4HCl \tag{1-71}$$

$$SiCl_4 + Si(s) = 2SiCl_2 \tag{1-72}$$

$$SiCl_2 + H_2 = Si(s) + 2HCl \tag{1-73}$$

$$SiHCl_3 + H_2 = Si(s) + 3HCl \tag{1-74}$$

$$SiHCl_3 = SiCl_2 + HCl \tag{1-75}$$

Other reactions can also be set out in a similar way. In all of these reactions, only three of them are fully independent. So $r = 3, C = 6 - 3 = 3$. If we consider more components, for example, SiH_2Cl_2, SiH_3Cl and SiH_4, more reactions may be written into the program. At last, for $r = 6, N = 9$, and $C = 9 - 6 = 3, C$ does not change. Using Brinkley's method, for both cases, we get $C = M = 3$.

It is illustrative from above example that Brinkley's method is very convenient when applied to high-temperature, complex systems. However, the Brinkley's method does have its own limitations.

3. Consider the system containing KCNS, $Fe(CNS)_3$, K_2SO_4, and $Fe_2(SO_4)_3$, with arbitrary quantities. There is one common independent reaction among them:

$$Fe_2(SO_4)_3 + 6KCNS = 2Fe(CNS)_3 + 3K_2SO_4 \tag{1-76}$$

Here $N = 4, M = 6$ then $M > N$. As mentioned above, Brinkley's method is invalid in this case, and Jouguet's method is the unique alternative.

$$C = N - r = 4 - 1 = 3$$

4. The equilibrium system of an electrolyte solution [Zemansky, 1968]. Supposing KH_2PO_4 is dissolved in water, KH_2PO_4 undergoes three ionization steps, forming $H_2PO_4^-$, HPO_4^{2-}, PO_4^{3-} and K^+, and the water may also ionize. There are four elements and eight components: KH_2PO_4, $H_2PO_4^-$, HPO_4^{2-}, PO_4^{3-}, K^+, H^+, H_2O and OH^- in the system.

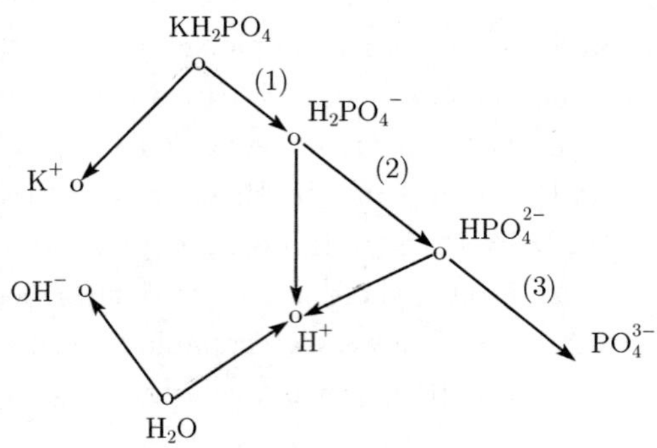

Fig. 1.1 The ionization of KH_2PO_4 and water.

According to Jouguet's method, we must first determine which reactions are independent.

$$H_2O = H^+ + OH^- \tag{1-77}$$

$$KH_2PO_4 = K^+ + H_2PO_4^- \tag{1-78}$$

$$H_2PO_4^- = H^+ + HPO_4^{2-} \tag{1-79}$$

$$HPO_4^{2-} = H^+ + PO_4^{3-} \tag{1-80}$$

There are two constraining conditions with respect to the concentrations, arising from the initial composition and ionization conditions:

$$[K^+] = [PO_4^{3-}] + [HPO_4^{2-}] + [H_2PO_4^-] \tag{1-81}$$

$$[H^+] = 2[PO_4^{3-}] + [HPO_4^{2-}] + [OH^-] \tag{1-82}$$

$[K^+]$, $[H^+]$ *etc.* are the concentrations of the ions in the solution. In addition, there is also an electroneutrality condition:

$$[K^+] + [H^+] = 3[PO_4^{3-}] + 2[HPO_4^{2-}] + [H_2PO_4^-] + [OH^-] \tag{1-83}$$

Since eq.(1-81)+eq.(1-82)=eq.(1-83), there are only two independent equations for the concentrations of ions. Then, $r = 4, Z = 2, N = 8$, and $C = N - Z - r = 8 - 2 - 4 = 2$.

In the Brinkley's method, only the value of Z must be considered: $Z = 2$ (eqs. (1-81) and (1-82)), so $C = M - Z = 4 - 2 = 2$.

5. Partial precipitation in an electrolyte solution [Zemansky, 1986]

Consider the system of $AlCl_3$ dissolved in water as an example. $AlCl_3$ may dissociate, hydrolyze, and the Al^{3+} partially precipitate in the form of $Al(OH)_3$. There are eight components: H_2O, $AlCl_3$, $Al(OH)_3$, HCl, H^+, Al^{3+}, Cl^- and OH^-, and each can react with each other (see Fig. 1.2).

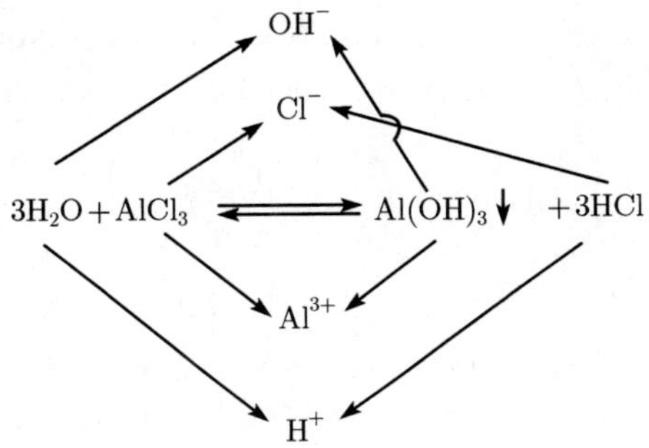

Fig. 1.2 $AlCl_3$ dissolved in water; it may dissociate, hydrolyze, and Al^{3+} partially precipitates.

According to Jouguet's method, the independent reaction must be determined first.

$$H_2O = H^+ + OH^- \tag{1-84}$$

$$AlCl_3 = Al^{3+} + 3Cl^- \tag{1-85}$$

$$Al(OH)_3 = Al^{3+} + 3OH^- \tag{1-86}$$

$$HCl = H^+ + Cl^- \tag{1-87}$$

At first glance, another reaction also seems to exist:

$$3H_2O + AlCl_3 = Al(OH)_3 + 3HCl \tag{1-88}$$

However, it can be seen that eq.(1-88) is not independent, because it is a linear combinations of four other equations: 3× eq.(1-84) + eq.(1-85) – eq.(1-86) – 3×eq.(1-87) = eq.(1-88). Actually, other possible species may also be written down. Because both the numbers of species and the number of independent reactions increase simultaneously, they contribute nothing to the final result of counting the number of independent components. Besides, there is only one electroneutrality condition, because of the partial precipitation of $Al(OH)_3$.

$$3[Al^{3+}] + [H^+] = [OH^-] + [Cl^-] \tag{1-89}$$

Unlike the fourth example, here $N=8, r=4, Z=1$ (eq.(1-89)) and $C=3$. It is a very interesting case where there are now three independent components, at equilibrium, in a system that was composed of two chemical substances in its initial state. This is ascribed to the partial precipitation of the $Al(OH)_3$ phase.

By the Brinkley's method: $M = 4, Z = 1, C = 4 - 1 = 3$. The result is the same, but the treatment is simpler.

Next, we will provide three examples of the determination of independent components found in complex phase diagrams.

6. Phase diagram of the system Ga-Al-As. Two compounds, GaAs and AlAs, exist in this system. With the Jouguet's method, we can write down the following independent reactions:

$$\mathrm{Ga + As = GaAs}$$
$$\mathrm{Al + As = AlAs}$$

By Jouguet's method, $N = 5, r = 2, Z = 0$ and $C = 5 - 2 = 3$. According to the Brinkley's method: because Ga, As, GaAs and AlAs can react with each other at high temperature, $r^* = 0, C = M = 3$. The application of Brinkley's method is easier. Usually, Ga, Al and As are chosen as the independent components, the system is a ternary one.

7. Phase diagram of the system made up of complex oxides. Consider the system of FeO-Fe_2O_3-SiO_2 for example, it being important during several metallurgical and geological processes. There exists many other components: *e.g.* Fe_2O_3, $FeO{\cdot}SiO_2$, $(FeO)_2{\cdot}SiO_2$ and $Fe_2O_3{\cdot}FeO{\cdot}SiO_2$ *etc*, and there are also three elements in the system, if $Z = r^* = 0, C = M = 3$. FeO, Fe_2O_3 and SiO_2 may be selected as independent components among the overall components. In the chemical formulas for the three components, each element appears at least once. It is a matter of fact that the actual phase diagram is represented by these three components. But the application of Jouguet's method is rather complicated, it is omitted here.

8. Phase diagram of the complex saline system of Mg^{2+}-Na^+-Cl^--SO_4^{2-}-H_2O system.

In this system, there are many stable solid compounds: $MgSO_4{\cdot}7H_2O$, $MgSO_4{\cdot}6H_2O$, $MgSO_4{\cdot}H_2O$, $Na_2Mg(SO_4)_2{\cdot}4H_2O$, $Na_{12}Mg_7(SO_4)_{13}{\cdot}15H_2O$, $Na_6Mg(SO_4)_4$, $Na_{21}MgCl_3(SO_4)_{10}$, NaCl, $Na_2SO_4{\cdot}10H_2O$, and Na_2SO_4 *etc.* In addition, some metastable compounds are also possible. It would be a very complicated exercise to use the Jouguet's method to deal with this system.

According to the Brinkley's method, $M=5$, since S, O and H form one invariant atomic radical and one invariant compound SO_4^{2-} and H_2O, they are counted as two "elements" only [Zhao, 1981], in addition, there is an electroneutrality condition:

$$2[Mg^{2+}] + [Na^+] = [Cl^-] + 2[SO_4^{2-}] \tag{1-90}$$

so $Z = 1$, and

$$C = M - Z = 5 - 1 = 4$$

Therefore this system is a quaternary one. The application of the Brinkley's method is rather simple.

Conclusion: as indicated above, the Brinkley's method does have its particular merit in counting the number of the independent components. This section may be useful for the teachers of Physical Chemistry and Chemical Thermodynamics.

1.4 Some Remarks on the Application of the Phase Rule

The phase rule is an important regulation. Though concrete equilibrium conditions and concentrations can not be gained from it, the phase rule has important and general guiding significance. Even for the system whose theoretical relation is still not clear, the phase rule can describe the fundamental characteristics of its equilibrium state. The extent of the application of the phase rule is probably wider than that of any other law in Physical Chemistry.

Formally, the phase rule is a very simple expression. It is easy to use the phase rule in summarizing the known experimental facts. While using the phase rule to study an unknown system, one may find that much circumspection is needed. The correct conclusion will be drawn only when the distinct physical concepts are held. In science history, there were such instances that the abuse of the phase rule interrupted people to probe deeply into the essence of matters, with the result that erroneous conclusions have remained for a long time without being redressed.

The correct use of the phase rule depends on the correct determination of the values of N, C and ϕ and if there are other parameters, than p, T, x_i, affecting the system equilibrium. On this basis, it is easier to calculate the number of the degrees of freedom.

Bear in mind that the phase rule treats actual thermodynamic equilibrium systems only. This is very significant, when analyzing mineral systems and silicate systems, for these systems are usually not in real equilibrium states.

For a known equilibrium system, the chemical species and the number of them are given. But, for an unknown multicomponent, multiphase equilibrium system, it is hard to determine the number of N, because only the initial composition is known. Of course, according to the initial compositions and abundant thermodynamic data, it is possible to evaluate the species and their relative amounts in the equilibrium system. Nevertheless, it is also troublesome. In these cases, the Brinkley's method is most appropriate.

For a known equilibrium system, the number of phases of the system is known. For an unknown system, *e.g.* when dealing with a complex chemical equilibrium system or a system whose phase diagram is "uncharted", one may "estimate" the possible phases and the total number of them, approximately, from the possible species and their forms in the equilibrium.

Sometimes, one may reversely reckon the probable maximum of the number of the phases, based on the phase rule:

$$\phi = C - f + 2$$

With constant pressure, because $f \geqslant 0$, then $\phi \leqslant C + 1$, or $\phi_{\text{max}} = C + 1$.

Under some particular circumstances, it is advantageous to scrutinize whether there are other parameters than T, p, and x_i affecting the equilibrium of the system, such as the intensity of the electromagnetic field, the surface tension and internal elastic stress, and so on. For instance, according to the phase rule, the vapor pressure and solubility of pure solid substances are constant, if the parameters p and T are taken into account. If the dispersivity is large, then the influence of the surface tension must be considered. At a given temperature, the vapor pressure and the solubility of pure solid substance in another solvent increases with the dispersivity.

The following examples of reduction of zinc oxide [Fu, 1963], illustrate the application of the phase rule.

For the smelting of zinc, the zinc sulphide ore is usually calcined to zinc oxide, and then it is reduced with carbon at 1200°C. There are ZnO (solid), Zn (vapor, liquid or solid), C (solid), CO and CO_2 in the equilibrium system. Initially, we discuss the case in which the Zn is present in the gaseous state.

We will determine the number of independent components using the Brinkley's method, then derive the number of degrees of freedom for the system from the phase rule and then explain the meanings of the results.

M=3, for the system considered, CO and CO_2 are produced from the reactions between the C and ZnO. The oxygen in the CO and CO_2 comes from the ZnO. So long as there is a Zn atom in the vapor phase, there will be an O atom in the CO or CO_2 present in the vapor phase, too.

$$p_{\text{Zn}} = p_{\text{CO}} + p_{\text{CO}_2} \tag{1-91}$$

$Z = 1$, then $C = M - Z = 3 - 1 = 2$. There are three phases in the system (vapor, ZnO (s) and C). According to the phase rule:

$$f = C - \phi + 2 = 2 - 3 + 2 = 1$$

The system has only one degree of freedom.

If the smelting furnace is directly connected to atmosphere (*i.e.* at atmospheric pressure), the total pressure should be

$$p = p_{Zn} + p_{CO} + p_{CO_2} = 1 \times 10^5 \text{Pa} \tag{1-92}$$

so ZnO can be reduced continuously to form Zn vapor. With the p fixed, the equilibrium state can only be established when the temperature approaches a definite fixed value, T^0, because of the premise $f = 1$.

The number of independent components is two; if ZnO and C are selected as independent components, all of the elements are involved. As mentioned above, whether Z=0 or not, one has

$$r = N - M - r^* = 5 - 3 - 0 = 2 \tag{1-93}$$

The number of independent reactions is two. They may be written as

$$\text{ZnO(s)} + \text{C(s)} = \text{CO} + \text{Zn(g)} \tag{1-94}$$

$$2\text{CO(g)} = \text{CO}_2 + \text{C(s)} \tag{1-95}$$

Thus, all of the five components appear. The other possible reactions are not independent. According to the mass action law:

$$p_{CO}p_{Zn} = K_{p_4} = f_4(T) \tag{1-96}$$

$$p_{CO_2}/p_{CO}^2 = K_{p_5} = f_5(T) \tag{1-97}$$

The variables in the system are: p_{CO}, p_{CO_2}, p_{Zn}, T, and p, five in all. There are four equilibrium conditions, eqs.(1-91), (1-92), (1-96) and (1-97), so the number of independent variables is only one. If the total pressure, p, is set at 10^5 Pa, then T^0 (the equilibrium temperature), p_{CO}, p_{CO_2} and p_{Zn} could be solved from the above four equations, the equilibrium state of the system could therefore be determined.

Next, we discuss the circumstance where liquid zinc is generated. Here, we consider that the temperature of the whole system is identical and no cool condenser is used. Suppose that the temperature is higher than T^0 as mentioned above, the total vapor pressure will then exceed atmospheric. As the temperature increases, the p_{Zn} rises quickly. Once the equilibrium partial pressure p_{Zn} (owing to the chemical reaction) in the system comes up to or slightly over the vapor pressure of pure liquid zinc at that temperature, liquid zinc will start to be condensed. This may be attributed to the fact that, due to the chemical reaction, the equilibrium p_{Zn} in the system increases more quickly than the vapor pressure of liquid zinc, when the temperature is increasing. Because of the formation of liquid zinc, a new phase appears in the system. In this case, eq. (1-91) is untenable because of the existence of the liquid zinc. The number of degree of freedom of the system is still one. The reader may write out the relevant equations applicable to this circumstance and thence analyze the meaning of the process degrees of freedom.

This example fully illustrates that the phase rule can determine the fundamental characteristics of the equilibrium system. For more detailed information on the system in question, we need to have the thermodynamic knowledge and the process data to calculate the complex chemical equilibrium involved in this example of an important everyday metallurgical process.

References-1

S. R. Brinkley. 1946. Note on the Conditions of equilibrium for systems of many constituents. J. Chem. Phys., 14: 563, 564, 686

Ying Fu. 1963. Introduction to Chemical Thermodynamics. Beijing: Science Press (in Chinese)

J. W. Gibbs. 1950. The Collected works of J. W. Gibbs. Vol.1. New Haven: Yale University Press

F. Van Zeggeren, S. H. Storey. 1970. The computation of chemical equilibria. Chapter 2 The foundations of chemical equilibrium computation. Cambridge: Cambridge University Press

M. W. Zemansky. 1968. Heat and Thermodynamics. 5th ed. New York: McGraw-Hill Inc.

Muyu Zhao, Zichen Wang, Liangzhi Xiao. 1992. The determination of the number of independent components by Brinkley's method. J. Chem. Education, 69(7): 539

Summary of Part One

We start this book by refreshing our knowledge of the famous Gibbs' phase rule.

$$f = N + 2 - \phi$$

The different methods to derive this rule, be rigorous or be concise, all are full of the forerunners' wisdom and fascinating for the successive scholars and students. We trust that reader's acquaintance of these fundamental scientific trains of thoughts and skills, will be much helpful to understand the major content of this book.

The determination of the number of independent components in an equilibrium system is critical for the application of the phase rule. We introduce two well established methods here, Brinkley's and Jouguet's methods, and compare the merits and shortcomings of these two methods. Brinkley's method is generally difficult to find in textbooks, but very useful for the researchers, engineers and students in the fields of chemical engineering and materials science.

Part Two

The Boundary Theory of Isobaric Phase Diagrams and Its Application

Chapter 2

The Boundary Theory of Isobaric Phase Diagrams

—Rules for Phase Diagram Construction

2.1 Introduction

A phase diagram is constituted by the phase regions displayed and their boundaries. The relationship among neighboring phase regions (abbreviated to NPRs), and the NPRs' boundaries is of a certain regularity. In other words, the phase regions and their boundaries must follow certain rules in order to constitute a correct phase diagram. The phase rule, which defines the relation among the number of components, number of phases and degrees of freedom of an equilibrium system, is infallibly applicable in every phase diagram. However, it does not cover the relationship and the regularity among the NPRs and their boundaries in the phase diagrams. For example, it would be difficult to answer the following questions:

(1) If the phase assemblages of two NPRs are known, what are the characteristics of the boundaries between them?

(2) If the phase assemblage of the first NPR and the characteristic of the boundary between two NPRs are known, what is the phase assemblage of the second NPR?

In practice, understanding the relationship among NPRs and their boundaries is very important. Firstly, a thorough comprehension and interpretation of a phase diagram is impossible until one masters the relationship among the NPRs and their boundaries within the phase diagram, especially the complicated phase diagrams.

Secondly, when the available experimental data are not adequate, the rules governing the boundaries may help to "sketch in" the relevant boundary lines between the NPRs, and to then design the further experimental points. Knowledge of the relationship among the NPRs and their boundaries is particularly useful when judging the authenticity of a phase diagram.

We have now developed a method, for applying our boundary theory and other thermodynamic principles, in order to determine the isobaric, multicomponent horizontal (isothermal) sections, the particular method used will be presented in

Chapter 7.

Thirdly, the rules concerning boundaries are helpful in setting up the thermodynamic equations for the calculation of phase diagrams.

Since these rules concerning boundaries are so important for phase diagram studies, many scientists have been engaged, over recent decades, in contributing to this project. Thus, in 1915, Schreinmakers "worked out" Schreinmakers' rule [Schreinmakers, 1915]. This rule points out that a given phase region containing N phases would either be: a) a neighbor in a phase region containing (N+1) phases, or b) in contact with a phase region containing (N+2) phases by a boundary point. This rule is usually known as the "cross rule". Vogel-Masing's rule is similar to that of Schreinmakers'. Later, Palatnik and Landau (here abbreviated to P-L) theoretically deduced the "contact rule of phase regions" [Palatnik and Landau, 1955, 1964]. Around the same time, Rhines summarized the "ten rules which must be obeyed when constructing ternary phase diagrams" [Rhines, 1956]. Much later, Gupta *et al.* deduced the overlapping ZPF (Zero Phase Fraction) lines method [Gupta *et al*, 1986]. The concept of the ZPF line is that the line for each phase divides a two dimensional, multicomponent section into two regions; where, on the one side of the line, the phase is generated, while on the other side, it is not. By overlapping the ZPF lines, the two- dimensional, multicomponent section with limited information may be constructed. Gupta's method is a very practical one and it has been widely applied in phase diagram calculation. M. Hillert and A. Pelton [Hillert, 1988, 1993, 1998; Pelton, 2001] have also contributed to the theory concerning the boundary features of phase diagrams.

In the present Chapter, some basic concepts that underlie the construction of phase diagrams are discussed. Based on these concepts, and on fundamental thermodynamic principles, the Theorem of Corresponding Relationship (abbreviated to TCR), and its corollaries, are deduced. Furthermore, the relation between the dimensions of the boundary R_1', and the dimensions of the phase boundary R_1, and its theoretical proof, are presented. These are the main components of the boundary theory of isobaric phase diagrams.

2.2 Several Basic Concepts for Underlying the Phase Diagram

2.2.1 Coordinate axes

There are two types of axes involved: (a) the molar axes, for example, x_i (mole fraction of i-th component in the system), and $S_{\rm m}$ (molar entropy) *etc.*, and (b) the potential axes, for example, temperature T and pressure p, *etc., i.e.* the intensive properties. As most scientific and technological literatures apply the axes of mixed type, *i.e.* T, p and x_i, we use the same nomenclature here in this publication.

2.2.2 The phase point and the system point

There are two categories of "point" used in a phase diagram.

The system point is the representative point (T, p, x_i) of a system in a phase diagram under a defined condition. T and p represent the temperature and pressure respectively; x_i is the mole fraction of the i-th component in the system. Obviously, every point within a phase diagram could be the system point. In other words, the system points can fill the whole available space of the phase diagram, see Fig. 2.1(c).

The phase point is a representative point (T, p, x_{ij}) in a phase. x_{ij} is the mole fraction of the i-th component in the j-th phase. Phase points exist only in single-phase regions and their boundaries, see Fig. 2.1(b). In a single-phase region, the phase points and the system points are identical. For two- or multi- phase regions, there are no phase points in their interior parts but phase points can occur on the boundaries between the two- or multi-phase regions, with the single phase regions.

For the general case, there is no phase point on those boundaries lying between the two- or multi- phase regions with other two- or multi- phase regions. In a few special cases, however, there may be a phase point between those pairs of phase regions, see later discussion.

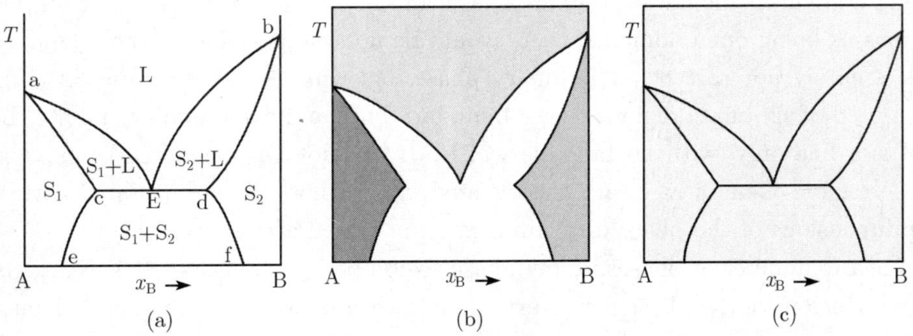

Fig. 2.1 (a) One typical binary isobaric phase diagram; (b) phase points exist only in the single phase region; (c) but the system points are everywhere. p=const.

2.2.3 The isobaric phase diagram and its dimensions

In the isobaric phase diagram, pressure p is kept constant. The variables of the system are T and x_i(i=1, 2, $\cdots$, N). The variables of the phase point are T and x_{ij} $(i = 1, 2, \cdots, N; j = 1, 2, \cdots, \phi)$, there exist:

$$\sum_{i=1}^{N} x_i = 1$$

$$\sum_{i=1}^{N} x_{i,j} = 1 \quad (j = 1, 2, \cdots, \phi)$$

So, for both the system point and the phase point, the number of their independent variables is N($N - 1$ from the molar relationship, either for system point or phase point; and one from temperature). The space of N dimensions may be used to describe the system point, the phase point, the phase region and the phase diagram. Therefore, the dimension of the isobaric phase diagram, R, is equal to the number of components N.

$$R = N \tag{2-1}$$

2.2.4 The phase, the phase region and the number of phases existing in the phase region

A phase is a homogeneous part of the system, of which the physical and chemical state is uniform; no demarcation exists inside the part. There are boundaries between the different phases. If a phase region consists of only one phase, it is called a one-phase or a homogeneous phase region. If a phase region consists of more than one phase, it is called a two- or multi-phase region; or a heterogeneous phase region.

A phase region is a part of a phase diagram, it is so defined that the dimensions of which are equal to the dimensions of the phase diagram. The phase region is a closed domain, it includes the interior part and its boundary. If we define all phase regions as being open domains, there would be no system point on the boundaries, this is surely not correct. The binary phase diagram, as shown in Fig. 2.1(a), is composed of six phase regions, seven boundary lines and five boundary points. Line cEd is a line only, with no tangible width. It can not be considered to exist as a phase region. Generally, in our theory, any region whose dimensions are inferior to the dimensions of the phase diagram is not considered a phase region.

Let the number of phases in any phase region be ϕ, evidently $\phi \geqslant 1$. Next, since the dimensions of the phase region are equal to the dimensions of the phase diagram, then the temperature of the system must be an independent variable. So, $f \geqslant 1, f$ is the degrees of freedom of an equilibrium system. According to the phase rule, $\phi = N + 1 - f$, at constant pressure, when $f \geqslant 1$, $\phi \leqslant N$. So, in any phase region of a phase diagram, there is

$$N \geqslant \phi \geqslant 1 \tag{2-2}$$

2.2.5 Neighboring phase regions (abbreviated to NPRs) and the total number of all the different phases present in them, Φ

Here, let us initially discuss the case of two NPRs with a common boundary. Assume that the first NPR contains ϕ_1 phases, they are $f_1, f_2, \cdots, f_{\phi_C}, f_{\phi_C+1}, \cdots,$

$f_{\phi_C+q_1}$, $\phi_1 = \phi_C + q_1$; and the second NPR contains ϕ_2 phases, they are $f_1, f_2, \cdots,$ $f_{\phi_C}, f_{\phi_C+1'}, f_{\phi_C+2'}, \cdots, f_{\phi_C+q_2}$, $\phi_2 = \phi_C + q_2$. Among all of these, phases $f_1, f_2, \cdots,$ f_{ϕ_C} belong to both NPRs, so that the number of these common phases is ϕ_C. The total number of all different phases in the two NPRs is denoted by Φ. For two NPRs, $\Phi = \phi_C + q_1 + q_2$. Evidently, $\Phi = \phi_1 + \phi_2 - \phi_C$, then

$$\phi_C = \phi_1 + \phi_2 - \Phi \tag{2-3}$$

The total number of all the different phases, Φ, is an important characteristic of the phase equilibrium represented in the boundary between NPRs in the phase diagram, this has not been revealed or underlined in the previous researches numerated in section 2.1. We have distinguished this concept in 1983 [Zhao, 1983], it is an important concept of our boundary theory.

2.2.6 The maximum phase number in any phase region of the two or more NPRs, $\phi_{\max}$

It has been proved (eq. (2-2)) that the number of phases which exist in any phase region in the isobaric phase diagram of N-components, $\phi \leqslant N$, so, the maximum number of phases in any phase regions is

$$\phi_{\max} = N \tag{2-4}$$

2.2.7 The boundary and the phase boundary among two or more NPRs

2.2.7.1 Boundary

Conventionally, people call the geometrical demarcation among two or more NPRs as the "boundary". According to the number of components of the phase diagram, a boundary could be a point, a line, a surface $\cdots$ until $(N-1)$ dimensions of the entity occupies the space. This concept of the boundary is widely used in most references to phase diagrams, in addition to Palatnik and Landau's contact rule. In our boundary theory, we use it in its conventional meaning, and recognize that a boundary is the set of system points and its dimensions are denoted as R_1'.

2.2.7.2 Phase boundary

From the viewpoint of the phase point (see subsection 2.2.2) in the study of the boundary between two NPRs, we can define the phase boundary as the set of the equilibrium phase points of the equilibrium system existing on the common boundary. The dimensions of the phase boundary are denoted by R_1.

Example 2-2-1. See the NPRs $(L+S_1)/L$ in Fig. 2.1(a), the phase region $(L+S_1)$ neighbors the phase region L. $\phi_1=2(L,S_1)$; $\phi_2 = 1(L)$; $\phi_{\max} = 2$; $\Phi = 2(L, S_1)$; $\phi_C =$

1(L); $\phi_C = \phi_1 + \phi_2 - \Phi = 1 + 2 - 2 = 1$, the common phase is the liquid phase, L. The boundary between NPRs (L+S_1)/L is the line aE, $R'_1 = 1$. But we consider that the phase boundary lines between (L+S_1)/L are lines aE and ac! Note: line ac is actually not between the NPRs (L+S_1)/L. According to the level rule, all components of the system existing on the boundary are distributed over the common phase, L, existing on the phase boundary, aE, but an infinitesimal amount of the components is distributed over the non-common phase, S_1, existing on the phase boundary line ac in principle. This is why we consider that the phase boundary lines between NPRs (L+S_1)/L are the lines aE and ac, but aE is the main phase boundary line.

In this case, $R_1 = R'_1 = 1$, the dimension of the boundary being equal to the dimension of the phase boundary.

Example 2-2-2. Two NPRs (S_1+L)/(S_1+S_2) see Fig.2.1(a), ϕ_1=2(S_1, L), ϕ_2 =2 (S_1, S_2), $\phi_{\max}$=2, Φ=3(L,S_1, S_2), $\phi_C = 1(S_1)$. For the boundary line cE, R'_1=1, it is composed of system points. The phase boundary consists merely of three phase points: c(S_1), d(S_2) and E(L), R_1=0. In this example, the phase boundary does not coincide with the "boundary" and $R'_1 \neq R_1$. This example demonstrates the difference that exists between the boundary and the phase boundary.

2.2.7.3 The relationship among the NPRs and their boundaries

The most important physical parameters that determine the relationship among NPRs and their boundaries are Φ, ϕ_C, R_1 and R'_1. If the assemblages of two NPRs are known, then the values of Φ and ϕ_C can be readily calculated. According to the boundary theory, the value of R_1 can be calculated from Φ, while the value of R'_1 can be calculated from R_1 and ϕ_C (see later paragraphs). The relationship among the NPRs and their boundaries can be determined by use of the following parameters: Φ, ϕ_C, R_1 and R'_1.

2.2.8 More on the phase boundary concept

In many literature references, the term "phase boundary" is often mentioned and is usually used to indicate the boundary of a phase, or of a single-phase region. However the meaning of "phase boundary" in our boundary theory is different, here we define that the phase boundary should be the set of "equilibrium phase points" of the equilibrium system existing on the boundary. Meanwhile, we deem that the phase point is more important than the system point, and the phase boundary is more important than the boundary, when problems of the phase equilibrium are being discussed.

The phase boundary is a "real entity" in the structure of phase diagram, the existence of this entity is no longer in doubt. From the examples listed in the previous section, it can be seen that a system, existing on the boundary between NPRs under a given condition, is usually distributed in the different phases that are present. Consequently, the conventional "boundary" does not necessarily coincide with the "phase boundary".

There is no such "concept" in Palatnik-Landau's contact rule; this makes it difficult to apply their rule in certain boundary between NPRs in the phase diagram. For example, when explaining the "boundary" line cEd, in Fig. 2.1(a), they have to introduce the extra concept of "degenerate region", that expands the line into a two-dimensional phase region to thereby explain the shift of the phase number in NPRs. There are many other similar examples, please see Chapter 3, section 3.6.

Based on the concept of the phase boundary, and on other thermodynamic principles, we have worked out a systematic boundary theory for phase diagrams. All of the difficulties that Palatnik-Landau's theory was not able to resolve, may now be otherwise resolved by the boundary theory (see the detailed theory description in Chapter 3).

The conception of the "phase boundary" has been generally accepted and is highly appreciated by many Chinese scientists. A few books on phase diagram topics, and some professors at various universities in China, have now introduced this concept and apply it in their pedagogic practices. Professor Chu-Kun Kuo *et al.* (Shanghai Institute of Ceramics, Chinese Academy of Science) have presented the boundary theory, especially the concept of the phase boundary, in their book "*High Temperature Phase Equilibrium and Phase Diagrams*" (Shanghai Scientific and Technical Publisher, 1987, in Chinese). This book has also been published in English by Pergamen Press (New York). Professor J. K. Liang (Institute of Physics, Beijing, Chinese Academy of Science) presented the boundary theory, including the concept of the phase boundary, in greater detail, in his book "*Phase Diagrams and Phase Structures*" (Science Press, Beijing, 1993, in Chinese) Section 1.7. Professor Hui-An Yin (Chengdu University of Technology) presented the boundary theory, more completely, in the book "*Multicomponent Phase Diagram*" (Peking University Press, Beijing, 2002, in Chinese). He emphasized that "the phase boundary is different from other theories and that it is thus a very important concept." There are also other books (in Chinese), which apply the concept of the phase boundary to investigate the phase diagrams. Professor Yun-Sheng Chen (Northwest University, Xi'an) had taught the "boundary theory" concept in his course "*Phase Diagrams*" for several years, and he reported that students are interested in the theory and learn much from the study of it.

2.3 The Theorem of the Corresponding Relationship between the Total Number of All the Different Phases in NPRs Φ and the Dimensions of the Phase Boundary R_1 in Phase Diagrams, and Its Theoretical Deduction

2.3.1 The theorem of the corresponding relationship between Φ and R_1

The theorem of the corresponding relationship between Φ (the total number of all the different phases in NPRs) and R_1 (dimensions of the phase boundary) in phase diagrams, is abbreviated as TCR in this text and is expressed as follows:

For p-T-x_i phase diagrams in the general case

$$R_1 = (N - Z - r) - \Phi + 2 \tag{2-5'}$$

For isobaric phase diagrams

$$R_1 = (N - Z - r) - \Phi + 1 \tag{2-6'}$$

Here, p, pressure; T, temperature; N, the number of components; r, the number of independent chemical reactions occurring in the system; Z, the number of independent conditions which constrain the concentrations of components, except the condition $\sum_i x_i = 1, \sum_i x_{i,j} = 1$, where x_i and $x_{i,j}$ denote the mole fractions of the i-th component in the system and the j-th phase, $j = 1, 2, \cdots, \phi$ respectively. The item $(N-Z-r)$ is "called" the number of independent components in the references of chemical thermodynamics (see Chapter 1). TCR expounds the corresponding relationship between Φ and R_1.

In general cases, $Z = r = 0$ for p-T-x_i phase diagrams, TCR is expressed as

$$R_1 = N - \Phi + 2 \tag{2-5}$$

For isobaric phase diagrams,

$$R_1 = N - \Phi + 1 \tag{2-6}$$

2.3.2 The theoretical deduction of TCR

The boundary is a part "in common" between the two NPRs. The system existing on the boundary must satisfy the phase equilibrium conditions for both NPRs. Let the first NPR and the second NPR contain $(\phi_C + q_1)$ phases, and $(\phi_C + q_2)$ phases, respectively. We now write the phase equilibrium conditions of the system in the first and the second NPRs, respectively. For a given temperature and pressure condition, the equilibrium system in the first NPR must satisfy the following phase equilibrium conditions:

$$\mu'_{i,1} = \mu'_{i,2} = \cdots = \mu'_{i,\phi_c} = \mu'_{i,(\phi_c+1)} = \cdots = \mu'_{i,(\phi_c+q_1)} \qquad (i = 1, 2, \cdots, N)$$

$$\sum_{i=1}^{N} x'_{i,j} = 1 \quad (j = 1, 2, \cdots, \phi_C, \phi_C + 1 \cdots, \phi_C + q_1)$$

Here, $\mu_{i,j}$ denotes the chemical potential of the i-th component in the j-th phase. Similarly, there exist phase equilibrium conditions for the equilibrium system in the second NPR:

$$\mu''_{i,1} = \mu''_{i,2} = \cdots = \mu''_{i,\phi_c} = \mu''_{i,(\phi_c+1')} = \cdots = \mu''_{i,(\phi_c+q_2)} \quad (i = 1, 2, \cdots, N)$$

$$\sum_{i=1}^{N} x''_{i,j} = 1 \quad (j = 1, 2, \cdots, \phi_C, \phi_C + 1', \cdots, \phi_C + q_2)$$

Since the boundary is a part "in common" of the two NPRs, when the equilibrium systems exist on the boundary, they must have

$$x'_{i,j} = x''_{i,j} = x_{i,j} \quad (i = 1, 2, \cdots, N; j = 1, 2, \cdots, \phi_C)$$

$$\mu'_{i,j} = \mu''_{i,j} = \mu_{i,j} \quad (i = 1, 2, \cdots, N; j = 1, 2, \cdots, \phi_C)$$

By applying the equilibrium relation on the boundary, the following unique phase equilibrium equations are obtained:

$$\mu_{i,1} = \mu_{i,2} = \cdots = \mu_{i,\phi_c} = \mu'_{i,(\phi_c+1)} = \cdots = \mu'_{i,(\phi_c+q_1)} = \mu''_{i,(\phi_c+1')} = \cdots = \mu''_{i,(\phi_c+q_2)}$$

$$(i = 1, 2 \cdots, N)$$

$$\sum_{i=1}^{N} x_{i,j} = 1 \quad (j = 1, 2, \cdots, \phi_C)$$

$$\sum_{i=1}^{N} x'_{i,j} = 1 \quad (j = \phi_C + 1, \cdots, \phi_C + q_1)$$

$$\sum_{i=1}^{N} x''_{i,j} = 1 \quad (j = \phi_C + 1', \cdots, \phi_C + q_2)$$

The number of independent equations in this set of equations is

$$N(\phi_C + q_1 + q_2 - 1) + \phi_C + q_1 + q_2$$

Since $\mu_{i,j}$ is a function of T, p, $x_{i,j}$, the unknown parameters describing the equilibrium phase points of the system at the phase boundary are: T, p and $x_{i,j}, x'_{i,j'}, x''_{i,j}$, there are a total of $N(\phi_C + q_1 + q_2) + 2$ unknowns. Therefore, the equilibrium phase points may exist in the space of R_1 dimensions,

$$\begin{aligned} R_1 &= N(\phi_C + q_1 + q_2) + 2 - N(\phi_C + q_1 + q_2 - 1) - (\phi_C + q_1 + q_2) \\ &= N - (\phi_C + q_1 + q_2) + 2 \end{aligned}$$

The total number of different phases in the two NPRs, Φ is

$$\Phi = \phi_C + q_1 + q_2$$

So

$$R_1 = N - \Phi + 2 \tag{2-5}$$

If p=const

$$R_1 = N - \Phi + 1 \tag{2-6}$$

If there are r independent chemical reactions, and Z other independent constrained conditions, for the system existing on the boundary, then

$$R_1 = (N - r - Z) - \Phi + 2 \tag{2-5$'$}$$

At constant pressure,

$$R_1 = (N - r - Z) - \Phi + 1 \tag{2-6$'$}$$

Let us apply this theorem to analyze the phase boundary of NPRs in Fig. 2.1(a), for NPRs L/(L+S_1), the dimension of the phase boundary

$$R_1 = (2 - 0 - 0) - 2 + 1 = 1 \qquad \text{(See eq.(2-6$'$))}$$

It is the line aE, which implies that when the liquid phase, L and the phase region, (S_1+L) in the phase diagram (Fig. 2.1a) meet together, its phase boundary (also "boundary" in this case) has only one degree of freedom. It is not uncommon for students to interrogate the following problem when they are studying phase diagrams, "if a system exists exactly on the line aE in Fig.2.1(a), has the system: 1) only one homogenous liquid phase, or 2) two mixed liquid-solid phases? If there is only one phase, then, by the phase rule, $f = N - \phi + 1 = 2 - 1 + 1 = 2$. But this line has only one independent variable. Why?" By applying the boundary theory, the concepts of the boundary and the phase boundary are rigorously distinguished, and thus this question may be easily responded too. According to TCR, the dimension of the phase boundary line, aE, "really is equal to 1".

For NPRs (S_1+L)/ (S_1+S_2), from TCR, the dimension of their phase boundary,

$$R_1 = 2 - 3 + 1 = 0$$

From Fig. 2.1(a), the phase boundary between NPRs (S_1+L)/ (S_1+S_2) contains three invariant phase points; c (S_1), E (L) and d (S_2). Their dimension really is zero.

If ϕ_C =0, eq.(2-5) is still valid. When more than two NPRs meet at a common boundary, one may write different phase equilibrium equations for the systems in different NPRs, the same conclusion as eq. (2-5), may be derived. Detailed discussion on this matter is omitted here.

2.4 The Theorem of the Corresponding Relationship (TCR) is an Independent Theorem, Not a Variant of the Phase Rule

In contrivance of TCR, many query that TCR is essential the phase rule, or at the most, a variant of it in presentation. "Is not 'the phase number of equilibrium system ϕ', the same as 'the number of total different phases in all the neighboring phase regions Φ'? If so, why use two different symbols?" It is a good question. Actually, this is a key point in this theory. Many consider it redundant in conceptions at the first glance over it. This is a very important issue to clear up before we are to go further in the boundary theory.

We emphasize that f and R_1, ϕ and Φ are different in definition (see Table below) and they treat different objects.

	The Phase Rule	TCR
Object	Equilibrium system	NPRs and their boundaries
The parameters	f—The freedom of the equilibrium system	R_1—The dimension of phase boundary
	ϕ—The phase number of the equilibrium system	Φ—The total phase number in all neighboring phase regions

When discussing the equilibrium system existing on the boundary, the phase rule reads:

$$f = N - \phi + 2$$

Here f is the number of degrees of freedom, ϕ is the number of phases in the equilibrium system.

When considering the relationship among NPRs and their boundaries, the TCR asserts that:

$$R_1 = N - \Phi + 2 \tag{2-7}$$

Here Φ is the total number of all different phases existing in the NPRs, R_1 is the dimensions of the phase boundary between NPRs.

These two rules are similar in form, and particularly, when the equilibrium system is on the boundary, $R_1 = f$. However, they are indeed different in "essence". For example, suppose the system is on point E in the binary phase diagram shown in Fig. 2.1(a). The degree of freedom of the system equals zero, implying that the system does not have any freedom in changing either its temperature or its molar fraction, if three phases co-exist. $f = N - \phi + 1 = 2 - 3 + 1 = 0$. On the other hand, TCR gives $R_1 = N - \Phi + 1 = 2 - 3 + 1 = 0$. Here the zero is the dimension of the phase boundary, which actually involves the three invariant point c, E and d.

Indeed, when the equilibrium system is on the boundary, "the phase number of equilibrium system ϕ" and "the total phase number of different phases in NPRs Φ" are the same in value, but only in value, they are not the same thing. When the system considered is not on the boundary but in other part of a phase diagram, the ϕ and Φ may be different in value. Let's go into following scenarios, see Fig. 2.2 and Fig. 2.3 in next page.

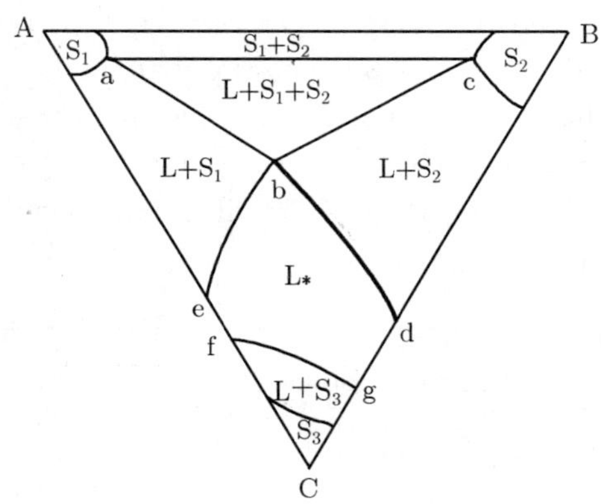

Fig. 2.2 A typical ternary phase diagram.

At point b (see Fig. 2.2 and Fig. 2.3(a)), the system at this point involves three phases: liquid, S_1 and S_2. The phase rule counts the number of phases in equilibrium as, ϕ =3. But TCR considers that that point "b" is neighboring four phase regions, and there are three (in all) different phases in these 4-phase regions, Φ=3. Here, ϕ and Φ are equal in value.

At the star position (in liquid phase region L) (see Fig. 2.2 and Fig. 2.3(b)), the system contains only L phase, ϕ=1. The TCR always looks at the boundary in phase diagram, so (1) if it is over the boundary point b, as discussed above, Φ=3;

(2) if over the boundary bd (heavy black line), Φ=2. In these two cases, we may see clearly, ϕ and Φ are talking different things.

(a)

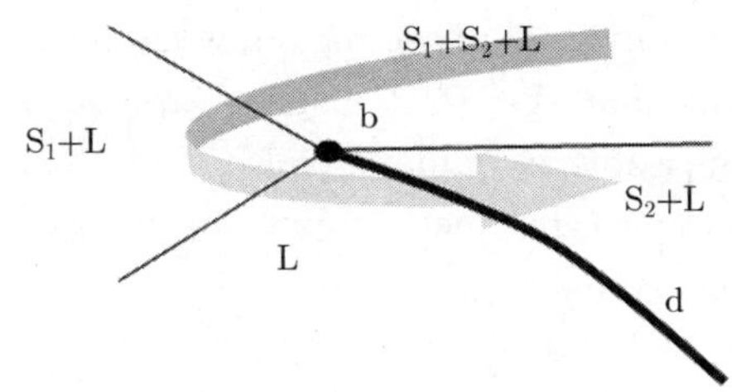

Phase rule: At the point b, there are three phases S_1, S_2, and L, coexisting in system, thus ϕ=3.
TCR: Around the point b, there are 4 neighboring phase regions, and the total different phases Φ=3.

(b)

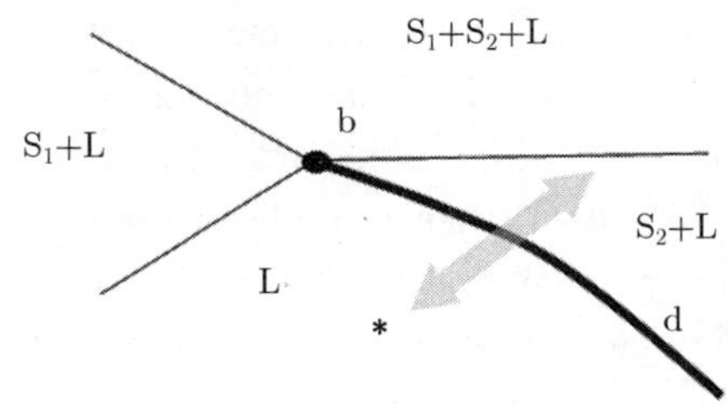

Phase rule: At the point ∗, the system contains liquid phase only, ϕ =1.
TCR: Over the line bd, there are 2 neighboring phase regions, and the total different phases Φ=2.

Fig. 2.3 ϕ and Φ are of different physical meaning and they are used from different stand points.

Generally speaking, in the phase diagram, when we are using the phase rule, we stand on "point" (0-dimension), *i.e.*, system point. We determine how many phases may be coexisting under this equilibrium condition.

While using TCR to investigate the phase diagram, we are thinking in N-dimension ($N \geqslant 2$, the dimension of phase diagram or section). We first focused on the boundary, be point, or line *etc.*, then we count how many NPRs there are and how many different phases there are. This outlook is illuminated in Fig. 2.3(a), and 2.3(b), which may be helpful to understand the method of this theory.

In this book, we have explained that we can deduce the phase boundary dimension if we know Φ, *vise versa*. We also give some examples to show that the phase rule cannot solve the problems.

Let us consider an isobaric, quinary eutectic phase diagram as another example, where there are 32 NPRs meeting at the eutectic point. When the equilibrium system existing at this point, by the phase rule, $f = N - \phi + 1, f = 0$, so ϕ=6. We are sure that there are 6 phases present in the equilibrium system at this eutectic point, but can we be certain of the total number of different phases in all of the 32 phase regions? What is the situation if it is, in reality, a phase diagram of 6-components or an even greater number system? In particular, could we deduce the phase number in any individual phase region, when just some of the cases are given?

It is on this point that the TCR distinguishes itself from the phase rule. By applying the TCR in isobaric, quinary phase diagrams, when the phase boundary existing at the eutectic or peritectic point. If given the dimension of the phase boundary R_1=0, then

$$\Phi = N - R_1 + 1 = 5 - 0 + 1 = 6$$

We are confident that the total number of different phases in all of the 32 NPRs, in contact at the eutectic or peritectic point, is 6. Further, if we know the concrete phase combination in any phase region, and the boundary between the NPRs, we could also know the situation in its neighboring phase region, thanks to TCR and its corollaries. Though when discussing the system on the boundary and the relationship among the NPRs and their boundaries, the value of f or ϕ equals the value of R_1 or Φ, respectively. They are equal to each other in value only, their meanings are different and they refer to different objects. From the parameters R_1 and Φ, we may obtain many useful results that the phase rule cannot deal with (See Chapter 3 to Chapter 6).

The phase rule was deduced more than one hundred years ago by J. W. Gibbs. However, the mere application of the phase rule did not solve all problems, for example, those concerning the relationship between NPRs and their boundaries in phase diagrams. This is why so many scientists have continued to "work out" various empirical and theoretical rules about these problems in respect to phase diagram science.

TCR is derived mathematically from thermodynamic principles and it is valid in all cases. By applying TCR, we may deduce a systematic boundary theory that can deal with all the problems concerning the relationship among the NPRs and their boundaries. The deduction of TCR didn't involve the application of the phase rule, and, as a matter of fact, TCR cannot be deduced from phase rule.

In summary, it is stated that TCR is an independent theorem, it is not a variant of the phase rule.

2.5 Corollaries of TCR for Isobaric Phase Diagrams

In combining TCR and some basic characteristics of isobaric phase diagrams, several corollaries of TCR may be obtained. These corollaries help to determine the ranges and regularities of variations in Φ, R_1 and ϕ_C values in isobaric phase diagrams of different types. In the general case, $Z = r = 0$, and for isobaric phase diagrams, $p =$ constant.

1st corollary: The range of variations in the value of Φ in binary and multicomponent isobaric phase diagrams.

Since $R_1 = N - \Phi + 1$ and $R_1 \geqslant 0, N + 1 \geqslant \Phi$; and two NPRs contain two phases at least, thence

$$(N+1) \geqslant \Phi \geqslant 2$$

2nd corollary: The range of variations in the value of R_1 in isobaric, binary and multicomponent phase diagrams.

Since $\Phi \geqslant 2$, and $R_1 = N - \Phi + 1, (N-1) \geqslant R_1$, that is

$$(N-1) \geqslant R_1 \geqslant 0$$

3rd corollary: For two NPRs of isobaric binary and multicomponent phase diagrams, there are two cases satisfying $R_1 = 0$ and $\phi_C = 0$.

(1) When two single-phase regions meet each other at a single phase point,

$$\phi_C = 0, \quad R_1 = 0.$$

For the general isobaric phase diagram, there is $Z = r = 0$ as a whole, but in this phase diagram, there may occur some single points, for which

$$Z \neq 0$$

If two single-phase regions, f_j and f_k should meet at a common phase boundary, every pair of phase points at this phase boundary satisfies

$$x_{1,j} = x_{1,k}, \quad x_{2,j} = x_{2,k}, \quad \cdots, \quad x_{N,j} = x_{N,k}$$

There are $(N-1)$ independent equations constraining the concentrations, *i.e.* $Z = N - 1$, and $r = 0$, $\Phi = 2, p =$ constant, so:

$$R_1 = N - (N-1) - 2 + 1 = 0$$

Since $R_1 = 0$, there is a single phase point satisfying this condition, $R_1 = 0$ and $\phi_C = 0$.

For examples, please see subsection 3.3.2.3, Fig. 3.4 or Rhines' first empirical rule in section 3.5.

(2) When $N \geqslant 2, R_1 = 0$, and the phase transition occurs at the invariant temperature. There is a boundary with $(\phi_{\max} + 1) = (N + 1)$ coexisting phases between two NPRs during the phase transition.

$$R_1 = 0, \quad \Phi = N + 1$$

If $$\phi_1 = N, \quad \phi_2 = 1$$

$$\phi_C = \phi_1 + \phi_2 - \Phi = N + 1 - (N+1) = 0$$

This case satisfies $R_1 = 0$ and $\phi_C = 0$.

4th corollary: Excluding the two cases mentioned in corollary 3, if $R_1 \geqslant 1$, the range of variations of the value of ϕ_C should be:

$$(\Phi - 1) \geqslant \phi_C \geqslant 1$$

We can use the "reduction to absurdity" method to prove this corollary. Two NPRs must have at least one common system point, otherwise they are not neighbors to each other. The system existing at the common system point must satisfy the equilibrium conditions for both of the two NPRs. Let the first and second NPRs contain ϕ_1 and ϕ_2 phases respectively, and assume ϕ_C=0. $m_1, m_2, \cdots, m_{\phi_1}$; $m_{1'}, m_{2'}, \cdots, m_{\phi_2}$; $x_{i,1}$, $x_{i,2}, \cdots, x_{i,\phi_1}$; $x_{i,1'}, x_{i,2'}, \cdots, x_{i,\phi_2} (i = 1, 2, \cdots, N)$ are the total amounts in moles and the mole fractions of different components in different phases in the first and the second NPRs, respectively. In the system, x_i $(i = 1, 2, \cdots, N)$, is the mole fraction of the i-th component in the system. Temperature T is also a variable. The total number of unknowns in the whole system is:

$$\phi_1 + \phi_2 + N\phi_1 + N\phi_2 + N + 1 = N(\phi_1 + \phi_2) + \phi_1 + \phi_2 + N + 1$$

The system has the following phase equilibrium conditions:

$$\mu_{i,1} = \mu_{i,2} = \cdots = \mu_{i,\phi_1} = \mu_{i,1'} = \mu_{i,2'} = \cdots = \mu_{i,\phi_2} \quad (i = 1, 2, \cdots, N)$$

there are total N $(\phi_1+\phi_2-1)$ phase equilibrium equations. The different components of the system satisfy the following mass balance equations: (Where M is the mole number of the system.).

For the first NPR,

$$x_{i,1}m_1 + x_{i,2}m_2 + \cdots + x_{i,\phi_1}m_{\phi_1} = Mx_i \tag{2-8}$$

$$(i = 1, 2, \cdots, N; N \text{ equations})$$

For the second NPR,

$$x_{x,1'}m_{1'} + x_{i,2'}m_{2'} + \cdots + x_{i,\phi_2}m_{\phi_2} = Mx_i \tag{2-9}$$

$$(i = 1, 2, \cdots, N; N \text{ equations})$$

And the following equations also hold:

$$\sum_{i=1}^{N} x_{i,j} = 1, (j = 1, 2, \cdots, \phi_1; \phi_1 \text{ equations}), \tag{2-10}$$

$$\sum_{i=1}^{N} x_{i,j'} = 1, (j' = 1', 2', \cdots, \phi_2; \phi_2 \text{ equations}), \tag{2-11}$$

From equations (2-8) and (2-10),

$$\sum_{j=1}^{\phi_1} x_{i,j} m_j = \sum_{j=1}^{\phi_1} m_j = \sum_{i=1}^{N} x_i \sum_{j=1}^{\phi_1} m_j$$

Then:

$$\sum_{i=1}^{N} x_i = 1$$

So this equation is not an independent equation. Since the system is the same, there induces another independent equation.

$$\sum_{j=1}^{\phi_1} m_j = \sum_{j'=1'}^{\phi_2} m_{j'}$$

The total number of independent equations is

$$N(\phi_1 + \phi_2 - 1) + N + N + \phi_1 + \phi_2 + 1 = N(\phi_1 + \phi_2) + \phi_1 + \phi_2 + N + 1$$

Therefore, the number of degrees of freedom of the equilibrium system, existing on the boundary with ϕ_C =0 is:

$$f = (N+1)(\phi_1 + \phi_2) + N + 1 - [(N+1)(\phi_1 + \phi_2) + N + 1] = 0$$

The dimension of the phase boundary, $R_1 = f$ =0. This is to say if $\phi_C = 0$, R_1 must be zero. By reduction to absurdity, when $R_1 \geqslant 1$, then $\phi_C \geqslant 1$.

On the other hand, $(\phi_C)_{\max}$ can not be equal to $\varPhi$, otherwise the two NPRs are identical, so $(\phi_C)_{\max} \leqslant (\varPhi - 1)$. Finally, we obtain, if $R_1 \geqslant 1$,

$$(\varPhi - 1) \geqslant \phi_C \geqslant 1$$

5th corollary: For isobaric binary and multicomponent phase diagrams, when R_1 =0, the phase transition occurs at an invariant temperature and there is a boundary with $(\phi_{\max}+1) = (N+1)$ coexisting phases between two NPRs during the phase transition;

$$(\varPhi - 2) \geqslant \phi_C \geqslant 0$$

When $R_1 = 0$, $\varPhi = N + 1$. $\phi_{\max} = N$ (eq.(2-4)), and ϕ_C can not be equal to $\phi_{\max}$, otherwise the two NPRs are identical, so

$$\phi_C \leqslant (\phi_{\max} - 1) = (N - 1) = (\varPhi - 2)$$

Thus $$(\Phi - 2) \geqslant \phi_C$$

The 3rd corollary has indicated that, when $R_1 = 0$, ϕ_C may be equal to zero, so the 5th corollary holds.

In summary, for binary and multicomponent isobaric phase diagrams with $Z = r = 0$, the ranges and regularities of variations of R_1, Φ and ϕ_C have been worked out.

2.6 The Relationship between the Dimensions of the Phase Boundary R_1 and the Dimensions of the Boundary R_1' for Isobaric Multicomponent Phase Diagrams

According to TCR, the value of R_1 may be calculated from Φ. But the most boundaries as shown on the phase diagrams, especially in the multicomponent phase diagrams, are sets of system points ("boundaries" as defined in section 2.2.7.1), and not phase boundaries (*i.e.*, sets of phase points). It is now appropriate to discuss how to derive the value of R_1' from R_1 and ϕ_C.

2.6.1 The qualitative explanation of the two formulas between R_1' and R_1

1. When $N \geqslant 2, R_1 = 0$, the phase transition occurs at an invariant temperature and there is a boundary with $(\phi_{\max}+1) = (N+1)$ coexisting phases between the two NPRs during the phase transition. The mass of the system may be distributed over ϕ_C common phases and one non-common phase (this will be proved theoretically later), there is a formula between R_1' and R_1:

$$R_1' = R_1 + \phi_C \quad (\text{since} \;\; R_1 = 0) \tag{2-12}$$

Consider two NPRs $(L+S_1)/(S_1+S_2)$ in Fig. 2.1(a) to illustrate the application of eq. (2-12). During the process of invariant phase transition (R_1 =0), for the system on the boundary between $(L+S_1)/(S_1+S_2)$, when it still exists in the phase region $(L+S_1)$, the mass of the system may be distributed among one common phase S_1 and one non-common phase L. Phases L, S_1 and S_2 coexist during the process of transition; since $(\phi_{\max}+1)=(N+1)=3$, this observation tallies with the condition mentioned above.

From $\Phi = 3, R_1 = N - \Phi + 1 = 0$, and $\phi_C = 1(S_1)$, according to the eq. (2-12), $R_1' = 0 + 1 = 1$. Thus the boundary between NPRs $(L+S_1)/(S_1+S_2)$ is one-dimensional, it is an isothermal line. Another example is the boundary between NPRs $L/(S_1+S_2)$ in Fig. 2.1(a); $R_1' = 0$. The phase transition occurs at an invariant temperature and there is a boundary with $(\phi_{\max} + 1)$ coexisting phases during the phase transition, and ϕ_C =0, then

$$R_1' = 0 + 0 = 0$$

The boundary is an invariant point.

Let us discuss how eq. (2-12) is obtained. Eq. (2-12) is used to calculate R_1' from R_1. The first step is to fix the equilibrium phase points at the given condition, and then find out the dimensions of the element in which the system points are distributed. For NPRs (L+S_1)/(S_1+S_2), the phase boundary has R_1 =0, the phase points are fixed themselves, see Fig. 2.4.

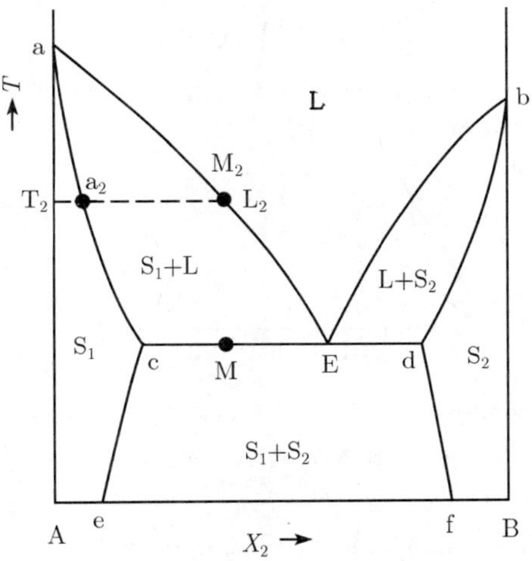

Fig. 2.4 A typical isobaric binary diagram.

The mass of the system is distributed in a common phase S_1, represented by point c, and a non-common phase L, represented by point E. According to mass balance principle, the system point M must exist at the tie-line of two phase points, c and E. In this case, the mass of the system may be distributed over a non-common phase, this is possible only for the condition: R_1 =0, the phase transition occurs at an invariant temperature, and there is a boundary with ($\phi_{\max}$+1) coexisting phases between the two NPRs during the invariant phase transition. Here, $\phi_C = 1$, the system points exist in the one-dimensional "tie-line" of two phase points, *i.e.* the tie-line with $\phi_C(= 1)$ dimension,

$$R_1' = R_1 + \phi_C = 0 + 1 = 1$$

The circumstances of isobaric, ternary phase diagrams are similar. Let us take an isobaric ternary, partially miscible, eutectic phase diagram, for example. We discuss the boundary with ($\phi_{\max}+1=4$) coexisting phases between the two NPRs ($L+S_1+S_2$)/($S_1+S_2+S_3$), the invariant phase transition occurs between two NPRs. $\phi_C=2(S_1, S_2)$, the mass of the system is distributed over two common phases S_1 and S_2, represented by point a and b, respectively, and one non-common phase, L represented by point E. According to the mass balance principle, the system points exist in the triangle formed by three phase points: a, b and E ($\phi_C+1=3$). This triangle is two-dimensional, *i.e.* $R_1'=\phi_C=2$, or $R_1'=R_1+\phi_C$ (see Fig. 2.5).

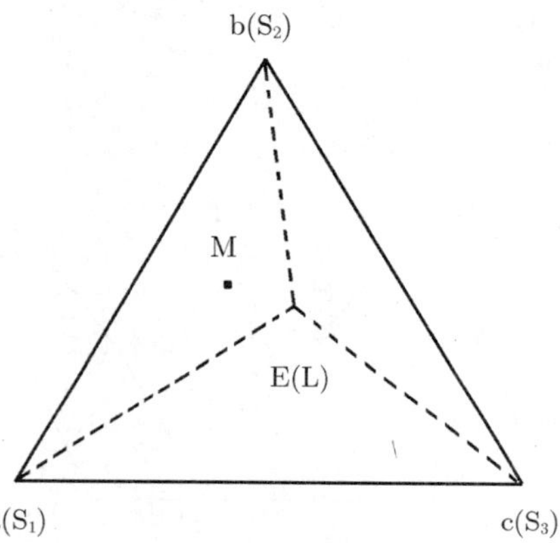

Fig. 2.5 System point and phase points of the system at the eutectic temperature in a ternary phase diagram.

For the isobaric phase diagrams of N-components ($N\geqslant3$), when $R_1=0$, the phase transition occurs at an invariant temperature, and there is a boundary with ($\phi_{\max}+1$) coexisting phases during the phase transition, the mass of the system being distributed over (ϕ_C+1) phases, represented by ϕ_C common-phase points and one non-common phase point. Similarly, it may be shown that the system points exist in an ϕ_C-dimensional boundary, formed by (ϕ_C+1) phase points as vertexes, *i.e.*

$$R_1'=\phi_C \quad \text{or} \quad R_1'=R_1+\phi_C$$

2. For other cases, for the system at the boundary, the mass of the system may be distributed only over common phases.

$$R_1'=R_1+(\phi_C-1) \tag{2-13}$$

For example, let us discuss the boundary of NPRs L/(L+S_1) in Fig. 2.4. $R_1=N-\varPhi+1=1, \phi_C$=1(L). $R_1'=1+1-1=1$, $R_1'=R_1$ =1, so it is a one-dimensional boundary and also a one-dimensional phase boundary.

Let us now discuss how eq. (2-13) is obtained. Initially, the phase points are fixed; after fixing the temperature (the phase points are the fixed points, a_2 and L_2 (see Fig. 2.4)). All of the system mass is distributed over the common phase L, at the phase point L_2. The system point, M_2, coincides with the common phase point L_2, it is a zero-dimensional point. Here, ϕ_C=1, so the system point exists at the point with $(\phi_C - 1) = 0$ dimension. When the temperature varies, the phase point varies with the temperature, so R_1=1; and the system point varies in the same way, R_1' =1, *i.e.*

$$R_1' = R_1 + (\phi_C - 1) = 1 + 1 - 1 = 1$$

For NPRs $(L+S_1)/(L+S_1+S_2)$ in a ternary isobaric phase diagram, one has $R_1 = N - \Phi + 1 = 3 - 3 + 1 = 1, \phi_C$=2. In fixing the temperature, the phase points are then fixed too. The phase points are L_1 of the common phases L and a_1, the phase point of another common phase, S_1 (see Fig. 2.6).

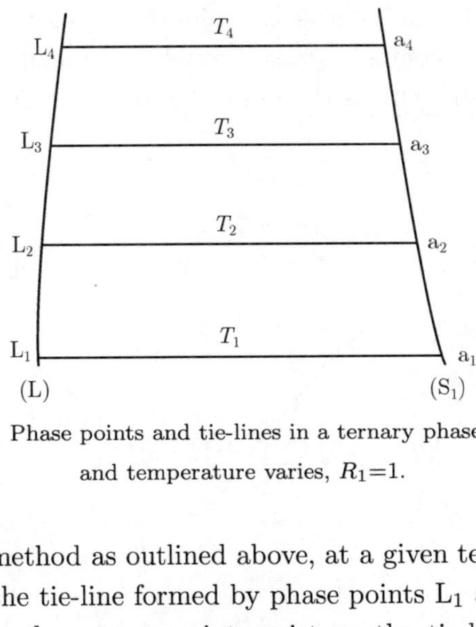

Fig. 2.6 Phase points and tie-lines in a ternary phase diagram, and temperature varies, R_1=1.

According to the method as outlined above, at a given temperature, the system points must exist on the tie-line formed by phase points L_1 and a_1, of the common phases L and S_1, *i.e.* the system points exist on the tie-line of the $(\phi_C - 1)$=1 dimension. The phase points vary as the temperature changes, R_1=1. The tie-line, on which the system points exist, also varies. The locus of the tie-line varying with the temperature is a plane of two dimensions. So

$$R_1' = R_1 + (\phi_C - 1) = 1 + 2 - 1 = 2$$

Similarly, eq. (2-13) can be obtained for the isobaric phase diagrams of N-components ($N \geqslant 3$).

2.6.2 The theoretical proof of the two formulae between R_1 and R_1' in $N \geqslant 2$ isobaric phase diagrams

2.6.2.1 Two types of phase transitions in the phase diagram

For the system in the first NPR transfers to the second NPR by the phase transition, there are two different types of the phase transitions, it is well known in phase equilibrium, let us just apply these characteristics to deduce the two formulae between R_1 and R_1'.

1. Type 1

$R_1 \geqslant 1$, when the phase transition just starts to occur or the two NPRs exist over the boundary in equilibrium, all the components of the system can distribute itself over the common phases of NPRs only.

Let us discuss the phase region (L) → phase region (L+S_1), see Fig.2.7. First, the system exists in the liquid phase (point p_1). If temperature T decreases, the system reaches the boundary line, aE, at point M_1, the phase transition then starts, and the NPRs L/ (L+S_1) still exists in equilibrium. All components of the system are distributed over the common phase L only, the amount of non-common phase S_1 is really infinitesimal. This is the basic characteristic of the phase transition of this first type.

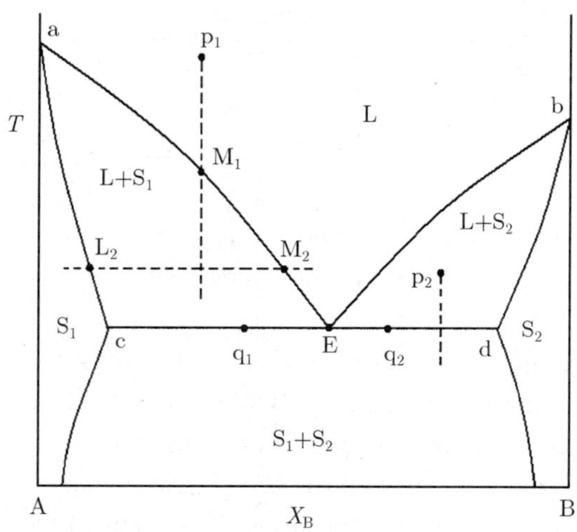

Fig. 2.7 Two types of phase transitions and a special case of phase region transfer.

Let T decreases further, the system is now divided into two phases, *i.e.* the system distributes over the common phase, L (at point M_2) and the non-common phase, S_1 (at point L_2). This really is another problem—the phase transition occurs inside the two-phase region (L+S_1), it is not the phase transition that occurs on the boundary between NPRs L/(L+S_1).

2. Type 2

When R_1=0, during the invariant phase transitions at the invariant temperature, the components of the system can be distributed over all of the coexisting phases of NPRs.

Let us now discuss the phase transition (L+S_2) → (S_1+S_2) (Fig.2.7). At first, the system exists at p_2, in the phase region (L+S_2). The temperature is now decreasing. When the system point reaches the Ed line but the invariant phase transition has not yet started, the system then contains one common phase, S_2, and one non-common phase, L. At this point, the invariant phase transition starts and continues. Another non-common phase, S_1, starts to form and increases, while the non-common phase, L, in the original phase region (L+S_2), decreases. In the course of the whole invariant phase transition, there are 3 phases $=(\phi_{\max+1}) = (N+1)$(*i.e.* S_2, L and S_1) coexisting in the system. These three phases may have definite and different amounts of components. When the phase transitions go further, the amount of S_1 increases while the amount of L gradually decreasing to zero at last. Following the invariant phase transition, the system now contains one common phase, S_2, and one non-common phase, S_1 the latter being the phase appearing during the phase transition.

2.6.2.2 A special case of the phase region transfer

Let the phase region (L+S_1) transfer to phase region (L+S_2) at the eutectic temperature. See Fig.2.7. Suppose the system point is q_1 at the beginning, then, at constant T_E (eutectic temperature), component B is gradually introduced into the system, whence x_B increases while x_A decreases. When the system point reaches point E, the system distributes over the phase L (the common phase of NPRs (L+S_1)/(L+S_2)) only (this is a very important characteristic!). By introducing more of component B into the system, while the temperature is maintained constant, the non-common phase, S_2 then appears and gradually increases. The non-common phase component of the original phase region, S_1 has already disappeared. The system then has one common phase, L and one non-common phase, S_2, the system representative point now being q_2.

This case just outlined is not a true real phase transition, it amounts only to a phase region transfer occurring when some additional component input into the system at the invariant temperature.

This case actually exists in the phase diagram. We have to discuss it in due course but it is not all that important.

2.6.2.3 The theoretical proof of eq. (2-13), $R_1'=R_1+\phi_C-1$

There are two cases of R_1 only: $R_1 \geqslant 1$ and $R_1=0$.

In the first instance, we will discuss the case of $R_1 \geqslant 1$ and the phase transition of the first type.

The system is in equilibrium on the boundary, the system components are distributed over the common phases.

For a given initial condition, *e.g.* T, p are kept constant, the phase compositions are then fixed. Assume that the first NPR contains phases: $f_1, f_2, \cdots, f_{\phi_C}$, $f_{\phi_C+1}, \cdots, f_{\phi_C+q_1}$, the second NPR contains: $f_1, f_2, \cdots, f_{\phi_C}, f_{\phi_C+1'}, \cdots, f_{\phi_C+q_2}$, where $f_1, f_2, \cdots, f_{\phi_C}$ are those common phases existing in both NPRs. And $f_{\phi_C+1}, \cdots, f_{\phi_C+q_1}$ are those phases existing only in the first NPR, and $f_{\phi_C+1'}, \cdots$, $f_{\phi_C+q_2}$ are those phases existing only in the second NPR. Now, in accord with the 4th corollary, and for this case where $R_1 \geqslant 1$, $(\Phi-1) \geqslant \phi_C \geqslant 1$, there are, during the phase transition, q_1 original phases disappearing and q_2 new phases appearing. According to the mass balance principle (*i.e.* the level rule, the center of gravity rule and the extended center of gravity rule, [P-L, 1964]), when the system point is exactly on the boundary, all components of the system are distributed among the common phases of the NPRs and the total of the masses of the "disappearing" phases and the newly "appearing" phases are infinitesimal.

Since all components of the system existing at the boundary are distributed over the common phases, the following equations stand (m_j and M are the mole number of j-th phase, and the mole number of the overall system, respectively):

$$\begin{aligned} x_{1,1}m_1 + x_{1,2}m_2 + \cdots + x_{1,j}m_j + \cdots + x_{1,\phi_C}m_{\phi_C} &= Mx_1 \\ x_{2,1}m_1 + x_{2,2}m_2 + \cdots + x_{2,j}m_j + \cdots + x_{2,\phi_C}m_{\phi_C} &= Mx_2 \\ &\vdots \\ x_{N,1}m_1 + x_{N,2}m_2 + \cdots + x_{N,j}m_j + \cdots + x_{N,\phi_C}m_{\phi_C} &= Mx_N \end{aligned}$$

The both sides of each equation mentioned above are now divided by M, and thus

$$y_j = \frac{m_j}{M}$$

$$x_{i,1}y_1 + x_{i,2}y_2 + \cdots + x_{i,j}y_j + \cdots + x_{i,\phi_C}y_{\phi_C} = x_i (i = 1, 2, \cdots, N)$$

$$\sum_{j=1}^{\phi_C} y_j = 1$$

From linear algebra, applied to the set of equations above, the ϕ_C common phase points on the boundary form ϕ_C concentration vectors $\{x_{1,j}, x_{2,j}, \ldots, x_{i,j}, \ldots, x_{N,j}\}$, $j = 1, 2, \cdots, \phi_C$ in N-dimensional space. These ϕ_C concentration vectors are linearly independent in the phase diagram space of N dimensions, with the exception that they are related, one to another, with the phase equilibrium conditions; they (serving as vertexes) are able to construct a hyperplane of $(\phi_C - 1)$ dimensions. On the other hand, the N concentration vectors of system points $\{x_1, x_2, \ldots, x_N\}$ are linear combinations of the ϕ_C concentration vectors of phase points. Because $1 \geqslant y_j \geqslant 0$ and $\sum_{j=1}^{\phi_C} y_j = 1$, the vectors of the system points $\{x_1, x_2, \ldots, x_N\}$ must be within the same hyperplane of $(\phi_C - 1)$ dimensions and cannot be outside of it.

Let the conditions now be changed, for example, by T, *etc.* being varied. If there are R_1 parameters being varied, the equilibrium phase points of the common phases (*i.e.* the vertexes of hyperplane of $(\phi_C - 1)$ dimensions mentioned above) may move in the space of R_1 dimensions, and the hyperplane over which the system points exist, may also move in this space of R_1 dimensions (Please see the example in section 2.6.1.1 and Fig.2.4 and its explanation, this argument may then be more easily understood). So now the total dimensions of the space in which the system points exist on the boundary, are $(R_1 + \phi_C - 1)$, *i.e.*

$$R_1' = R_1 + (\phi_C - 1) \tag{2-13}$$

Next, we discuss the case of $R_1 = 0$ and $R_1' = R_1 + (\phi_C - 1)$. This actually occurs on the invariant isothermal line, for example, the eutectic line. The transfer from one NPR to another NPR is driven by the change of system composition. When the system exists at this boundary, then, by mass balance principle, all masses of the system components are distributed over the common phases, *i.e.* the masses of components, in those original phases disappearing and in those phases newly appearing, are infinitesimal. In this case, $\phi_C \geqslant 1$, between these two NPRs, there are ϕ_C common phase points. These phase points construct a hyperplane of $(\phi_C - 1)$ dimensions, all of the components are distributed over the common phases. This situation is similar to the case: $R_1 \geqslant 1$ and $R_1' = R_1 + (\phi_C - 1)$, as discussed previously. When the values of the phase points $\{x_{i,j}\}$ $(i = 1, 2, \cdots, N; j = 1, 2, \cdots, \phi_C)$ are given, all those system points $\{x_i\}(i = 1, 2, \cdots, N)$ satisfying the phase equilibrium conditions are distributed over the concentration hyperplane of $(\phi_C - 1)$ dimensions and so fill the whole hyperplane but can not exceed it. So, in this case, the dimensions of the hyperplane over which the system points are distributed, are: $(\phi_C - 1)$. Although the equilibrium phase points are invariant, $R_1 = 0$, the relation between R_1 and R_1' is still in the form of

$$R_1' = R_1 + (\phi_C - 1).$$

This case is not really a phase transition, it is only a phase region transfer.

2.6.2.4 The theoretical proof of R_1 =0, there is an invariant phase transition between two NPRs and $R_1' = R_1 + \phi_C$

Let us now discuss the phase transition of the second type (ref. subsection 2.6.1.1).

Consider the case, $N \geqslant 2$, R_1=0 and the phase transition occurring at the invariant (eutectic or peritectic) temperature, there exists an invariant region of $(\phi_{\max} + 1) = (N + 1)$ coexisting phases between the two NPRs during the phase transition.

When the temperature decreases, the system reaches the invariant region from the first NPR while the phase transition has not yet started. All components of the system are distributed over the phases of the first NPR. As the phase transition proceeds, the non-common phases of the first NPR decrease continuously while the non-common phases, existing within the second NPR, newly appear and increase gradually. In the course of this invariant phase transition, all phases in both NPRs simultaneously exist, while the amounts of all of these phases vary continuously. Until the invariant phase transition ends, all components are distributed over those phases existing in the second NPR.

In the case of: R_1 =0 and $\varPhi = (N + 1)$, and according to eq.(2-4), $\phi_{\max} = N$; then $\phi_1 \leqslant N$, $\phi_2 \leqslant N$; since $\varPhi > N$, in this case, even $\phi_1 = \phi_2 = N$, two NPRs are still not identical.

Let the phases in the first NPR be $f_1, f_2, \cdots, f_{\phi_1}$. When the system just reaches the invariant phase transition temperature, all components still being distributed over the phases of the first NPR, the following relation among the compositions of the system points $\{x_i\} (i = 1, 2, \cdots, N)$ and the compositions of the phase points $\{x_{i,j}\}$ $(i = 1, 2, \cdots, N; j = 1, 2, \cdots, \phi_1)$ are valid:

$$\begin{aligned} x_{1,1}m_1 + x_{1,2}m_2 + \cdots + x_{1,\phi_1}m_{\phi_1} &= Mx_1 \\ x_{2,1}m_1 + x_{2,2}m_2 + \cdots + x_{2,\phi_1}m_{\phi_1} &= Mx_2 \\ &\vdots \\ x_{N,1}m_1 + x_{N,2}m_2 + \cdots + x_{N,\phi_1}m_{\phi_1} &= Mx_N \end{aligned} \qquad (2\text{-}14)$$

$m_1, m_2, \cdots, m_{\phi_1}$ are the sum of all the masses of the components $(i = 1, 2, \cdots, N)$ in the j-th phase $(j = 1, 2, \cdots, \phi_1)$ in the first NPR, M is the total amount of these component masses in the system. When the invariant phase transition is just terminated, the mass of the system is wholly distributed over the second NPR. The following relation, then existing among the compositions of the system points $\{x_i\}$ and the phase compositions of the phase points in the second NPR $\{x_{i,j'}\} (i = 1, 2, \cdots, N; j' = 1', 2', \cdots, \phi_2)$, is valid. Then:

$$\begin{aligned} x_{1,1'}m_{1'} + x_{1,2'}m_{2'} + \cdots + x_{1,\phi_2}m_{\phi_2} &= Mx_1 \\ x_{2,1'}m_{1'} + x_{2,2'}m_{2'} + \cdots + x_{2,\phi_2}m_{\phi_2} &= Mx_2 \\ &\vdots \\ x_{N,1'}m_{1'} + x_{N,2'}m_{2'} + \cdots + x_{N,\phi_2}m_{\phi_2} &= Mx_N \end{aligned} \qquad (2\text{-}15)$$

where $m_{1'}, m_{2'}, \cdots, m_{\phi_2}$ are the sum of the masses of all the components ($i = 1, 2, \cdots, N$) in the j'-th phase ($j' = 1', 2', \cdots, \phi_2$) in the second NPR. In the case of an invariant phase transition at an invariant temperature, the phase compositions are also invariant, so all $\{x_{i,j}\}$ and $\{x_{i,j'}\}$ are known fixed values. Since there are ϕ_C common phases in the two NPRs, some concentration vectors of $\{x_{i,j}\}$ and $\{x_{i,j'}\}$ are in common, but the masses of the common phases in the two NPRs are still different in values. So $m_1, m_2, \cdots, m_{\phi_1}, m_{1'}, m_{2'}, \cdots, m_{\phi_2}; x_i (i = 1, 2, \cdots, N)$ are the independent variables. Since $\sum_{j=1}^{\phi_1} m_j = M$, so M is not an independent variable.

For the same system, the following relation holds:

$$\sum_{j=1}^{\phi_1} m_j = \sum_{j'=1}^{\phi_2} m_{j'} \tag{2-16}$$

Considering eqs.(2-14), (2-15) and (2-16) to be true independent equations, thence

$$\sum_{i=1}^{N} x_i = 1$$

is not an independent equation. There are a total $(2N + 1)$ of independent equations in eqs (2-14)–(2-16). The independent variables are $x_i (i = 1, 2, \cdots, N)$, $m_j (j = 1, 2, \cdots, \phi_1)$, $m_{j'} (j' = 1', 2', \cdots, \phi_2)$. The number of independent variables is;

$$N + \phi_1 + \phi_2 = N + \Phi + \phi_C = 2N + 1 + \phi_C$$

The dimensions of the solution for equations (2-14)~(2-16) are

$$2N + 1 + \phi_C - (2N + 1) = \phi_C$$

so the dimensions of the system points R_1' are ϕ_C. Although $R_1 = 0$, for uniformity, we write

$$R_1' = R_1 + \phi_C \tag{2-12}$$

If $\phi_C = 0$, $R_1' = 0$, the system point has a unique solution, the two NPRs have only one common system point.

When $\phi_C \neq 0$, the hyperplane of dimensions, ϕ_C, over which the system points of the boundary are distributed, is constructed in such a way. ϕ_C common phases have ϕ_C common phase points, furthermore, when $\phi_C = 0$, there is still a common system point so there are $(\phi_C + 1)$ common phase points or common system points. According to the 5th corollary, $\phi_C \leqslant (\Phi - 2) = N - 1$, so

$$(\phi_C + 1) \leqslant N$$

Besides, these (ϕ_C+1) common phase points or system points are related one to another within the phase equilibrium conditions. Further, they are linearly independent within their concentration space of N dimensions. These (ϕ_C+1) points serve as vertexes to form a hyperplane of ϕ_C dimensions, over which the system points are distributed. The hyperplane of ϕ_C dimensions is a common component of both of the NPRs. The dimensions of boundary R_1 are ϕ_C, and eq.(2-12) is therefore valid.

Finally, we may now try to explain the character of the only common system point existing between the two NPRs. When R_1=0, phase transition occurs at the invariant temperature, and there exists an invariant region containing $(\phi_{\max}+1)$=$(N+1)$ phases, situated between two NPRs during the invariant phase transition. When $\phi_C=0$, and $\phi_1=N$ and ϕ_2 =1, in this case, the only single common system point, situated between the two NPRs, is the equilibrium phase point of the only one phase of the second NPR.

Since all equilibrium phase points over the invariant region are indeed invariants, these equilibrium phase points of the second NPR are therefore invariants also. In this single-phase region, the phase point coincides with the system point, therefore this phase point is also a system point on the boundary of the second NPR. It has been shown that, when $R_1'=R_1+\phi_C, \phi_C=0$ and $R_1=0$, the "common" system point of the two NPRs is unique. So the common system point is the only single phase point of the second NPR located in the invariant region.

As indicated above, we have presented equations for the calculation of R_1' from values of R_1 and ϕ_C, and the corresponding theoretical proof of these equations. The difference between these equations

$$R_1'=R_1+\phi_C \tag{2-12}$$

$$R_1'=R_1+(\phi_C-1) \tag{2-13}$$

is not simply due to "plus or minus" one artificially, it reflects on the difference between the two different types of phase transitions in the phase diagram. Further, these two equations are deduced theoretically when treating the different types of phase transitions.

2.7 The Summary of the Boundary Theory of Isobaric Phase Diagrams

The basic points of the boundary theory of isobaric phase diagrams are:

1. The concept of the phase boundary has been put forward and the relation between the "phase boundary" and the "boundary" and their differences, has determined. We have revealed the concept of Φ, *i.e.*, the total number of different phases

present in all NPRs. The assemblage of NPRs phases is the important feature of the phase diagram. From these assemblages of NPRs phases, the important parameters Φ and ϕ_C are able to be calculated. From Φ and ϕ_C, according to the later points, the parameters R_1 and R_1' may also be obtained.

2. Based on the above concepts, along with the phase equilibrium equations for the equilibrium system existing on the boundary, the theorem of corresponding relationship (TCR) between Φ and R_1 is obtained. For use in isobaric phase diagrams, and in general cases, Z=0, r=0, $R_1 = N - \Phi + 1$. This is eq. (2-6).

We have demonstrated that TCR is an independent theorem, not a variant of the phase rule.

3. Through logical deduction, we have obtained five corollaries for the TCR, which determine both the ranges and regularities in the variation of Φ, ϕ_C and R_1. These corollaries are useful in dealing with problems concerning the phase diagram.

4. Based on the relation between the phase point compositions, the system point compositions, and the mass balance principle, the two equations for calculating R_1' from the values of R_1 and ϕ_C are theoretically demonstrated. For phase transitions of the first type, $R_1 \geqslant 1$. When the phase transition commences, the equilibrium system can be distributed over the common phases between the NPRs only, $R_1' = R_1 + (\phi_C - 1)$, eq.(2-13). For phase transitions of the second type, when R_1=0, the phase transition occurs at an invariant temperature, and there is an invariant region of coexisting (N+1) phases between the two NPRs during the phase transition, $R_1' = R_1 + \phi_C$, eq.(2-12).

The difference between eqs(2-13) and (2-12) is not due to artificial plus or minus one, but due to the difference of two types of phase transitions in the real phase diagram.

5. Eqs. (2-6), (2-12) and (2-13) are the three principal formulas for the boundary theory of isobaric phase diagrams.

If Φ, ϕ_C, R_1 and R_1' are given parameters, then the relationship among the NPRs and their boundaries can be well explained. With the aid of the boundary theory of phase diagrams, one now may well understand how phase regions and their boundaries can be manipulated to construct both the "elegance" and the "utility" of phase diagrams!

References-2

P. Gordon. 1968. Principles of phase diagrams in materials systems. New York: McGraw-Hill

M. Hillert. 1985. Principles of phase diagrams. International Metals Rev., 30(2): 45

M. Hillert. 1993. Gibbs' phase rule applied to phase diagrams and transformations. J. Phase Equilibrium, 14: 418

M. Hillert. 2007. Phase equilibria, phase diagrams and phase transformations, their thermodynamic basis. 2nd ed. Cambridge: Cambridge University Press

L. S. Palatnik, A. I. Landau. 1964. Phase equilibria in multicomponent phase diagrams. New York: Holt Rinehart and Winston, Inc

F. A. H. Schreinemakers, K. Akad. 1915. Wetenschappen (Section of Sciences). 18: 116 Amsterdam

Muyu Zhao, Xiaobao Fan. 1985. The relation between the dimensions of the boundary and phase boundary in isobaric phase diagrams. Scientia Sinica, Ser, B, 28(5): 458

Muyu Zhao. 1983. The theorem of corresponding relation between neighboring phase regions and their boundaries in phase diagrams. CALPHAD, 7(3): 185-199

Chapter 3

Application of the Boundary Theory to Unary, Binary and Ternary Phase Diagrams – Comparison of the Boundary Theory Application and Palatnik-Landau's Contact Rule of Phase Regions

According to the boundary theory of isobaric phase diagrams, the relationship among NPRs and their boundaries in unary, binary and ternary phase diagrams of all types (including isothermal and isopleth sections), could, with advantage, be systematically clarified. With the aid of boundary theory, Rhines' ten empirical rules concerning the construction of complicated ternary phase diagrams from phase diagram units are well expounded. A comparison, made between the boundary theory and Palatnik-Landau's contact rule of phase regions, is also presented in this chapter.

3.1 Determination of Phase Assemblages of NPRs and the Characteristics of Their Boundaries by the Boundary Theory

3.1.1 Determination of the phase assemblage of the second NPR, when the phase assemblage of the first NPR, and the characteristics of the boundary between the two NPRs, are known

According to eq. (2-12) or (2-13)

$$R_1' = R_1 + \phi_C$$

$$R_1' = R_1 + \phi_C - 1$$

From R_1' and R_1, the value of ϕ_C can be obtained.

$$\phi_C = \phi_1 + \phi_2 - \Phi$$

$$\phi_2 = \Phi + \phi_C - \phi_1$$

The number of the common phases of the two NPRs is ϕ_C, the phase number of those phases existing only in the first NPR is $(\phi_1 - \phi_C)$. Therefore, the phase number of those existing only in the second NPR is:

$$\phi_2 - \phi_C = (\Phi + \phi_C - \phi_1) - \phi_C = \Phi - \phi_1$$

Thus, the number of phases of the second NPR, ϕ_2, the number of common phases of the two NPRs, ϕ_C, and the phase number belonging only to the second NPR $(\phi_2 - \phi_C)$, are all determined.

3.1.2 The determination of the characteristics of the boundary between the two NPRs

When the phase assemblages of the two NPRs are given, the characteristics of the boundary between them can be determined as follows. If the values of ϕ_1, ϕ_2, ϕ_C and Φ are known, then, by the boundary theory, the value of R_1 may be calculated with Φ, while the value of R_1' may be obtained with eq.(2-12) or (2-13), from the values of R_1 and ϕ_C. Therefore, the characteristics of the boundary can be well determined.

3.1.3 Examples

Take NPRs L/(S$_1$+L) and their boundary, as shown in Fig. 3.1, as an example.

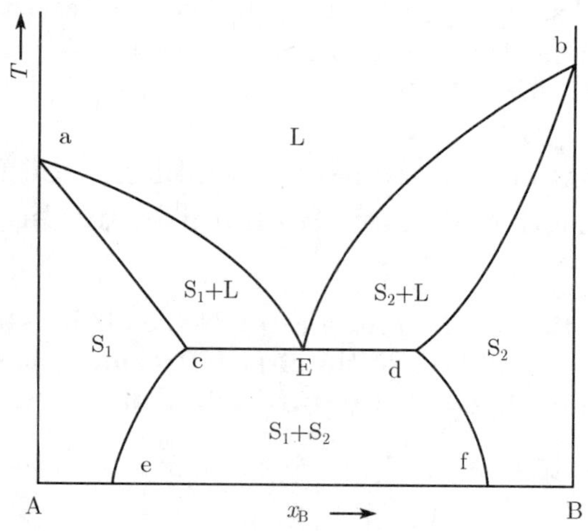

Fig. 3.1 The isobaric, eutectic binary phase diagram.

If the first NPR and the characteristics of the boundary, aE, are already given, *i.e.* $\phi_1 = 1, R_1' = 1, R_1 = 1$, then the phase assemblage of the second NPR may be determined.

$$\Phi = N + 1 - R_1 = 2 + 1 - 1 = 2$$

Through eq. (2-13), the number of the common phases existing in both NPRs, becomes:

$$\phi_C = R_1' + 1 - R_1 = 1 + 1 - 1 = 1$$

The phase number of the second NPR,

$$\phi_2 = \Phi + \phi_C - \phi_1 = 2 + 1 - 1 = 2$$

The number of phases existing only in the second NPR,

$$\phi_2 - \phi_C = \Phi - \phi_1 = 2 - 1 = 1$$

Therefore, the phase number of the second NPR is 2. It has one phase "in common" with the first NPR and one phase belonging only to itself, so the phase assemblage of the second NPR is well determined.

If the phase assemblage of the first NPR is ($L+S_1$), and the phase assemblage of the second NPR is (S_1+S_2), then the characteristics of their boundary are able to be determined. The dimension of their phase boundary is given by

$$R_1 = N + 1 - \Phi = 2 + 1 - 3 = 0$$

The dimension of the boundary may be determined through eq. (2-12),

$$R_1' = R_1 + \phi_C = 0 + 1 = 1$$

By this means, the characteristics of the boundary between the two NPRs have been able to be well determined.

3.2 Application of the Boundary Theory to Unary Phase Diagrams

The phase diagrams for unary systems are very simple (see Fig. 3.2). They can be readily interpreted by means of the TCR approach without the need for use of any additional concepts. According to the TCR for unary phase diagrams ($N = 1$),

$$R_1 = N - \Phi + 2 = 3 - \Phi$$

Φ	2	3
R_1	1	0
The phase boundary	line	point
example	oa, ob, oc	o

Fig. 3.2 is a real p-T phase diagram, excluding composition variables. This is not the type of isobaric T-x_i phase diagram, but the phase diagram of **potential axes** only.

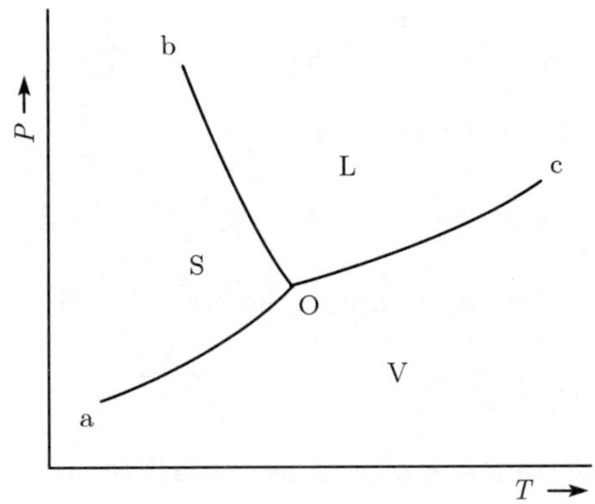

Fig. 3.2 A typical phase diagram for a unary system.

Palatnik-Landau's contact rule can not treat such a simple phase diagram , see later section 3.6.3.

3.3 Application of the Boundary Theory to Binary Phase Diagrams

3.3.1 The general analyses of isobaric binary phase diagrams

The relationship among NPRs and their boundaries for isobaric phase diagrams is shown in Table 3.1.

Table 3.1 The variations of Φ, R_1, ϕ_C, $\phi_{\max}$ and R_1' of a binary phase diagram

($r = Z = 0, p = constant,\ R_1 = 3 - \Phi$)

$\Phi(3 \geqslant \Phi \geqslant 2)$	2	3
$R_1(1 \geqslant R_1 \geqslant 0)$	1	0
$\phi_{\max}$	2	2
ϕ_C	$\phi_C = 1$	$1 \geqslant \phi_C \geqslant 0$
R_1'	$R_1' = R_1 + \phi_C - 1$	$R_1' = R_1 + \phi_C$
The phase assemblages of two NPRs	$f_i/(f_i + f_j)$	$\phi_C = 1, R_1' = 1$ $(f_i + f_j)/(f_j + f_k)$
		$\phi_C = 0, R_1' = 0$ $L/(S_1 + S_2)$ $(f_i + f_j)/f_k$

Where f_i, f_j and f_k denote different phases (i, j, k=1, 2, 3; $i \neq j \neq k$).

3.3.2 Analyses of some typical isobaric binary phase diagrams

3.3.2.1 A typical isobaric binary phase diagram

A typical isobaric binary phase diagram is shown in Fig.3.1. A few particular points only are now discussed,

(1) The boundary point, E, between NPRs L/(S_1+S_2) in Fig. 3.1. $\Phi = 3, R_1 = 0$, NPRs L and (S_1+S_2) exist on the opposite sides of the invariant region; during the invariant phase transition, there coexist $(\phi_{\max}+1)=(N+1) = 3$ phases in this invariant region, and $\phi_C=0$.

$$R_1' = R_1 + \phi_C = 0 + 0 = 0$$

(2) The point a, b in Fig. 3.1. This may be considered from two different view points. Take the point "a" as an example. Point *a* may be considered as the melting point of the pure component, A. Since N=1,

$$R_1 = N + 1 - \Phi = 1 + 1 - 2 = 0$$

Or, from the viewpoint of the binary phase diagram, point a may be considered as the boundary of NPRs L/S_1. Φ=2, and the compositions of the liquid and solid phases are identical, $x_{1,\mathrm{L}} = x_{1,\mathrm{S}_1}$, Z=1,

$$R_1 = N + 1 - Z - \Phi = 2 + 1 - 1 - 2 = 0$$

Therefore, point a is a phase boundary point.

Palatnik-Landau's contact rule cannot treat such a simple phase diagram, see later section 3.6.3.

3.3.2.2 SiO_2-Al_2O_3 phase diagram

The SiO_2-Al_2O_3 phase diagram is shown in Fig. 3.3 see next page (where, S or A represents SiO_2 or Al_2O_3 respectively). The boundary point, M, may be considered as the melting point of the $3Al_2O_3{\cdot}2SiO_2$, it is a phase boundary point between the two single-phases. In the single-phase region, the phase point coincides with the system point, so it also serves as a boundary point between the two single-phase regions. The boundary line, Me, is the single, solid phase line of the composite-oxide, $3Al_2O_3{\cdot}2SiO_2$.

3.3.2.3 The phase diagram of the system, KCl-NaCl, with a melting point minimum

The NaCl-KCl phase diagram is shown in Fig. 3.4. M is the boundary point between the two single-phase regions, L and S, Φ=2, while the compositions of the solid and liquid phase are identical, $x_{1,S} = x_{1,L}$, Z=1,

$$R_1 = (N - Z) - \Phi + 1 = (2 - 1) - 2 + 1 = 0$$

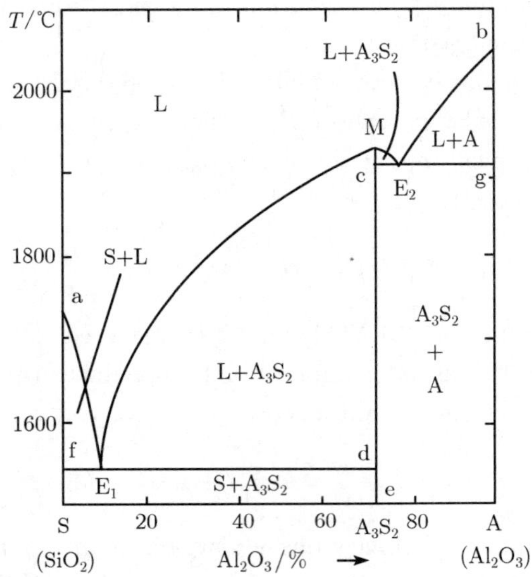

Fig. 3.3 SiO_2-Al_2O_3 phase diagram.

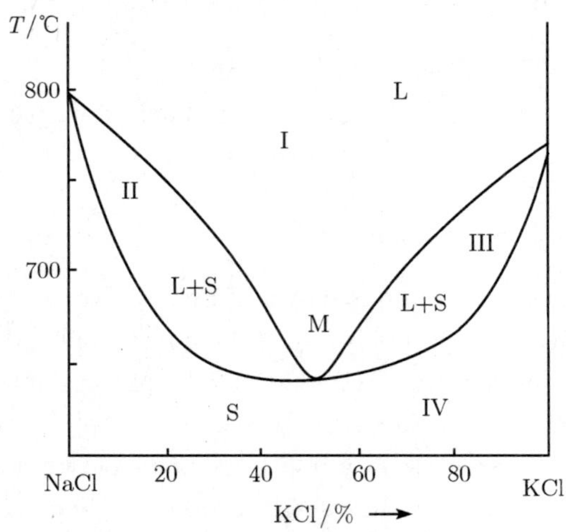

Fig. 3.4 NaCl-KCl phase diagram.

The point M is a phase boundary point between the two NPRs L and S. In the single-phase region, the phase point tallies with the system point, therefore this phase boundary point is also a boundary point.

3.3.3 A few cases are beyond the scope of the boundary theory

3.3.3.1 The line Mcde in the SiO_2-Al_2O_3 binary phase diagram (Fig. 3.3)

Take line de as an example. There are three different phases, S, A_3S_2 and A, in the NPRs on either side of line de. The total compositions of the systems, presented in NPRs on either side of line de are different. The transfer, from the phase region ($S+A_3S_2$) to that of (A_3S_2+A), can only be realized by changing the system composition. As discussed in section 2.6.2, this "change" is really not an equilibrium phase transition. The three phases, S, A_3S_2 and A, cannot "coexist in equilibrium" on the line, de. This is an important difference between line de and other boundary lines between the NPRs. Since the boundary theory only deals with the case where different equilibrium phases are coexisting in two or more NPRs. Thus, the boundary theory does not apply to this particular case certainly.

3.3.3.2 The case of the phase region II (L+S), is shown in Fig. 3.4 to be passing to the phase region III (L+S), through the point M, as indicated in Fig. 3.4.

The phase regions, II and III, are really the same two-phase regions, (L+S), point M being a "singular point" in this phase region. Because the NPRs discussed in the boundary theory must be different phase regions in the phase diagram, the point M is "out of the question" with respect to the relationship among the NPRs and their boundary, nor does the boundary theory "work" in such cases.

3.3.4 Critical point

There is a critical point, K, within the phase diagram, as shown in Fig. 3.5.

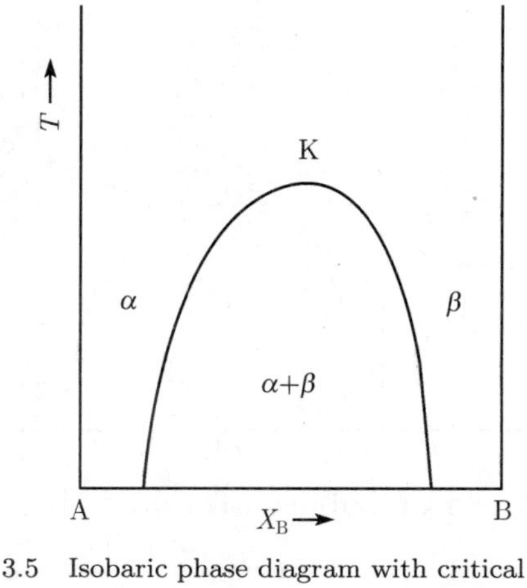

Fig. 3.5 Isobaric phase diagram with critical point.

The critical point satisfies the following two equations:

$$\left(\frac{\partial \mu}{\partial x}\right)_{p,T} = 0$$

$$\left(\frac{\partial^2 \mu}{\partial x^2}\right)_{p,T} = 0$$

The critical point is also a "singular" point; thus it may be "discussed", along with other principles of the phase equilibrium, and it cannot be treated by the boundary theory.

As these 3 cases are beyond the scope of the boundary theory, therefore, the boundary theory cannot treat these cases surely.

3.4 Application of the Boundary Theory to Ternary Phase Diagrams

3.4.1 The general analysis

In a ternary phase diagram, there are three, and only three, types of phase equilibrium that can exist on the boundaries, *i.e.* two-, three- and four-phase equilibrium. The general relationship among NPRs and their boundaries in ternary phase diagrams are summarized in the following Table 3.2.

Table 3.2 The variations of Φ, R_1, ϕ_C and R_1' of ternary phase diagrams

($r = Z = 0, p =$ constant, $R_1 = 4 - \Phi$)

$\Phi(4 \geqslant \Phi \geqslant 2)$	2	3	4
$R_1(2 \geqslant R_1 \geqslant 0)$	2	1	0
$\phi_{\max}$	2	3	3
ϕ_C	$\phi_C = 1$	$2 \geqslant \phi_C \geqslant 1$	$2 \geqslant \phi_C \geqslant 0$
R_1'	$R_1 + \phi_C - 1 = 2$	$R_1 + \phi_C - 1 = \phi_C$	$R_1 + \phi_C = \phi_C$
The phase(s) assemblages of two NPRs $i, j, k, m = 1, 2, 3, 4$ $i \neq j \neq k \neq m$	$f_i/(f_i + f_j)$	$\phi_C = 1, R_1' = 1$ … $f_i/(f_i + f_j + f_k)$ $(f_i + f_j)/(f_j + f_k)$	$\phi_C = 0, R_1' = 0$ … $f_i/(f_j + f_k + f_m)$ $(f_i + f_j)/(f_k + f_m)$
		$\phi_C = 2, R_1' = 2$ … $(f_i + f_j)/(f_i + f_j + f_k)$	$\phi_C = 1, R_1' = 1$ … $(f_i + f_j)/(f_j + f_k + f_m)$
			$\phi_C = 2, R_1' = 2$ … $(f_i + f_j + f_k)/(f_j + f_k + f_m)$

3.4.2 Isothermal sections of isobaric, ternary phase diagrams

The isothermal section is also called the horizontal section. In isothermal sections, the temperature is kept constant, therefore, in regular sections, the dimensions of the phase boundaries $(R_1)_{\text{H}}$ (H is an abbreviation of "Horizontal")and the dimensions of boundaries $(R_1')_{\text{H}}$ of isothermal sections are one less than the dimensions of the phase boundaries, R_1, and the dimensions of boundaries, R_1' of the space phase diagrams, respectively, *i.e.*

$$(R_1)_{\text{H}} = R_1 - 1 \tag{3-1}$$

$$(R_1)_{\text{H}} = 3 - \Phi \tag{3-1$'$}$$

$$(R_1')_{\text{H}} = R_1' - 1 \tag{3-2}$$

For the special case, where the isothermal section crosses the extreme point or the invariant transition point, the phase boundary, or the boundary, is associated with this special point when it satisfies the following equations:

$$(R_1)_{\text{H}} = R_1 \tag{3-3}$$

$$(R_1')_{\text{H}} = R_1' \tag{3-4}$$

If all boundaries and phase boundaries in the isothermal section satisfy eqs.(3-1) and (3-2), this section is called the "regular section". If a particular boundary or phase boundary of an isothermal section exist, which does not satisfy eq. (3-1) or (3-2), this section is called the "irregular section".

Here, only the regular, isothermal ternary sections are analyzed.

There are two types of boundaries, *i.e.* boundary lines and boundary points, in the isothermal ternary section.

For isobaric, ternary phase diagrams,

$$R_1 = N + 1 - \Phi = 4 - \Phi$$

In the isobaric phase diagram, when $R_1 \geqslant 1$, then $\phi_C \geqslant 1$ (4th corollary, see section 2.5),

$$\begin{aligned} R_1' &= R_1 + \phi_C - 1 = 4 - \Phi + \phi_C - 1 \\ &= 3 - \Phi + \phi_C \end{aligned}$$

For regular, isobaric isothermal sections,

$$(R_1)_{\text{H}} = R_1 - 1 = 3 - \Phi \tag{3-5}$$

$$(R_1')_{\text{H}} = R_1 - 1 = 2 - \Phi + \phi_C \tag{3-6}$$

Let us discuss the two types of boundaries separately. They are the boundary line and the boundary point.

3.4.3 The two types of boundaries

3.4.3.1 The boundary line

The condition of the boundary line is $(R_1')_{\mathrm{H}} = 1$, by eq.(3-6):

$$1 = 2 - \Phi + \phi_C$$

$$\phi_C = \Phi - 1$$

According to the different values of Φ, one can divide the boundary lines into two classes:

(1) Φ=2, $(R_1)_{\mathrm{H}} = 3-\Phi$=1, so the boundary and phase boundary have the same dimensions, and ϕ_C=1.

$$\phi_1 = 1, \phi_C = 1, \text{ so } \phi_2 = 2.$$

$$\phi_1 = 2, \phi_C = 1, \text{ so } \phi_2 = \Phi - \phi_1 + \phi_C = 2 - 2 + 1 = 1$$

These two cases are similar: the phase assemblages of the NPRs on the two sides of the boundaries of both cases, may be expressed as NPRs $f_i/(f_i + f_j)$.

(2) $\Phi = 3, (R_1)_{\mathrm{H}} = 3 - \Phi = 0$. Since $(R_1')_{\mathrm{H}} \neq (R_1)_{\mathrm{H}}$, these boundary lines are no longer phase boundary lines. These boundary lines therefore consist only of system points.

By eq. (3-6),

$$(R_1')_{\mathrm{H}} = 2 - \Phi + \phi_C = \phi_C - 1$$

$$1 = (R_1')_{\mathrm{H}} = \phi_C - 1$$

thence

$$\phi_C = 2$$

$$\Phi - \phi_C = 1$$

If ϕ_1=2,

$$\phi_2 = \Phi - \phi_1 + \phi_C = 3 - 2 + 2 = 3$$

The phase assemblages of the two NPRs on both sides of these boundaries are of the type of NPRs: $(f_i + f_j)/(f_i + f_j + f_k)$.

If $\phi_1 = 3$, $\phi_2 = 2$, the phase assemblages of the two NPRs are NPRs $(f_i + f_j + f_k)/(f_i + f_j)$. These two cases are similar, only the order of the NPRs is inverted.

3.4.3.2 The boundary point

The condition of the boundary point is $(R_1')_{\mathrm{H}}$=0, $(R_1)_{\mathrm{H}} \leqslant 0$, so $\Phi \leqslant 3$, see eq. (3-1′).

Suppose that $\Phi \leqslant 2, R_1 = (N+1) - \Phi = 3 + 1 - \Phi = 4 - \Phi \geqslant 2$,

$$(R_1)_{\mathrm{H}} = R_1 - 1 \geqslant 1$$

This contradicts the "premise" of $(R_1')_{\rm H}=0$ and $(R_1)_{\rm H} \leqslant 0$, and thus the case is impossible.

Therefore, there is only one solution, *i.e.* $\Phi=3$.

$$(R_1)_{\rm H} = 3 - \Phi = 0$$

$$0 = (R_1)_{\rm H} = 2 - \Phi + \phi_C = 2 - 3 + \phi_C = \phi_C - 1$$

$$\phi_C = 1$$

and

$$\Phi - \phi_C = 2$$

The number of non-common phases in the two NPRs is 2, and $(R_1')_{\rm H} = 0$, so the two NPRs can intersect with each other only at a fixed point.

If $\phi_1 = 1$: since $\phi_C=1$ and $\Phi=3$, $\phi_2=3$, the two NPRs are the type of NPRs, $f_i/(f_i + f_j + f_k)$, and can intersect at a point which is a phase point of the "phase in common", f_i.

If $\phi_1=2$: since $\phi_C=1$ and $\Phi=3$, $\phi_2=2$, the two NPRs are of the type of NPRs $(f_i+f_j)/(f_j+f_k)$; NPRs intersect at a boundary point which is also a phase point of the common phase f_j .

Through discussion of the isobaric, isothermal ternary section, in conjunction with the "boundary theory of phase diagrams", the characteristics of the boundaries of sections of this type, are well determined.

The results of the boundary theory of the isobaric, isothermal ternary section may be summarized, as follows:

The cases	Φ	$(R_1')_{\rm H}$	$(R_1)_{\rm H}$	ϕ_C	The phase assemblages of two NPRs
$R_1 \geqslant 1, \phi_C \geqslant 1$	2	1	1	1	$f_i/(f_i+f_j)$
$R_1' = R_1 + \phi_C - 1$	3	1	0	2	$(f_i+f_j)/(f_i+f_j+f_k)$
	3	0	0	1	$f_i/(f_i + f_j + f_k)$ $(f_i + f_j)/(f_j + f_k)$

Notice: In regular isobaric, isothermal ternary phase diagrams, there is no case of Φ=4.

We will compare these results from the boundary theory viewpoint with those of Palatnik-Landau's theory, for isothermal ternary sections, later in section 3.6.

3.4.4 Typical isopleth sections (or vertical sections) of isobaric ternary phase diagrams

3.4.4.1 A brief analysis of the isobaric ternary isopleth section

The ternary isopleth section is a much more complicated structure than the isothermal ternary section. Although the isopleth section is depicted as being on a plane, only the total composition of the system is constrained by a certain condition, the temperature of the system being a variable and the two phase compositions concentrations are also variables. The number of the independent variables of the equilibrium section is still three, *i.e.* the same as in the spatial ternary phase diagram. However, there are some differences between the isopleth section and the spatial ternary phase diagram, but, from the viewpoint of the phase equilibrium, both exhibit much similarity.

3.4.4.2 The characteristics of the boundary lines on a typical, regular isobaric ternary isopleth section

Based on the phase assemblages of those NPRs situated on the isobaric ternary isopleth section, the characteristics of the boundary lines between these NPRs may also be determined. Fig. 3.6 shows a typical, isobaric ternary isopleth section.

There are three types of boundary lines and two types of boundary points in this section. These are now discussed separately.

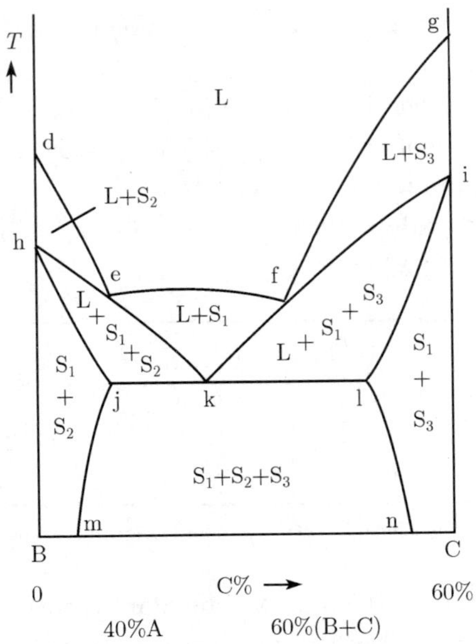

Fig. 3.6 Isobaric eutectic ternary isopleth section.

(1) The boundary lines of the first type are the lines de, ef, fg; the NPRs on the two sides of these lines have $\varPhi = 2, \phi_C = 1$ (the common phase is L).

According to the boundary theory,

$$R_1 = (N + 1) - \varPhi = 4 - 2 = 2$$

And $R_1 \geqslant 1$,

$$R_1' = R_1 + \phi_C - 1 = 2 + 1 - 1 = 2$$

$$(R_1)_i = R_1 - 1 = 1, \quad (R_1')_i = R_1' - 1 = 1$$

$$(R_1)_i = (R_1')_i$$

The boundary and the phase boundary in the corresponding space of the isobaric ternary phase diagram are both of the same phase boundary plane of the common phase, L. This boundary plane intersects the isopleth section on a curved line. This is a phase boundary line, constituted by the equilibrium phase points.

(2) The boundary lines of the second type are lines mj, jh, he, ek, kf, fi, il and ln. Consider line "he" as an example.

The NPRs (L+S_2)/(L+S_1+S_2), on both sides of line he, have Φ=3, ϕ_C=2, so $R_1 = 4 - \Phi = 1$. In this case, the phase boundary of the corresponding spatial phase diagram, is a one-dimensional curved phase boundary line. Since ϕ_C=2, there are two such boundaries. At constant temperature, one may find two equilibrium phase points on the two phase boundary lines and the tie-line connects these two phase points. As the temperature changes, the loci of the moving tie-lines form the curved, two-dimensional boundary plane which is made up of system points. The boundary line, he, is the intersection of the boundary plane on the isopleth section. So line "he" also consists of system points. In addition to "he", all of the other lines may be discussed in a similar way.

(3) The boundary line of the third type is that of line jkl, the NPRs on both sides of this boundary line satisfy the condition: $\Phi = 4, R_1$=0; so temperature of boundary line being invariant. Consider, as an example, the boundary line, jk, lying between NPRs (L+S_1+S_2)/(S_1+S_2+S_3). The phase transition is an invariant one, there is a (N+1)=4 four-phase region coexisting between these NPRs and ϕ_C=2, thus:

$$R_1' = R_1 + \phi_C = 0 + 2 = 2$$

The corresponding boundary in the spatial phase diagram is a boundary plane (since temperature is maintained constant). Line jk is the intersection line of this boundary plane on the isopleth section; it also consists of system points only.

There are also four equilibrium phase points; they are not shown in the regular sections. They do not occur on the line jkl.

3.4.4.3 The characteristics of the boundary points in the regular, isobaric ternary isopleth section

There are two types of boundary points:

(1) The phase boundary points, e and f, the NPRs on both sides of these phase points satisfy the conditions Φ=3, ϕ_C=1 and R_1=1,

$$R_1' = R_1 + \phi_C - 1 = 1 + 1 - 1 = 1$$

$$R_1' = R_1 = 1$$

So, in the corresponding spatial phase diagram, the boundary and phase boundary are both of the same phase boundary line of the common phase, L. Point e (or f) is the crossing point of this phase boundary line on the isopleth section. It is an equilibrium phase point of the common phase, L.

(2) The boundary point. The three boundary points, j, k, and l (see Fig. 3.6), have been discussed earlier in the discussion on the boundary lines of the third type. Within the regular isopleth sections, they are all system points.

3.4.5 The boundary theory of isobaric ternary isopleth sections

3.4.5.1 The basic principles

The independent variables of the isobaric, ternary phase diagram are: T, x_1 and x_2 (the mole fractions of the composition of the ternary system, x_i, i=1,2,3; $\sum x_i = 1$), the isobaric ternary phase diagram being three-dimensional. If one mole fraction of the system composition (*e.g.* x_1)is kept constant, the dimensions of the phase boundary $(R_1)_i$ and boundary $(R_1')_i$ of the isopleth section are one dimension less than the dimensions of the phase boundary R_1 and boundary R_1' of the corresponding spatial phase diagram, respectively.

$$\left.\begin{aligned}(R_1)_i = R_1 - 1\\(R_1')_i = R_1' - 1\end{aligned}\right\} \tag{3-7}$$

We now discuss the characteristics of phase boundaries and the boundaries of the isopleth section, associated with the values of the phase boundaries dimensions of the corresponding spatial phase diagram.

3.4.5.2 The case of $R_1 \geqslant 1$

(1) When $R_1 \geqslant 1$, then $\phi_C \geqslant 1$ and $R_1' = R_1 + \phi_C - 1$

If $R_1 \geqslant 1$, and there are boundary lines with $(R_1')_i = 1$, then, in accord with the boundary theory, the following equations may be deduced for the isobaric ternary isopleth section:

$$(R_1)_i = R_1 - 1 = N + 1 - \Phi - 1$$

$$(R_1)_i = 3 - \Phi \tag{3-8}$$

$$(R_1')_i = R_1' - 1 = (R_1 + \phi_C - 1) - 1 = (N + 1 - \Phi) + (\phi_C - 1) - 1$$

$$(R_1')_i = \phi_C + 2 - \Phi \tag{3-9}$$

When $(R_1')_i = 1$,

$$1 = \phi_C + 2 - \Phi$$

$$\Phi - \phi_C = 1 \tag{3-10}$$

The number of phase differences, between the two NPRs with a boundary line, is one.

The phase assemblages of the two NPRs in this case are of the types: NPRs $f_i/(f_i + f_j)$ and $(f_i + f_j)/(f_i + f_j + f_k)$.

If $f_i/(f_i + f_j)$, Φ=2, ϕ_C=1.

$$(R_1)_i = 3 - \Phi = 1$$

$$(R_1')_i = \phi_C + 2 - \Phi = 1$$

$$(R_1)_i = (R_1')_i = 1$$

So, the boundary line is also a phase boundary line.

In NPRs, $(f_i + f_j)/(f_i + f_j + f_k)$, $\Phi = 3, \phi_C = 2$.

$$(R_1)_i = 3 - \Phi = 0$$

$$(R_1')_i = \phi_C + 2 - \Phi = 1$$

$$(R_1')_i = 1 > (R_1)_i = 0$$

Thus, the boundary line is a boundary line only, and it does not act as a phase boundary line.

We may now summarize the above descriptions in a table. For isobaric ternary isopleth sections, when $R_1 \geqslant 1$, $(R_1')_i = 1$.

Phase assemblages	ϕ_C	$(R_1)_i$	$(R_1')_i$
$f_i/(f_i + f_j)$	1	1	1
$(f_i + f_j)/(f_i + f_j + f_k)$	2	0	1

(2) When the case of $R_1 \geqslant 1$ and there are boundary points at the isobaric ternary isopleth section, *i.e.* $(R_1')_i = 0$.

For the case: $(R_1')_i = (R_1)_i = 0$, *i.e.* the boundary points are also phase boundary points.

When $(R_1')_i = (R_1)_i = 0$, according to eq. (3-8),

$$0 = (R_1)_i = 3 - \Phi$$

Φ=3. In this case, the boundary point in the isobaric ternary isopleth section may also be a phase boundary point.

$$\because \quad 0 = (R_1')_i = \phi_C + 2 - \Phi \text{ (see eq.(3-9))}$$

$$\phi_C = \Phi - 2$$

Since Φ=3, ϕ_C=1, the phase assemblages of two NPRs in this case must be of the type of NPRs $f_i/(f_i + f_j + f_k)$ or $(f_i + f_j)/(f_j + f_k)$ with $(R_1')_i = (R_1)_i = 0$.

3.4.5.3 The case of the isobaric, ternary spatial phase diagram, R_1=0; and two NPRs exist on the same side, above the invariant phase transition temperature. There is no $(3+1) = 4$ four-phase coexisting invariant region between the two NPRs, then $R_1' = R_1 + \phi_C - 1$

(1) In this case, in the isopleth section, there is no boundary line with $(R_1')_i$=1. This may be proved as follows:

since

$$R_1 = 0$$

$$(R_1')_i = R_1' - 1 = (R_1 + \phi_C - 1) - 1$$

if $1 = (R_1')_i = 0 + \phi_C - 2$,

$$\phi_C = 3$$

Since $\phi_{\max} = N = 3$, see (2-4), now, $\phi_C = 3$, the phase assemblages of the two NPRs are identical, it is meaningless; so, in this case, $R_1 = 0$ and $R_1' = R_1 + \phi_C - 1$ in the isopleth section, thus there is no boundary line with $(R_1')_i = 1$.

(2) So $(R_1')_i$=0

$$R_1 = 0, R_1' = R_1 + \phi_C - 1,$$

$$(R_1')_i = (0 + \phi_C - 1) - 1 = 0$$

$$\phi_C = 2$$

$R_1 = 0$, $\Phi = 4, \phi_{\max} = 3$, so the phase assemblages of the two NPRs of this case is of the type of NPRs $(f_i + f_j + f_k)/(f_j + f_k + f_m)$. The transfer between $(f_i + f_j + f_k)/(f_j + f_k + f_m)$ is not a phase transition, it occurs only when the composition of the system changes.

3.4.5.4 The case: in the isobaric ternary phase diagram, R_1=0; an invariant phase transition from one NPR to another exists, and there is a (N+1)= 4 four-phase invariant region, situated between the two NPRs, so $R_1' = R_1 + \phi_C$

In this case, in the isopleth section, there may be boundary lines and boundary points between the two NPRs.

(1) The case: there exists the boundary line with $(R_1')_i = 1$ between the two NPRs

since

$$R_1 = 0, \Phi = N + 1 = 4, (R_1)_i = R_1 - 1 = -1$$
$$1 = (R_1')_i = R_1' - 1 = (R_1 + \phi_C) - 1 = \phi_C - 1$$

Then ϕ_C=2 and $\phi_{\max}$=3.

So, in this case, the phase assemblages of the two NPRs are of the type of NPRs $(f_i + f_j + f_k)/(f_i + f_k + f_m)$.

(2) The case: there is the boundary point $(R_1')_i = 0$ between the two NPRs.

$$R_1 = 0, \Phi = N + 1 - R_1 = 3 + 1 = 4, (R_1)_i = -1.$$
$$0 = (R_1')_i = R_1' - 1 = (R_1 + \phi_C) - 1 = \phi_C - 1$$
$$\phi_C = 1$$

and $\phi_{\max}$=3, so the phase assemblages of the two NPRs in this case must be of the type of NPRs $(f_i + f_j)/(f_j + f_k + f_m)$.

We now summarize the results of the boundary theory examination of the isobaric isopleth ternary section, see Table 3.3.

Table 3.3 The variations of Φ, $(R_1')_i, (R_1)_i$ and ϕ_C of the isobaric ternary isopleth

No.	The cases	Φ	$(R_1')_i$	$(R_1)_i$	ϕ_C	The phase assemblages of two NPRs
1	$R_1 \geqslant 1, \phi_C \geqslant 1$	2	1	1	1	$f_i/(f_i + f_j)$
		3	1	0	2	$(f_i + f_j)/(f_i + f_j + f_k)$
	$R_1' = R_1 + \phi_C - 1$	3	0	0	1	$f_i/(f_i + f_j + f_k)$ $(f_i + f_j)/(f_j + f_k)$
2	$R_1 = 0$ $R_1' = R_1 + \phi_C - 1$	4	0	−1	2	$(f_i + f_j + f_k)/(f_j + f_k + f_m)$
3	$R_1 = 0$	4	0	−1	1	$(f_i + f_m)/(f_i + f_j + f_k)$
	$R_1' = R_1 + \phi_C$	4	1	−1	2	$(f_i + f_j + f_k)/(f_i + f_j + f_m)$

3.4.5.5 The analysis of regular and irregular isopleth sections with the boundary theory

For the regular isopleth section, when R_1=0,

$$(R_1)_i = R_1 - 1 = -1$$

That is to say, the equilibrium phase points at the invariant phase transition region are unable to be shown on the regular isopleth section, since an isopleth section does not usually cross the invariant equilibrium phase point.

But, the position of a special isopleth section is chosen here in such a way that the isopleth section does cross one or two invariant phase points, this or these invariant phase points are shown naturally in this isopleth section, then it does not satisfy the rule of $(R_1)_i = -1$ (since R_1=0). This section is irregular.

A eutectic ternary system is taken as an example to explain the characteristics of the boundaries in the isopleth sections. The projection of this ternary system is shown in Fig. 3.7.

Figs. 3.8, 3.9 and 3.10 are of three further isopleth sections of this system.

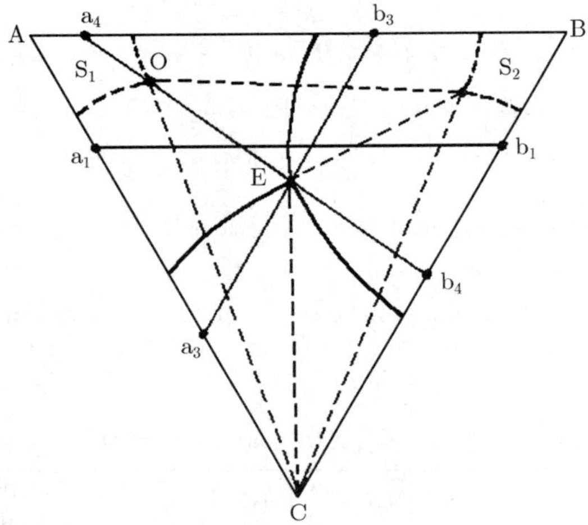

Fig. 3.7 The projection of a ternary eutectic phase diagram.

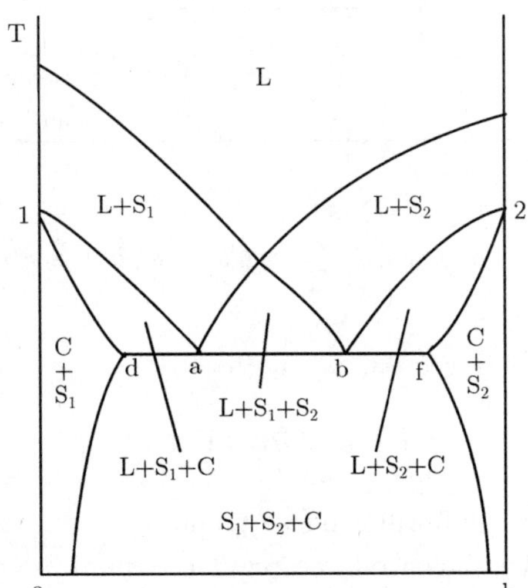

Fig. 3.8 A regular isopleth section.

The composition lines a_1b_1, a_3b_3 and a_4b_4 are shown in Fig. 3.7 also.

(1) The discussion on Fig. 3.8.

This section is a typical, regular isopleth section. The boundaries with $R_1 > 0$ have been discussed in section 3.4.4. Here we discuss the case of R_1=0 only.

Initially, the phase region L does not come into contact with the phase region (S_1+S_2+C),(C is pure solid phase, not a solid solution). Let us explain this case. Though phase regions L and (S_1+S_2+C) do not contact each other, the value of Φ for these two non-neighboring phase regions, L and (S_1+S_2+C), may still be counted.

$$R_1 = 4 - \Phi = 4 - 4 = 0$$

$$(R_1)_i = R_1 - 1 = -1$$

and there is an invariant phase transition, from one NPR to another, along with a (N+1)=4 four-phase invariant region between NPRs and ϕ_C=0,

$$R_1' = R_1 + \phi_C$$

$$(R_1')_i = R_1' - 1 = (R_1 + \phi_C) - 1 = -1$$

$$(R_1)_i = (R_1')_i = -1 < 0$$

Therefore, the boundary between phase regions L/(S_1+S_2+C) can not exist in the regular isobaric, ternary isopleth section.

Boundary points, a and b, between NPRs (L+S_1)/(S_1+S_2+C) and (L+S_2)/(S_1+S_2+C), have R_1=0, $(R_1)_i = -1$, ϕ_C=1.

$$(R_1')_i = (R_1 + \phi_C) - 1 = 0$$

So, the boundary points a, b, are system points only.

The boundary lines, da, ab and bf, between the NPRs (L+S_1+C)/(S_1+S_2+C), (L+S_1+S_2)/(S_1+S_2+C) and (L+S_2+C)/(S_1+S_2+C), respectively, have Φ=4, R_1=0. There is also an invariant phase transition and a (N+1)=4 four-phase, coexisting invariant region, between the NPRs, and ϕ_C=2,

$$R_1' = R_1 + \phi_C = 2$$

$$(R_1')_i = R_1' - 1 = 1$$

So, lines da, ab and bf are boundary lines which consist of system points.

At last, we now discuss the boundary points a and b between NPRs (L+S_1+C)/(L+S_1+S_2) and (L+S_1+S_2)/(L+S_2+C) respectively. These NPRs exist on the same side of the invariant transition region, ϕ_C=2. There is no (N+1=4) four-phase, coexisting region between the NPRs, and the equation, $R_1' = R_1 + \phi_C - 1$, is valid.

$$R_1' = 0 + 2 - 1 = 1$$

$$(R_1')_i = R_1' - 1 = 1 - 1 = 0$$

So, the NPRs in this case can only make contact at individual points. The transfer between ($L+S_1+C$)/($L+S_1+S_2$) or ($L+S_1+S_2$)/($L+S_2+C$) is not a phase transition, the phase region transfer from one NPR to another can occur only when the composition of the system changes.

Let us discuss point 1 and 2 (Fig. 3.8) further. According to the boundary theory, since the points 1 and 2 are the boundaries in the two binary systems (A-C) and (B-C), respectively. Take point 1 to discuss, it is the boundary between NPRs ($L+S_1$)/(S_1+C) (it is similar to (S_1+L)/(S_1+S_2) in Fig. 3.1),

$$R_1' = R_1 + \phi_C = 0 + 1 = 1$$

But, the composition of one component is fixed in the isopleth section, $(R_1')_i = R_1' - 1 = 0$, therefore the boundary in the isopleth section is a point, it is point 1; it is not necessary to pull point 1 open to a line section 1-1' (This is what Palatnik-Landau did, please see Fig. 3.12.). The discussion on the point 2 is similar to that of point 1.

(2) The discussion of one irregular isopleth section, see Fig. 3.9. In this figure, there is only one irregular boundary, *i.e.* the boundary point e (E) between NPRs L/(S_1+S_2+C).

As discussed previously, for this boundary to exist in a regular isopleth section, it would have:

$$(R_1)_i = -1$$

$$(R_1')_i = -1$$

i.e., in the regular isopleth section, there cannot have any common boundary between these NPRs L/(S_1+S_2+C). But, the composition line of the system a_3b_3 in Fig. 3.7 just crosses the ternary eutectic point——the phase point E of phase L, and it is the only one common system point e(E) between NPRs L/(S_1+S_2+C), as shown in Fig. 3.9. This boundary point e(E) exists on this four-phase coexisting plane, it is naturally shown in Fig. 3.9. The reason for this is very clear from the viewpoint of geometry.

Palatnik-Landau simply pointed out that the contact rule is not valid in this case, without their offering any plausible explanation for the invalidity [Palatnik-Landau, 1964].

(3) The discussion of Fig. 3.10, another irregular isopleth section.

In Fig. 3.10, there are two equilibrium phase points O(S_1) and e(L) (point e is also the ternary eutectic point E,) existing on this isopleth section. The tie-line, Oe, of these two equilibrium phase points occurs naturally in this isopleth (see line a_4b_4 in Fig. 3.7). Line a_4b_4 in Fig. 3.7 is just the tie-line, Oe, shown in Fig. 3.10. According to the previous discussion, the tie-line, Oe, has to be the boundary line between NPRs (L+S_1)/(S_1+S_2+C), therefore, the boundary line between (L+S_1)/(S_1+S_2+C) occurs fully on this isopleth section. (In general cases, when the number of phase differences between the two phase regions is three, these two phase regions cannot be in contact with each other in a regular isopleth section)

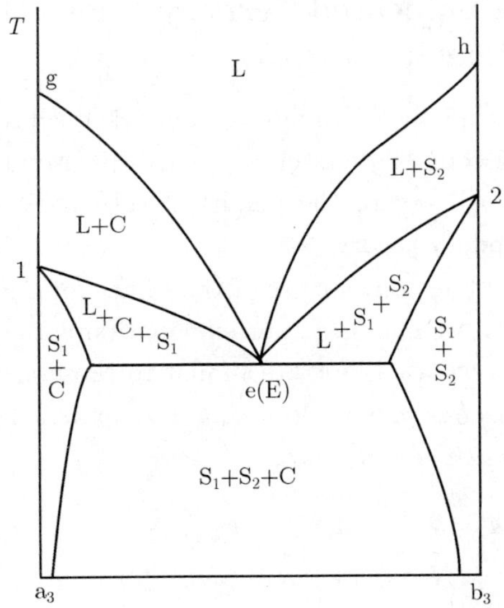

Fig. 3.9 An irregular isopleth section.

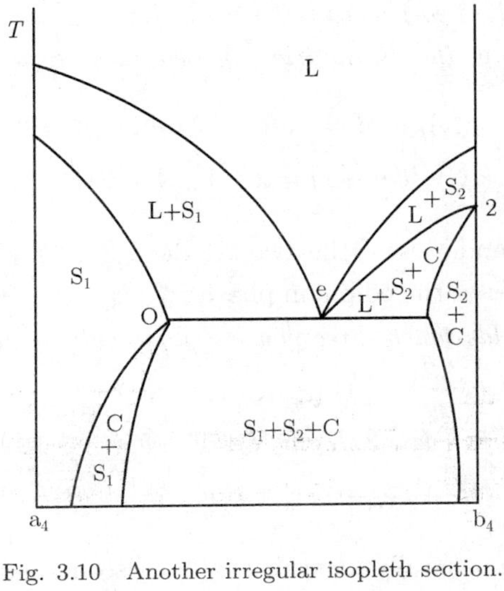

Fig. 3.10 Another irregular isopleth section.

Surely, the Palatnik-Landau's contact rule is invalid in all of these cases shown in Figs. 3.8, 3.9 and 3.10, they modified the real phase diagrams into other unacceptable forms [Palatnik and Landau, 1964].

3.5 Explanation of Rhines' Ten Empirical Rules for Constructing Complicated Ternary Phase Diagrams with the Bounary Theory

Now let us turn to explain N. Rhines' ten empirical rules which must be obeyed in the construction of a complicated, ternary phase diagram from the phase diagram units [Rhines, 1956]. All ten of the empirical rules may well be expounded by application of the boundary theory.

For assisting the reading convenience of the same empirical rule, we cite Rhines' description at first; then we elaborate our explanation with the use of symbols and equations. All the symbols used here are similar to those used for Table 3.2.

(1) *"Single-phase regions may meet one another at single points, these points are also the temperature maxima or minima."*

$$f_i/f_j, \Phi = 2, Z = 2(x_{1,i} = x_{1,j}, x_{2,i} = x_{2,j}), \phi_C = 0,$$
$$R_1 = (N - Z) + 1 - \Phi = (3 - 2) + 1 - 2 = 0$$

In the single-phase region, the phase point coincides with the system point. Therefore, $R_1' = 0$ also. Only single points satisfy these conditions.

(2) *"One-phase regions are elsewhere separated from each other by two-phase regions representing the two phases concerned; thus the bounding surfaces of single-phase regions are always the 'boundaries' of two-phase regions."*

$$f_i/(f_i + f_j)/f_j, \Phi = 2, R_1 = N + 1 - \Phi = 2, \phi_C = 1$$
$$R_1' = (R_1 + \phi_C - 1) = 2 + 1 - 1 = 2, R_1' = R_1 = 2$$

Therefore, the boundaries of the two NPRs $f_i/(f_i{+}f_j)$, or $(f_i{+}f_j)/f_j$ are the phase boundary planes of the common phases; f_i or f_j .

(3) *"One-phase fields touch three-phase regions only at lines which are generally non-isothermal."*

$$f_i/(f_i + f_j + f_k), \Phi = 3, R_1 = N + 1 - \Phi = 3 + 1 - 3 = 1, \phi_C = 1$$
$$R_1' = (R_1 + \phi_C - 1) = 1 + 1 - 1 = 1, R_1' = R_1 = 1$$

So, boundaries are generally identified by non-isothermal, phase boundary lines ($\because$ $R_1 = 1$).

(4) *"One-phase regions touch four-phase reaction planes only at a single point."*

$$f_i/(f_j+f_k+f_m), \Phi=4, R_1=N+1-\Phi=3+1-4=0, \phi_C=0$$
$$R_1'=R_1+\phi_C=0+0=0, R_1'=R_1=0$$

Thus, single-phase regions can meet at single phase boundary points with two-dimensional, four-phase boundary planes.

(5) *"Two-phase regions touch each other along lines, which are, in general, non-isothermal."*

$$(f_i+f_j)/(f_j+f_k), \Phi=3, R_1=N+1-\Phi=3+1-3=1, \phi_C=1$$
$$R_1'=(R_1+\phi_C-1)=1+1-1=1, R_1'=R_1=1$$

So, the boundaries are constituted of non-isothermal phase boundary lines, they are sets of phase equilibrium points of the systems.

In addition, there is also one condition which has not been considered by Rhines. In isobaric ternary phase diagrams involving peritectic transitions, two two-phase regions, $(f_i+f_j)/(f_k+f_m)$, meet at a single point with the four-phase plane, since:

$$\Phi=4, R_1=N+1-\Phi=3+1-4=0, \phi_C=0,$$
$$R_1'=R_1+\phi_C=0+0=0.$$

Because the phase assemblages of the two-phase regions are different, there are no common phases, and thus the boundaries between the NPRs $(f_i+f_j)/(f_k+f_m)$, consist of common system points only.

(6) *"Two-phase regions are elsewhere separated by one- and three-phase regions, by the bounding surfaces that they are enclosing."*

(7) *"Two-phase regions meet three-phase regions upon 'ruled' bounding surfaces generated by the limiting tie-lines."*

The case of (6):

$$\mathrm{NPRs}(f_i+f_j)/f_j/(f_j+f_k), \Phi=2,$$
$$R_1=N+1-\Phi=3+1-2=2,$$
$$\phi_C=1, R_1'=R_1+\phi_C-1=2+1-1=2,$$
$$R_1'=R_1=2$$

Phase boundary planes between the NPRs, $(f_i+f_j)/f_j$ or $f_j/(f_j+f_k)$, are the common phase boundary planes of the common phases, f_j .

The cases of (6) and (7):

$$\text{NPRs}(f_i + f_j)/(f_i + f_j + f_k)/(f_j + f_k),$$
$$\Phi = 3, R_1 = N + 1 - \Phi = 3 + 1 - 3 = 1$$
$$\phi_C = 2, R_1' = R_1 + \phi_C - 1 = 1 + 2 - 1 = 2,$$
$$R_1 < R_1' = 2$$

The boundary planes are formed in such a manner. At a given temperature, the tie-line connects the two equilibrium phase points at the two phases, boundary lines. When the temperature changes, the loci of the moving tie-lines form the boundary planes; they consist of sets of system points and are not phase boundary planes.

(8) *"Two-phase regions touch four-phase region planes along single isothermal lines, which are the limiting tie-lines."*

$$\text{NPRs}(f_i + f_j)/(f_j + f_k + f_m), \Phi = 4, R_1 = N + 1 - \Phi = 3 + 1 - 4 = 0,$$
$$\phi_C = 1, R_1' = R_1 + \phi_C = 0 + 1 = 1$$
$$R_1' = 1 > R_1 = 0$$

So, this single isothermal line is the tie-line of one common phase point (of the common phase, f_j) and one common system point.

(9) *"Three-phase regions meet each other nowhere except at four-phase reaction isotherms."*

$$\text{NPRs } (f_i + f_j + f_k)/(f_j + f_k + f_m), \Phi = 4, R_1 = N + 1 - \Phi = 3 + 1 - 4 = 0, \phi_C = 2$$

If there is an invariant phase transition and a region of (N+1) coexisting phases between the two NPRs, then

$$R_1' = R_1 + \phi_C = 0 + 2 = 2$$

The boundary is the plane formed by connecting the two common phase points (since there are two common phases) and one common system point.

If the two three-phase regions exist on the same side of the invariant region, *i.e.* there is no invariant phase transition and no (N+1) phases coexisting region between the two three-phase regions, then

$$R_1 = 0, \phi_C = 2, R_1' = R_1 + \phi_C - 1 = 0 + 2 - 1 = 1$$

The boundary between the two three-phase regions is the tie-line of two phase points of the two common phases.

Except for the above conditions, two three-phase regions cannot meet each other elsewhere. For the isobaric ternary phase diagram, $2 \geqslant R_1 \geqslant 0$, besides the four-phase coexisting plane, there must be: R_1=1 or R_1=2.

If $R_1=1$, then $\phi_C \geqslant 1$. Assume the first NPR to be $(f_i+f_j+f_k)$, and $\phi_C=1$, then the second NPR must be $(f_k+f_m+f_n)$, so $\Phi=5$. But, in the isobaric ternary phase diagrams, $\Phi \leqslant 4$, so this case is impossible. If $\phi_C=2$, $\Phi=4$, $R_1=0$, then it is in contradiction with the premise of $R_1=1$. If $\phi_C=3$, then the two three-phase regions have become identical, *i.e.*, it is meaningless. The "maxima" of ϕ_C is three, thus it has no other possibility. If

$$R_1 = 2, \Phi = N + 1 - R_1 = 3 + 1 - 2 = 2,$$

but three-phase regions already have three phases, $R_1=2$, thus $\Phi=2$ is impossible in this particular case.

(10) *"Three-phase regions are elsewhere separated and bounded by two-phase regions involving those phases that are held in common by the neighboring three-phase regions."*

The NPRs in this case may thus be written as:

$$(f_i + f_j + f_k)/(f_j + f_k)/(f_j + f_k + f_m), \Phi = 3, R_1 = N + 1 - \Phi = 3 + 1 - 3 = 1,$$
$$\phi_C = 2, R_1' = R_1 + \phi_C - 1 = 1 + 2 - 1 = 2,$$
$$R_1 < R_1' = 2$$

The boundary planes are the loci of the moving tie-lines connecting two isothermal phase points, when the temperature changes.

Rhines' description is not complete. A supplement should be made so that three-phase regions may be separated by single-phase regions, *i.e.* NPRs $(f_i+f_j+f_k)/f_k/(f_k+f_m+f_n)$, in this case,

$$\Phi = 3, R_1 = 1,$$
$$\phi_C = 1, R_1' = R_1 + \phi_C - 1 = 1 + 1 - 1 = 1,$$
$$R_1' = R_1 = 1$$

The phase boundary lines are those phase boundary lines that lie between $(f_i + f_j + f_k)/f_k$ and $f_k/(f_k + f_m + f_n)$, respectively.

3.6 Comparison of the Boundary Theory and the P-L's Contact Rule of Phase Regions

3.6.1 The deduction of contact rules of phase regions by applying the boundary theory

Palatnik-Landau's contact rule of phase regions (title abbreviated to the "contact rule") [Palatnik-Landau, 1964] was deduced in 1955. In this respect, Palatnik-Landau's work is an important contribution to the phase theory.

The problem to be solved by the contact rule is that: when the phase assemblages of two NPRs are given, the dimensions of the boundary between these two NPRs may be determined. The equation is:

$$R_1' = R - D^+ - D^- \geqslant 0 \tag{3-11}$$

where, R is the dimension of the phase diagram(or its horizontal sections); D^+ or D^- is the number of phases, which respectively either appear newly or disappear in crossing the boundary from the first NPR to the second.

In Palatnik-Landau's publications [Palatnik-Landau, 1964], the dimensions of the boundary are denoted as "R_1". It is essential that "R_1'" appears in our boundary theory. In order to avoid confusion, we explicitly use R_1' for the boundaries in this text, when discussing P-L's contact rule.

The contact rule can be deduced from the boundary theory easily.

Through the definition of D^+ and D^-, $(D^+ + D^-)$ is the total number of the different phases, which exist merely in either one or other of the two NPRs. $(D^+ + D^-)$ does not include the number of common phases existing in both of the two NPRs, ϕ_C . The total phase number in the two NPRs is:

$$\Phi = D^+ + D^- + \phi_C \tag{3-12}$$

From the TCR of isobaric phase diagrams, and with $Z = r = 0$

$$R_1 = N + 1 - \Phi \tag{3-13}$$

For the system of (1) $N \geqslant 2$, $R_1 \geqslant 1$; or (2) $N \geqslant 2$, $R_1 = 0$, there is no invariant phase transition among the NPRs, and no invariant region of $(\phi_C + 1) = (N + 1)$ coexisting phases, among the two NPRs during the phase region transfer, from one NPR to another.

$$R_1' = R_1 + \phi_C - 1 \quad \text{(see (2-13))}$$

And for the isobaric phase diagrams:

$$R = N \quad \text{(see (2-1))}$$

We insert eqs. (3-12), (3-13) and (2-1) into eq. (2-13), so that

$$R_1' = R_1 + \phi_C - 1 = (N + 1 - \Phi) + [\Phi - (D^+ + D^-)] - 1$$

$$R_1' = N - (D^+ + D^-) = R - (D^+ + D^-) \tag{3-14}$$

This is the contact rule. This deduction is very simple. In the original work of Palatnik and Landau [Palatnik-Landau, 1964], their deduction is rather complicated.

On the other hand, none of the three important formulas of the boundary theory could be derived either from the contact rule or from the whole Palatnik-Landau's theory. The boundary theory may thus be considered to be both more fundamental and comprehensive.

3.6.2 The meanings of the parameters used in the boundary theory are clearer than those used in the Palatnik-Landau's theory

When discussing the crossing of the boundary, from the first NPR to the second NPR, besides D^+ and D^-, P-L introduced D^0 denotes the phases remaining from the first NPR to the second. This parameter really is the ϕ_C (the number of phases coexisting in both NPRs) referred to in the boundary theory.

By P-L's theory, the number of total different phases in all the NPRs is denoted by $(D^0 + D^+ + D^-)$, but parameter $\varPhi$ in our theory is more straightforward. Similarly, according to P-L's theory, the phase number in the first NPR and the second NPR, describing by (D^0+D$^+$) and $(D^0 + D^-)$, but our notation(ϕ_1 and ϕ_2) appears to be more concise.

The significant difference existing between the boundary theory and P-L's contact rule, is however, the application of the concept of "phase boundary". Without the use of this concept, the contact rule of phase regions encounters many difficulties in its applications.

3.6.3 The difficulties of applying the contact rule

In the course of deducing the contact rule by the application of boundary theory, some conditions have been introduced, *i.e.*"$Z = r = 0$; and the system of $N \geqslant 2$, $R_1 \geqslant 1$; or $N \geqslant 2$, $R_1=0$, however, there is no invariant phase transition between the NPRs and no invariant region of $(\varPhi + 1) = (N + 1)$ coexisting phases between the two NPRs during the phase region transfer, from one NPR to another, where $R_1' = R_1 + \phi_C - 1$." We are introducing these presumptive conditions to facilitate our deduction of the contact rule. And we found that the constraint of these conditions on the contact rule is universal. In normal phase diagram work, if any of these conditions should not be satisfied, then the contact rule would be invalid. In the following examples, we will present several difficult situations for the contact rule application, and how Palatnik and Landau have to transform the real phase diagrams to fit their own formula.

(1) When $N < 2$, *i.e.* N=1, they modified the real unary phase diagram (see Fig. 3.2 in section 3.2) into Fig. 3.11.

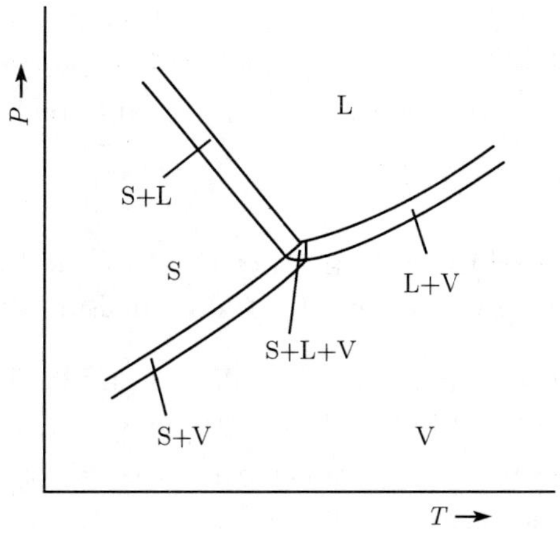

Fig. 3.11 The modified unary phase diagram (depicted by Palatnik-Landau).

(2) When $N \geqslant 2$, $R_1 = 0$, and there is an invariant phase transition among the NPRs, and an invariant region of (Φ+1)=(N+1) coexisting phases among the two NPRs during the phase transition, then the contact rule is invalid, see Fig. 3.1. In this case, Palatnik and Landau had to introduce the concept of degeneracy, thereby transforming Fig. 3.1 into Fig. 3.12.

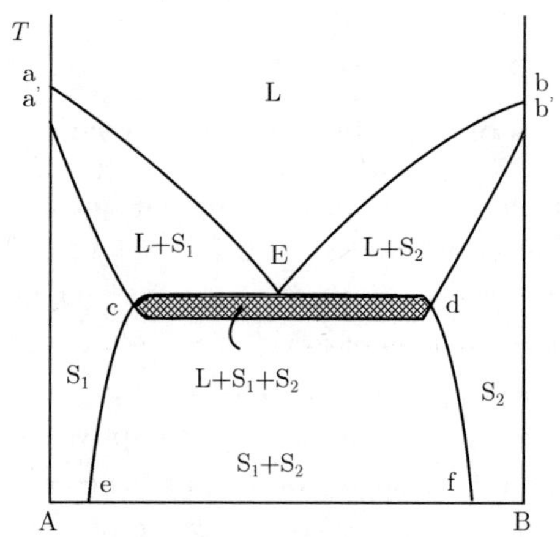

Fig. 3.12 The binary eutectic phase diagram depicted by Palatnik-Landau.

In P-L's figure, the melting points of components A and B are extended to two sections of lines, a-a' and b-b'; and the boundary line, cEd, is extended to a 3-phase region. Thus Palatnik and Landau are able to explain this figure by the contact rule. (The boundary theory is able to explain these types of phase transitions more naturally, see subsection 3.3.2.1)

3. When phase diagram with $Z \neq 0$ are examined; for example, $Z=1$, as the phase diagram with the minimum (or maximum) melting point, the contact rule cannot be applied either.

The boundary theory has been able to explain this type of phase diagram (Fig. 3.4), without resort to any "artificial supplementary modification" (see subsection 3.3.2.3). On the other hand, in order to apply the contact rule, the real phase diagram has to be transformed to the shape illustrated in Fig. 3.13. As with many other transformations illustrated previously, these "modified" phase diagrams appear to be both strange and unreasonable.

For ternary phase diagrams, there are more circumstances which could not be explained by the contact rule, they have been mentioned in subsection 3.4.5.5 of this chapter.

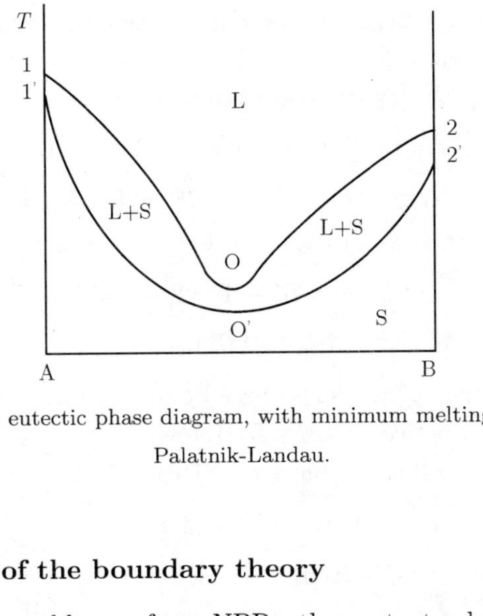

Fig. 3.13 The binary, eutectic phase diagram, with minimum melting point, as modified by Palatnik-Landau.

3.6.4 The merits of the boundary theory

Given the phase assemblages of two NPRs, the contact rule generates the boundary dimensions only, but the boundary theory can determine both the dimensions of the boundary, along with the dimensions of the phase boundary.

Consider Fig. 3.14 as an example.

This phase diagram is a phase diagram at constant T and p. It is one of the phase diagrams of the type with molar-molar axes only.

Here, we discuss the boundary lines, ab, between (S_1+L)/(L+S_1+S_2), and fg, between L/(L+S_3). According to the contact rule, ab and fg have the following characteristics:

$$R_1' = R - (D^+ + D^-) = 2 - 1 = 1$$

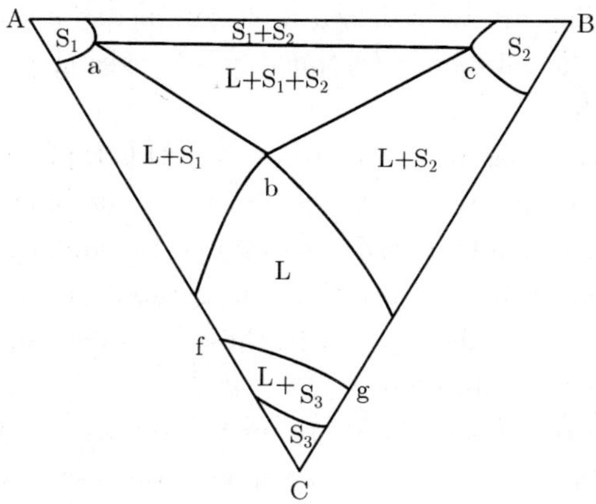

Fig. 3.14 A regular, isobaric, isothermal section of a ternary eutectic phase diagram.

They are both one-dimensional boundaries, their differences can not be distinguished by the contact rule.

Using the boundary theory, applied to line fg:

$$R_1 = (N+1) - \Phi = 3+1-2 = 2$$

$$(R_1)_{\mathrm{H}} = R_1 - 1 = 3 - \Phi = 3-2 = 1$$

$$R_1' = R_1 + \phi_C - 1 = 2+1-1 = 2$$

$$(R_1')_{\mathrm{H}} = R_1' - 1 = 2-1 = 1$$

$$(R_1)_{\mathrm{H}} = (R_1')_{\mathrm{H}} = 1$$

So, the boundary line, fg, is also a phase boundary line, being the boundary line of the common phase L between NPRs L/(L+S_3).

But, for the boundary line ab, between NPRs (S_1+L)/(L+S_1+S_2),

$$R_1 = (N+1) - \Phi = 3+1-3 = 1$$

$$(R_1)_{\mathrm{H}} = R_1 - 1 = 0$$

and ϕ_C=2,

$$R_1' = R_1 + \phi_C - 1 = 1+2-1 = 2$$

$$(R_1')_{\mathrm{H}} = R_1' - 1 = 2-1 = 1$$

$$(R_1)_{\mathrm{H}} < (R_1')_{\mathrm{H}} = 1$$

So, line ab is a boundary line only, but it is not a phase boundary line. It is actually the "tie-line" connecting two common phase points: a(S_1) and b(L), between NPRs (S_1+L)/(L+S_1+S_2).

Analyses above show this phase diagram can be treated by contact rule; but less information can be obtained by applying contact rule than those by applying the boundary theory.

All of the boundary lines displayed in Fig. 3.14 may be discussed in the similar way by reference to the boundary theory.

That is to say, the boundary theory is able to treat the phase diagram with mole fraction-mole fraction axes only, and its treatment is much better than that of the P-L's contact rule.

The boundary theory can provide the systematic analysis to even multicomponent phase diagrams, of all the different types (see early sections 3.2, 3.3, 3.4, 3.5 in this chapter and Chapters 4, 5 and 6).

The contact rule can only deal with those isobaric, molar-molar axes phase diagrams, but boundary theory has also been extended to treat the $p-T-x_i$ or high-pressure, multi- component types of phase diagrams.

Based on the boundary theory of these phase diagrams and on other thermodynamic principles, we have designed a method to calculate the phase diagrams of the high-pressure systems. With the aid of this method, the high-pressure binary and ternary phase diagrams of the Cd-Pb-Sn and Cd-Sn-Zn systems have been calculated. These calculated high-pressure phase diagrams tally well with the experimentally determined ones (see Chapters 8, 9, 10 and 11).

Summarizing, "the contact rule", developed by Palatnik and Landau, has been a very important achievement in the phase diagram research field. The formula is both concise and easy to apply. Unfortunately, its success is limited only to some general cases. As we have illustrated above, in many situations where the contact rule becomes invalid, researchers have had to introduce many "artificial transformations" in order to fit the data to the formula. As most published phase diagrams have been elaborately determined, either by experimental methods and/or through calculation with the aid of thermodynamic models, such alterations will result in, at least, some confusion in the understanding of phase diagrams, and thence make transformed phase diagrams both of impaired creditability and in becoming unacceptable with respect to supporting a theoretical deduction.

References-3

P. Gordon. 1968. Principles of Phase Diagrams in Materials Systems. New York: McGraw-Hill

L. S. Palatnik, A. I. Landau. 1964. Phase Equilibria in Multicomponent Phase Diagrams. New York: Holt Rinehart and Winston, Inc

F. N. Rhines. 1956. Phase Diagram in Metallurgy. New York: McGraw-Hill

Muyu Zhao. 1983. The theorem of corresponding relation between neighboring phase regions and their boundaries in phase diagrams. CALPHAD, 7(3): 185-199

Chapter 4

The Application of the Boundary Theory of Phase Diagrams to the Quaternary and Higher Number Component Phase Diagrams

4.1 Introduction

In the text books dedicated to phase diagrams, isobaric phase diagrams are presented primarily as unary, binary and ternary phase diagrams. In the case of displays of two dimensional planes, the quaternary and higher component multidimensional phase diagrams can only be presented as sections or projections. The isobaric, multicomponent horizontal and vertical sections are the particular sections of importance. In order to discuss sections of these types, the boundary theory of phase diagrams is helpful. Moreover, higher dimensional phase diagrams can be inferred from lower ones, for example, in the calculation of isobaric ternary sections, one usually starts from the "side lines" of the binary systems; in these cases, the application of boundary theory is very enlightening. For the construction, application or learning/teaching of quaternary or more component system phase diagrams, the boundary theory for these phase diagrams is both useful and indispensable, since most people are usually not familiar with such complicated phase systems and their diagrammatic representation.

4.2 The Relationship among NPRs and their Boundaries in a Typical, Isobaric, Quaternary Phase Diagram

Quaternary phase diagrams are generally complicated. In applying the boundary theory to these phase diagrams, the boundary theory for such types of phase diagrams may be obtained. To be concise, only the relationship among the NPRs and their boundaries of these phase diagrams, are cited in the tables.

For general use, isobaric phase diagrams, where $r = Z{=}0$, p=const., the regularities in the variations of R_1, Φ, ϕ_C and R_1' in the isobaric quaternary phase diagram, is shown in Table 4.1.

Table 4.1 Regularities in the variations of R_1, Φ, ϕ_C and R_1' in isobaric, quaternary phase diagrams

	$R_1 = 5 - \Phi$			
$R_1(3 \geqslant R_1 \geqslant 0)$	3	2	1	0
$\Phi(5 \geqslant \Phi \geqslant 2)$	2	3	4	5
$\phi_{\max}$	2	3	4	4
ϕ_C	1	$2 \geqslant \phi_C \geqslant 1$	$3 \geqslant \phi_C \geqslant 1$	$3 \geqslant \phi_C \geqslant 0$
R_1'	3	ϕ_C+1	ϕ_C	$\phi_C^{1)}$ or $\phi_C - 1$

1) There is an invariant phase transition between two NPRs.

Table 4.2 Phase assemblages under different conditions are shown for the isobaric quaternary phase diagrams

(1) $\Phi = 2, R_1 = 3, \phi_C = 1, R_1' = 3$	
$L/(L+S_i)(4)$	$S_i/(S_i+S_j)(12)$
(2) $\Phi=3,\ R_1=2$	
$\phi_C=1,\ R_1'=2$	$\phi_C=2,\ R_1'=3$
$L/(L+S_i+S_j)(6)$ $(L+S_i)/(L+S_j)(6)$ $(L+S_i+S_j)/S_i(12)$ $(L+S_i)/(S_i+S_j)(12)$ $S_i/(S_i+S_j+S_k)(12)$ $(S_i+S_j)/(S_j+S_k)(12)$	$(L+S_i)/(L+S_i+S_j)(12)$ $(L+S_i+S_j)/(S_i+S_j)(6)$ $(S_i+S_j)/(S_i+S_j+S_k)(12)$
(3) $\Phi=4,\ R_1=1$	
$\phi_C=1,\ R_1'=1$	$\phi_C=2,\ R_1'=2$
$L/(L+S_i+S_j+S_k)(4)$ $(L+S_i)/(L+S_j+S_k)(12)$ $(L+S_i)/(S_i+S_j+S_k)(12)$ $(L+S_i+S_j)/(S_j+S_k)(24)$ $(L+S_i+S_j+S_k)/S_k(12)$ $S_i/(S_1+S_2+S_3+S_4)(4)$ $(S_i+S_j)/(S_j+S_k+S_m)(12)$	$(L+S_i)/(L+S_i+S_j+S_k)(12)$ $(L+S_i+S_j)/(L+S_i+S_k)(12)$ $(L+S_i+S_j)/(S_i+S_j+S_k)(12)$ $(S_i+S_j+S_k)/(S_j+S_k+S_m)(6)$ $(S_i+S_j)/(S_1+S_2+S_3+S_4)(6)$
	$\phi_C=3,\ R_1'=3$
	$(L+S_i+S_j)/(L+S_i+S_j+S_k)(12)$ $(L+S_i+S_j+S_k)/(S_i+S_j+S_k)(4)$ $(S_i+S_j+S_k)/(S_1+S_2+S_3+S_4)(4)$
(4) $\Phi=5,\ R_1=0,\ R_1'=R_1+\phi_C$	
$\phi_C = 0, R_1' = 0$	$\phi_C = 1, R_1' = 1$
$L/(S_1+S_2+S_3+S_4)(1)$ $(L+S_i)/(S_j+S_k+S_m)(4)$ $(L+S_i+S_j)/(S_k+S_m)(6)$ $(L+S_i+S_j+S_k)/S_m(4)$	$(L+S_i)/(S_1+S_2+S_3+S_4)(4)$ $(L+S_i)/(L+S_j+S_k+S_m)(4)$ $(L+S_i+S_j)/(S_j+S_k+S_m)(12)$ $(L+S_i+S_j)/(L+S_k+S_m)(6)$ $(L+S_i+S_j+S_k)/(S_k+S_m)(12)$
$\phi_C=2,\ R_1'=2$	$\phi_C=3,\ R_1'=3$
$(L+S_i+S_j)/(S_1+S_2+S_3+S_4)(6)$ $(L+S_i+S_j)/(L+S_j+S_k+S_m)(12)$ $(L+S_i+S_j+S_k)/(S_j+S_k+S_m)(12)$	$(L+S_i+S_j+S_k)/(L+S_i+S_j+S_m)(12)$ $(L+S_i+S_j+S_k)/(S_1+S_2+S_3+S_4)(4)$
(5) $\Phi=2,\ Z=3,\ R_1=0,\ \phi_C=0,\ R_1'=0$	
L/S	

In Table 4.2, we explain all the cases of phase assemblages of NPRs with different values of R_1. The notations used are: L, liquid phase, assuming that all components are completely miscible with one another in the liquid state; S_1, S_2, S_3 and S_4 are four solid solutions, $i, j, k, m = 1, 2, 3, 4$, and $i \neq j \neq k \neq m$. For example, L/(L+S_i)(4), since i=1, 2, 3, 4, (4) denotes 4 different phase assemblages counted by the method of permutations and combinations.

In Table 4.2, only the cases given are: where (1) $R_1 \geqslant 1, R_1' = R_1 + \phi_C - 1$, (2) R_1=0 and there is an invariant phase transition between two NPRs, $R_1' = R_1 + \phi_C$.

All of the above discussion points are valid for the following types of phase diagram cases: (1) In liquid and solid states, all components are completely miscible with one another; (2) Components are soluble with one another only in the liquid state. They are only partially soluble with one another in the solid state. Eutectic events may occur in the system; and (3) Peritectic events may occur in the system.

4.3 During Temperature Decreasing, Some Cases of Variations of the NPRs and their Boundaries, May be Encountered for Several Types of Quaternary Isobaric Phase Diagrams

4.3.1 The simple quaternary phase diagram, in which, (a) the liquid state components are completely miscible, but (b) the same components are completely insoluble with one another, in the solid state

For further examination, these components are denoted by A, B, C and D. The pure solid state components remain denoted by the identities: S_1, S_2, S_3 and S_4. There also exists one invariant, quaternary eutectic transition.

$$L \rightarrow (S_1 + S_2 + S_3 + S_4)$$

In addition, binary and ternary eutectic transitions also exist. High-temperature, stable phase regions are the liquid-solid coexisting phase regions, these are as follows: L + S_i(4) (since i=1, 2, 3, 4, so there are 4 such phase regions, 4 being used to represent the number of such phase regions). Below, the notations are similar: (L + S_i + S_j)(6); (L + S_i + S_j + S_k)(4). The low-temperature, stable phase region is (S_1 + S_2 + S_3 + S_4) (1). Therefore there are 16 phase regions in the phase diagram. The binary, ternary and quaternary eutectic points are denoted respectively, by E_{ij}(6) (as i, j = 1, 2, 3, 4 and $i \neq j$, *i.e.* there are 6 binary, eutectic points.), E_{ijk}(4) and E_{1234}(1).

We now discuss the cases of the variations of the NPRs and their boundaries, during a decreasing temperature regime.

For this phase diagram, $R_1 = N - \Phi + 1 = 5 - \Phi$, $3 \geqslant R_1 \geqslant 0$.

At elevated temperature, the liquid phase L is stable. As the temperature decreases, phase transitions commence to occur in the system, R_1 decreases from 3 to 2, then to 1 and finally to 0.

1. For phase region L, when the temperature decreases, the regularities of the phase transitions are:

(1) With decreasing temperature, phase transition occurs, in most cases, within the composition tetrahedron, A, B, C, D: L $\rightarrow$ (L + S_i) (4) (since, i = 1, 2, 3, 4, there are 4 such phase transitions), $\Phi = 2$,

$$R_1 = 4 - \Phi + 1 = 5 - \Phi = 3$$

$$R_1' = R_1 + \phi_C - 1 = 3 - 1 + 1 = 3$$

$$R_1' = R_1$$

Thus, the 3-dimensional boundaries between L/(L+S_i) also act as phase boundaries, *i.e.* the boundaries are composed of "system points" which also act as phase points.

(2) If the total composition point of the system is located on the "special" curved surface, *i.e.* where the curved surface passes through points E_{ij}, E_{ijk}, E_{1234}, E_{ijm}, E_{ij} (6 such surfaces), and temperature decreases to a "certain temperature", then a phase transition occurs, L$\rightarrow$(L + S_i +S_j), where two solid phases are deposited from the liquid phase. There are 6 such phase transitions.

$$\phi_C = 1$$

$$\Phi = 3$$

$$R_1 = 5 - \Phi = 2$$

$$R_1' = R_1 + \phi_C - 1 = 2 + 1 - 1 = 2$$

The two-dimensional boundaries, lying between L/(L+S_i+S_j), are also phase boundaries, *i.e.* the boundaries are composed of the system points (also phase points).

(3) If the composition point of the system is located on the special curves, *i.e.* those curves that pass through $E_{ijk} \rightarrow E_{1234}$(4), then, when the temperature decreases further to a certain temperature, 3 solid phases commence to deposit from the liquid phase L, *i.e.* L$\rightarrow$(L+S_i+S_j+S_k) (6 such phase transitions),

$$\Phi = 4, \phi_C = 1$$

$$R_1 = 5 - \Phi = 1$$

$$R_1' = R_1 + \phi_C - 1 = 1 + 1 - 1 = 1$$

$$R_1' = R_1$$

The boundary lines between L/(L+ S_i+S_j+S_k) are phase boundary lines also.

(4) When the composition point of the system is located just at the point, E_{1234}, in the composition tetrahedron, the temperature decreases to the quaternary eutectic temperature, and a phase transition occurs, *i.e.* L→(L+S_1+S_2+S_3+S_4)(1), *i.e.* 4 phases deposit from the liquid phase, L.

$$\varPhi = 5, \phi_C = 0$$

$$R_1 = 5 - \varPhi = 5 - 5 = 0$$

$$R_1' = R_1 + \phi_C = 0 + 0 = 0$$

Since there is an invariant transition between two NPRs, equation $R_1' = R_1 + \phi_C$ is valid, the boundary point being a phase point, too.

2. For the phase region (L+S_i), when the temperature decreases, the regularities of the phase transitions occur:

(1) For the most of the systems for which the system points exist in the phase region, one more solid phase will be deposited, when the temperature decreases, *i.e.* (L+S_i) →(L+S_i+S_j) (the number of such phase transitions being 12).

For the boundaries between (L+S_i)/(L+S_i+S_j), $\varPhi$=3, ϕ_C=2,

$$R_1 = N - \varPhi + 1 = 2$$

$$R_1' = R_1 + \phi_C - 1 = 2 + 2 - 1 = 3$$

$$R_1' \neq R_1$$

So, the boundaries are of 3 dimensional boundaries only, they are not phase boundaries anyway!

(2) If the composition points of the system(s) are located on special curved surfaces, then the solid phase S_i deposits continuously, and the system point falls to "that of" the curves, E_{ijk}−E_{1234}, solid phases S_i, S_j and S_k, deposited from the liquid phase, *i.e.* (L+S_i) →(L+S_i+S_j+S_k) (12 such phase transitions), $\varPhi$ = 4, ϕ_C=2,

$$R_1 = 5 - \varPhi = 1$$

$$R_1' = R_1 + \phi_C - 1 = 2$$

$$R_1' \neq R_1$$

The boundaries between (L+S_i)/(L+S_i+S_j+S_k) are only of two dimensional boundaries (not phase boundaries).

(3) If the composition points of the systems are located on the curved line, connecting the pure S_i and E_{1234} of the composition tetrahedron, then, when the solid phase deposits continuously, and the system point falls to the point at E_{1234};

4 solid phases S_1, S_2, S_3 and S_4, would then be deposited simultaneously from the liquid phase, *i.e.* $(L+S_i) \rightarrow (S_1+S_2+S_3+S_4)$ (4)

$$\Phi = 5, \phi_C = 1,$$
$$R_1 = 0$$
$$R_1' = R_1 + \phi_C = 1$$

These boundaries are boundary lines only, not phase boundary lines.

3. The regularities of the variations of the phase region $(L+S_i+S_j)$, during the temperature decrease period:

(1) For "ordinary cases", when the solid phases, S_i and S_j, are depositing continuously, the system point would fall to that of the curved surface passing through E_{ijk} and E_{1234}, further solid phase would then be deposited, *i.e.* $(L+S_i+S_j) \rightarrow (L+S_i+S_j+S_k)$, Φ=4, $\phi_C = 3$,

$$R_1 = 5 - \Phi = 1$$
$$R_1' = R_1 + \phi_C - 1 = 3$$

The boundaries are 3-dimensional boundaries only (not phase boundaries).

(2) In a special case, when the solid phases S_i, S_j and S_k are being deposited continuously, the system point falls to that of the eutectic point, E_{1234}, then 4 solid phases, S_1, S_2, S_3 and S_4 would also deposit simultaneously, *i.e.* $(L+S_i+S_j) \rightarrow (S_1+S_2+S_3+S_4)$(6), Φ=5, ϕ_C=2,

$$R_1 = 0$$
$$R_1' = R_1 + \phi_C = 2$$

since there is an invariant phase transition. The boundaries are two dimensional boundaries only. The boundary is located on the non-variant, phase transition plane; it is a triangle tie-plane, formed by connecting the three boundary points.

4. The regularity of the phase transitions of the phase regions $(L+S_i+S_j+S_k)$ (4), during the temperature decrease period

When the solids (S_i, S_j, S_k) are depositing continuously, the system point falls to point E_{1234}; one further solid phase then deposits, $(L+S_i+S_j+S_k) \rightarrow (S_1+S_2+S_3+S_4)$ (4), $\Phi = 5$, $\phi_C = 3$,

$$R_1 = 0$$
$$R_1' = R_1 + \phi_C = 3$$

The boundaries are 3-dimensional boundaries only (not phase boundaries).

4.3.2 The isobaric quaternary phase diagram, in which the 4 components in the liquid state are completely miscible, but, in the solid state, they are partially soluble in one another

The liquid phase region and liquid-solid co-existing phase region of these phase diagrams are basically similar to those of the simple quaternary phase diagram, but here the solid phases are actual "solid solutions", so the case is a much more complicated one. The solid phase regions have $S_i(4)$, $(S_i+S_j)(6)$, $(S_i+S_j+S_k)(4)$, $(S_1+S_2+S_3+S_4)(1)$, and the liquid phase L(1), the solid-liquid co-existing phase regions being $(L+S_i)(4)$, $(L+S_i+S_j)(6)$ and $(L+S_i+S_j+S_k)$ (4). Thus, there are 30 phase regions to be included in this phase diagram.

There are also: binary, ternary and quaternary eutectic points, $E_{ij}(6)$, $E_{ijk}(4)$ and $E_{1234}(1)$ for consideration.

During the temperature decrease, the regularities of the variations of NPRs and their boundaries are much more complicated situations for this phase diagram. Let us now discuss it briefly.

The high-temperature-stable phase is the liquid phase, L. During the temperature decrease period, the regularities of variations of NPRs and their boundaries, are similar to that of a simple, isobaric quaternary phase diagram, but the deposited solid phases are all solid solutions.

During the temperature decrease, the phase regions for the three types: $(L+S_i)$, $(L+ S_i+S_j)$ and $(L+S_i+S_j+S_k)$, have the similar phase transitions of corresponding phase regions of the simple, quaternary phase diagram.

Since the deposited solids are true solid solutions, the phase region, for the three regions mentioned above, has another property in common: *i.e.* the value of R_1 does not decrease, it remains unchanged. Therefore, these phase regions all have the following phase transitions:

$$(L + S_i) \rightarrow S_i(4), \varPhi = 2, \phi_C = 1,$$
$$R_1 = 5 - 2 = 3$$
$$R_1' = 3 + 1 - 1 = 3$$

Here the boundaries between $(L+S_i)/S_i$ are 3-dimensional boundaries (also phase boundaries).

$$(L + S_i + S_j) \rightarrow (S_i + S_j)(6), \varPhi = 3, \phi_C = 2,$$
$$R_1 = 5 - 3 = 2$$
$$R_1' = 2 + 2 - 1 = 3$$
$$R_1' \neq R_1$$

The boundaries between $(L+S_i+S_j)/(S_i+S_j)$ are 3-dimentional boundaries only (not phase boundaries).

$$(\mathrm{L} + \mathrm{S}_i + \mathrm{S}_j + \mathrm{S}_k) \rightarrow (\mathrm{S}_i + \mathrm{S}_j + \mathrm{S}_k)(4),\ \varPhi = 4, \phi_C = 3,$$
$$R_1 = 5 - 4 = 1$$
$$R_1' = R_1 + \phi_C - 1 = 1 + 3 - 1 = 3$$
$$R_1' \neq R_1$$

i.e., the boundaries lying between $(\mathrm{L}+\mathrm{S}_i+\mathrm{S}_j+\mathrm{S}_k)/(\mathrm{S}_i+\mathrm{S}_j+\mathrm{S}_k)$ are 3-dimentional boundaries only.

Further, vertical sections of the isobaric quaternary phase diagrams of the various types may be explained with the use of the boundary theory.

Consider a typical vertical section, though, in this vertical section, the compositions of B% and D% of the systems are kept constant, the phase compositions of all components (including B and D) in the systems are otherwise variable. Thus, the characteristics of this vertical section are similar to the 4-dimensional quaternary phase diagram (see Fig. 4.1). Therefore, the relation, $R_1 = 5 - \varPhi$, still holds.

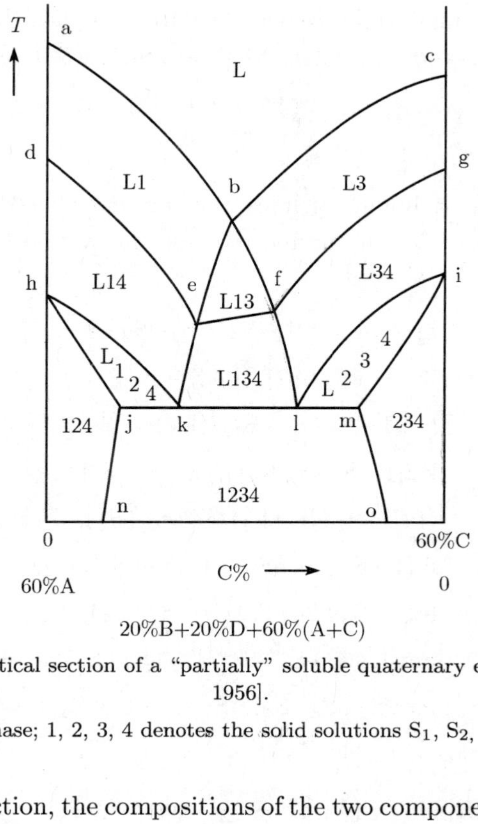

Fig. 4.1 A typical vertical section of a "partially" soluble quaternary eutectic system [Rhines, 1956].

L denotes the liquid phase; 1, 2, 3, 4 denotes the solid solutions S_1, S_2, S_3 and S_4 respectively.

In this vertical section, the compositions of the two components are held constant.

So, for the regular sections, the dimensions of the phase boundary and the boundary, $(R'_1)_V$ and $(R_1)_V$ (v is an abbreviation of "Vertical") have the following equations, where R_1 and R'_1 are the dimensions of the boundary and phase boundary in the corresponding, quaternary phase diagram.

$$(R'_1)_V = R'_1 - 2 \quad (4\text{-}1)$$

$$(R_1)_V = R_1 - 2 \quad (4\text{-}2)$$

Fig. 4.1 is a regular section, the meaning of the boundaries on this section will now be discussed.

4.3.2.1 The boundary lines

Lines ab and bc are the boundaries existing between the two NPRs with Φ=2. They have:

$$(R_1)_V = R_1 - 2 = (4 - \Phi + 1) - 2 = (4 - 2 + 1) - 2 = 1$$
$$(R'_1)_V = R'_1 - 2 = (R_1 + \phi_C - 1) - 2 = (1 + 2 - 1) - 2 = 1$$

Thus, ab and bc are boundary lines, and they are also phase boundary lines.

For lines: de, eb, bf and fg, the two NPRs around these lines have $\Phi = 3, \phi_C = 2$

$$(R_1)_V = R_1 - 2 = (4 - 3 + 1) - 2 = (2) - 2 = 0$$
$$(R'_1)_V = R'_1 - 2 = (R_1 + \phi_C - 1) - 2 = (2 + 2 - 1) - 2 = 1$$

Thus, these lines are only boundary lines, they are not phase boundary lines.

Lines, nj, jh, hk, ke, ef, fl, li, im and mo, and the two NPRs around these lines, have $\Phi = 4, \phi_C = 3$

nj:$(S_1+S_2+S_3+S_4)/(S_1+S_2+S_4)$,

jh:$(S_1+S_2+S_4)/(L+S_1+S_2+S_4)$,

hk:$(L+S_1+S_2+S_4)/(L+S_1+S_4)$,

ke:$(L+S_1+S_3+S_4)/(L+S_1+S_4)$,

ef:$(L+S_1+S_3+S_4)/(L+S_1+S_3)$,

fl:$(L+S_1+S_3+S_4)/(L+S_3+S_4)$,

li:$(L+S_2+S_3+S_4)/(L+S_3+S_4)$,

im:$(L+S_2+S_3+S_4)/(S_2+S_3+S_4)$,

mo:$(S_2+S_3+S_4)/(S_1+S_2+S_3+S_4)$,

$$(R_1)_V = R_1 - 2 = (4 - 4 + 1) - 2 = -1$$
$$(R'_1)_V = R'_1 - 2 = (R_1 + \phi_C - 1) - 2 = (1 + 3 - 1) - 2 = 1$$

Therefore, these lines are also boundary lines only.

Boundary line jklm, the NPRs around this line are $(L+S_i+S_j+S_k)/(S_1+S_2+S_3+S_4)$, $\Phi=5$, $R_1=0$. This means that there are only invariable phase points in the 4-dimensional phase diagram. But

$$(R_1)_V = R_1 - 2 = -2$$

So, these phase points cannot be presented in the two-dimensional vertical section. $\phi_C=3$, and there is an invariant phase transition between the two NPRs, then:

$$R_1 = 0$$
$$(R_1)_V = -2$$
$$R_1' = R_1 + \phi_C = 0 + 3 = 3$$
$$(R_1')_V = R_1' - 2 = 3 - 2 = 1$$

Therefore, boundary line jklm is also a boundary line only. The points, j, k, l and m, are boundary points, too.

4.3.2.2 Boundary points

(1) Boundary point b

Around point b, there are NPRs $L/(L+S_1+S_3)$, or NPRs $(L+S_1)/(L+S_3)$, or NPRs L, $(L+S_3)$, $(L+S_1+S_3)$ and $(L+S_1)$. For all these sets of NPRs, $\Phi=3$, $\phi_C=1$,

$$R_1 = 5 - 3 = 2$$
$$R_1' = R_1 + \phi_C - 1 = 2$$
$$(R_1)_V = R_1 - 2 = 0$$
$$(R_1')_V = R_1' - 2 = 0$$

So boundary b is a phase point.

(2) Boundary points e and f

The NPRs around them have $\Phi=4$, $\phi_C=2$,

$$R_1 = 5 - 4 = 1$$
$$R_1' = R_1 + \phi_C - 1 = 1 + 2 - 1 = 2$$
$$(R_1)_V = 1 - 2 = -1$$
$$(R_1')_V = 2 - 2 = 0$$

So point e and f are boundary points only.

Through the discussion above, the characteristics of different kinds of boundaries are differentiated.

Boundary lines ab and bc are also phase boundary lines. All other boundary lines are boundary lines only. Boundary point b is a phase point, while boundary point e and f are boundary points only.

We may now depict a series of vertical sections having different compositions, as shown in Fig. 4.2.

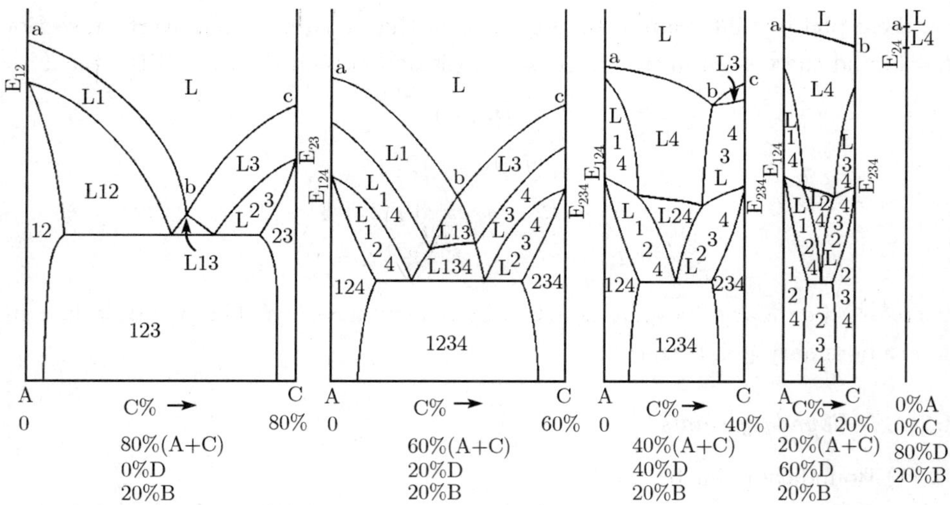

Fig. 4.2 A series of vertical sections of a quaternary eutectic system, in which the solid components are partially soluble with each other [Rhines, 1956].

All of the notations of Fig. 4.2 are similar to those of Fig. 4.1.

In Fig. 4.2, the binary eutectic points, E_{12}, E_{23} and E_{24}, and ternary eutectic points, E_{124} and E_{234}, present on the vertical axes. This figure can be readily explained as it is similar to Fig. 4.1. The explanation is however omitted here.

4.3.3 Isobaric quaternary phase diagrams with peritectic transitions

Peritectic transitions have three types:

$$(\mathrm{L}+\mathrm{S}_i) \rightarrow (\mathrm{S}_j+\mathrm{S}_k+\mathrm{S}_m)$$

$$(\mathrm{L}+\mathrm{S}_i+\mathrm{S}_j) \rightarrow (\mathrm{S}_k+\mathrm{S}_m)$$

$$(\mathrm{L}+\mathrm{S}_i+\mathrm{S}_j+\mathrm{S}_k) \rightarrow \mathrm{S}_m$$

In the phase diagrams for each type, the NPRs phase assemblages have different combinations. As a result, all of these phase diagrams are very complicated, on the whole. In comparison with the simpler eutectic phase diagrams, the peritectic ones have more peculiarities, *e.g.* the temperature ranges for liquid state existence are often greater, while the concentration ranges for the solid solutions existence are wider. Thus, phase diagrams of the peritectic types are both more diversified in form and are also more complicated. However, there are, in principle, no basic differences between the eutectic and the peritectic phase diagram.

For the purpose of space saving, only one typical vertical section of a quaternary peritectic phase diagram, with the phase transition of the type (L+S_i) →(S_j+S_k+S_m) is discussed here (see Fig. 4.3).

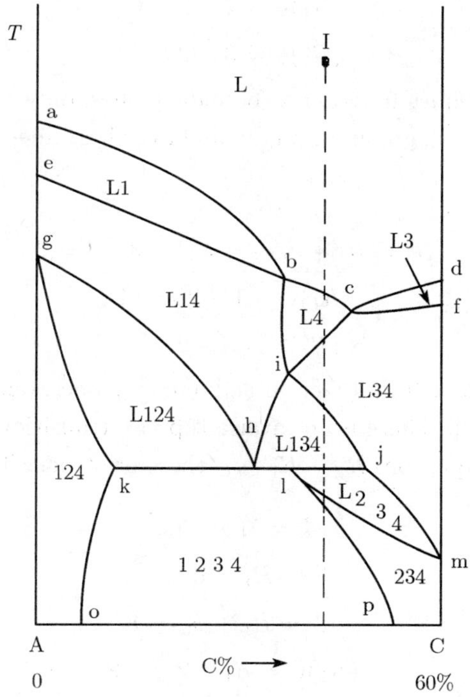

Fig. 4.3 A typical vertical section of a quaternary, peritectic system. L denotes the liquid phase, 1, 2, 3, 4 denote the solid solutions (S_1, S_2, S_3 and S_4) respectively [Rhines, 1956].

4.3.3.1 Boundary lines

Boundary lines, ab, bc, cd satisfy the combinations: $\varPhi$=2, ϕ_C=1

$$R_1 = 3$$

$$R_1' = R_1 + \phi_C - 1 = 3$$

Thus

$$(R_1')_V = R_1' - 2 = 1$$

$$(R_1)_V = R_1 - 2 = 1$$

Therefore, these three boundary lines are all boundary lines and phase boundary lines.

Boundary lines: eb, bi, ic and cf. These lines satisfy the combinations Φ=3, ϕ_C=2

$$R_1 = 2$$

$$R_1' = R_1 + \phi_C - 1 = 2 + 2 - 1 = 3$$

$$(R_1)_V = 2 - 2 = 0$$

$$(R_1')_V = 3 - 2 = 1$$

$(R_1)_V \neq (R_1')_V$, these lines function as boundary lines, only.

Boundary lines ok, kg, gh, hi, ij, jm, ml and lp. These lines satisfy the conditions, Φ=4, ϕ_C =3

$$R_1 = 1$$

$$R_1' = R_1 + \phi_C - 1 = 1 + 3 - 1 = 3$$

$$(R_1)_V = 1 - 2 = -1$$

$$(R_1')_V = 3 - 2 = 1$$

So, these eight boundary lines function as boundary lines, only.

Boundary line, khlj. There is an invariant phase transition, located between the two NPRs here, the equation, $R_1' = R_1 + \phi_C$ therefore holds. This line, khlj, satisfies the conditions:

$$\Phi = 5, \phi_C = 3,$$

$$R_1 = 0$$

$$R_1' = R_1 + \phi_C = 3$$

$$(R_1)_V = R_1 - 2 = -2$$

$$(R_1')_V = R_1' - 2 = 1$$

This line is a boundary line only, no phase point exists over it.

4.3.3.2 Boundary points

Point b and c. They satisfy the conditions: Φ=3, ϕ_C=1

$$R_1 = 2$$

$$R_1' = R_1 + \phi_C - 1 = 2 + 1 - 1 = 2$$

$$(R_1)_V = 2 - 2 = 0$$

$$(R_1')_V = 2 - 2 = 0$$

Thus, points b and c are both boundary points and phase boundary points.

Point i. It satisfies the conditions Φ=4, ϕ_C=2

$$R_1 = 1$$

$$R_1' = R_1 + \phi_C - 1 = 1 + 2 - 1 = 2$$

$$(R_1)_V = R_1 - 2 = -1$$

$$(R_1')_V = R_1' - 2 = 1$$

Thus, it is a boundary point only.

We can now discuss the cooling history of the system whose composition is represented by I.

The discussion starts from the liquid phase, L. With the declining temperature, the system point of phase L eventually touches line bc, the phase transition occurring: L→ (L+S_4). With further temperature decrease, the system point reaches line ci, and the phase transition occurs: (L+S_4) → (L+S_3+S_4). When the system point reaches line ij, the phase transition occurs: (L+S_3+S_4) → (L+S_1+S_3+S_4). With continuing temperature decrease, the system reaches the peritectic line, lj, and the peritectic reaction occurs:

$$(L + S_1 + S_3 + S_4) \rightarrow (L + S_2 + S_3 + S_4),\ \Phi = 5, \phi_C = 3,$$

$$R_1 = 0$$

$$R_1' = R_1 + \phi_C = 3$$

$$(R_1)_V = -2$$

$$(R_1')_V = 3 - 2 = 1$$

The boundary line, lj, is a boundary line only.

With the temperature decreasing further:

$$(L+S_2+S_3+S_4) \rightarrow (S_2+S_3+S_4) \rightarrow (S_1+S_2+S_3+S_4)$$

This process is easy to explain and so it is not discussed further here.

4.3.4 Quaternary phase diagrams, in which the systems have either compounds or intermediate phases or maximum (or minimum) melting points

In these cases, it is better to discuss the phase diagrams with the TCR in the form:

$$R_1 = (N - r - Z) - \Phi + 1$$

Or, one may divide the phase diagram into several, independent simpler parts, and then discuss them in the usual manner.

4.4 The Isobaric Quinary Phase Diagrams

Here, the boundary theory may be used to discuss the quinary or even higher number-component phase diagrams.

In the general case of the isobaric phase diagram, $Z = r$=0, the characteristic of the relation between NPRs and their boundaries is outlined in Table 4.3.

Table 4.3 $Z = r = 0$, the characteristic of the variations of R_1, $\varPhi$, ϕ_C and R_1' in isobaric, quinary phase diagrams

$R_1 = 6 - \varPhi$					
$R_1(4\geqslant R_1 \geqslant 0)$	4	3	2	1	0
$\varPhi(6\geqslant \varPhi \geqslant 2)$	2	3	4	5	6
ϕ_C	1	$2\geqslant \phi_C \geqslant 1$	$3\geqslant \phi_C \geqslant 1$	$4\geqslant \phi_C \geqslant 1$	$4\geqslant \phi_C \geqslant 0$
R_1'	4	ϕ_C+2	$\phi_C + 1$	ϕ_C	ϕ_C 1) or $\phi_C - 1$

1) There is an invariant phase transition between the two NPRs.

Similarly, we may also apply the comparable method, as applied in quaternary phase diagrams, to discuss isobaric, quinary phase diagrams, *i.e.* list all combinations of phase assemblages of NPRs under the conditions of different values for R_1 and $\varPhi$. Since there are no new things of basic manipulations and principles involved in these higher order component assemblages, the analysis and discussion being just more complicated, the analysis of the higher order structures are omitted from this present analysis.

4.5 Conclusion

The above "outline" discussions have shown that "the boundary theory" may be employed to both analyze and synthesize multicomponent phase diagrams. This examination has shown that "the boundary theory" of multicomponent phase diagrams, is both correct and useful.

References-4

F. N. Rhines. 1956. Phase Diagram in Metallurgy. New York: McGraw-Hill

Chapter 5

The Boundary Theory in Construction of Multicomponent Isothermal Sections

5.1 The Relationship among Neighboring Phase Regions (NPRs) and Their Boundaries in Isobaric Isothermal Multicomponent Sections

5.1.1 General rules

The general regular isothermal sections satisfy the condition of $R_1 \geqslant 1$.

In the regular isothermal sections of N-component system, besides T and p, the compositions of (N-3) components are also kept constant.

$$(R_1')_{\mathrm{H}} = R_1' - 1 - (N-3) = R_1' - (N-2) \tag{5-1}$$

$$(R_1)_{\mathrm{H}} = R_1 - 1 - (N-3) = R_1 - (N-2) \tag{5-2}$$

where $(R_1')_{\mathrm{H}}$ and $(R_1)_{\mathrm{H}}$ are the dimensions of the boundary and the phase boundary in the regular isobaric isothermal section of the N-component system respectively.

In isobaric phase diagrams, the theorem of corresponding relationship (TCR) is as follows:

$$R_1 = N - \Phi + 1$$

then

$$(R_1)_{\mathrm{H}} = (N - \Phi + 1) - (N-2) = 3 - \Phi \tag{5-3}$$

$$(R_1')_{\mathrm{H}} = (R_1 + \phi_C - 1) - (N-2) = \phi_C - \Phi + 2 \tag{5-4}$$

For the isobaric isothermal section, if

$$(R_1)_{\mathrm{H}} = (R_1')_{\mathrm{H}} \tag{5-5}$$

Then the boundary coincides with the phase boundary each other, *i.e.*, the system points on the boundary are phase points at the same time. If in any case

$$(R_1)_{\mathrm{H}} < (R_1')_{\mathrm{H}} \tag{5-6}$$

The boundary in the regular section is no longer a phase boundary.

5.1.2 The two types of boundaries in isobaric isothermal multicomponent sections

5.1.2.1 The boundary lines

When
$$\Phi - \phi_C=1 \tag{5-7}$$

$$(R_1')_{\mathrm{H}} = \phi_C - \Phi + 2 = 1$$

This is to say, if the number difference of the phases between two NPRs is one, there should be a boundary line between them.

When
$$\Phi = 2,\ \phi_C = 1,$$

$$(R_1)_{\mathrm{H}} = 3 - \Phi = 1$$

$$(R_1')_{\mathrm{H}} = (R_1)_{\mathrm{H}}$$

In this case, the boundary line is also a phase boundary line.

When $\Phi = 3$,
$$(R_1)_{\mathrm{H}} = 3 - \Phi = 0$$

The boundary line consists of system points only.

5.1.2.2 The boundary point

When
$$\Phi = 3,\ \phi_C = 1, \text{ and}$$

$$\Phi - \phi_C = 2 \tag{5-8}$$

$$(R_1')_{\mathrm{H}} = \phi_C - \Phi + 2 = 0$$

Therefore, if the number of phase differences between two NPRs is two, there could be only one boundary point between these two NPRs. Since $(R_1)_{\mathrm{H}} = 3 - \Phi=0$, the boundary point between two NPRs is a phase boundary point at the same time.

If $\Phi \geqslant 4$, according to the boundary theory, $(R_1)_{\mathrm{H}}$ should be less than zero, *i.e.*,

$$(R_1)_{\mathrm{H}} \leqslant -1 \tag{5-9}$$

It means that the boundary point between the two NPRs could not be a phase boundary point. The meaning of the negative dimension of the phase boundary will be explained in the next section.

The cross rule, well-known in the phase diagram research community, describes a fundamental regulation in phase regions transfer. This rule points out that a phase region containing N phases would either be a neighbor to a phase region containing $(N+1)$ phases, demarcated by a boundary line, or would be in contact with a phase region containing $(N+2)$ phases by a boundary point. From the view point of the results of phase region transfer: "A boundary point is equivalent to two boundary lines."

In Fig. 5.1, it can be seen that the boundary between those NPRs is a boundary line if there is only one phase difference between the two NPRs, for example, phase region AOB to BOC, BOC to COD, COD to DOA *etc.* For two phase differences, the boundary dividing them is a boundary point, for example AOB to COD, BOC to AOD *etc.* Following the course of the phase region evolution from one NPR to another, the system in the NPR AOB could reach COD by crossing the boundary point O; or by passing the AO and OD two boundary lines. This is to say, from the result of the phase region transfer, one boundary point O between two NPRs AOB/COD is equivalent to two boundary lines, AO and OD, among the three NPRs AOB/AOD/COD. From the discussion above (eqs. (5-3) to (5-9)), we can see that the boundary theory interprets the "cross rule" clearly, and more information can be derived from the boundary theory.

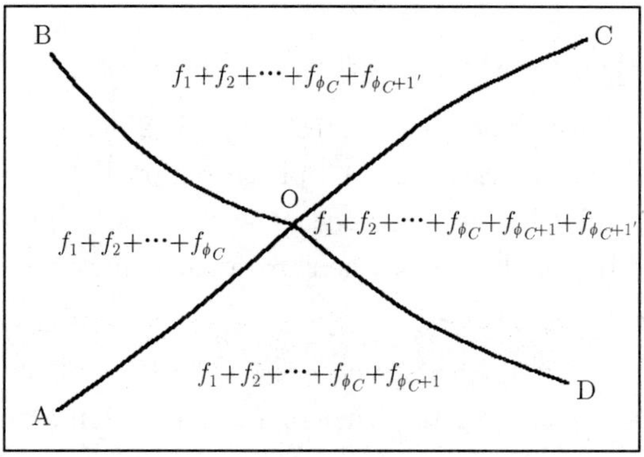

Fig. 5.1 One boundary point is equivalent to two boundary lines.

5.1.2.3 *In case* $\Phi - \phi_C \geqslant 3$

$$(R_1')_{\mathrm{H}} = \phi_C - \Phi + 2 \leqslant -1 \tag{5-10}$$

The unrealistic negative dimension of the boundary implies that it is actually impossible for these two phase regions to contact each other in a regular isobaric isothermal section. They are non-contact or non-neighboring phase regions. This is a useful guide line for constructing multicomponent isothermal sections, which helps us to judge the situations where certain phase regions will never be neighbours to each other, due to their make-up from a particular combination of phases.

The above conclusions have nothing to do with the value of N, so they apply to the regular isothermal sections of all the ternary and multicomponent systems.

It is worthy mentioning here that the "cross rule" describes well the situations that four phase boundaries meet at a single point; however, there are cases in which one cross-over points connecting more than four lines, or the cases where less than four lines meet together. Such "violation" of the "cross rule" is often seen at special points, for example, at a "nodal plexus" or "nodal foci", where the phase regions degeneration occurred [Prince, 1966]. With the exception of this kind of "violation", the "cross rule" restrictions hold true in general. This chapter discusses only the general regular isothermal sections, we will not involve those exceptions.

5.2 The Non-Contact Phase Regions and the Boundaries between Them

5.2.1 The number of boundaries existing between non-contact phase regions

Assume two non-contact (or non-neighboring) phase regions be

$$\mathrm{PR}_1/\ldots\ldots/\mathrm{PR}_k$$

$$f_1+f_2+\cdots+f_{\phi_C}+f_{\phi_C+1}+\cdots f_{\phi_C+q}/\cdots/f_1+f_2+\cdots+f_{\phi_C}+f_{\phi_C+1'}+\cdots+f_{\phi_C+q'}$$

The system in the phase region PR_1 goes through a series of phase regions and boundaries, and eventually arrives at the phase region PR_k at last. Although the phase regions PR_1 and PR_k do not contact each other, the total number of the different phases existing in these two phase regions, Φ may be counted also.

$$\Phi=\phi_C+q+q' \tag{5-11}$$

The number of phases belonging to either one phase region alone is

$$\Phi-\phi_C=q+q' \tag{5-12}$$

According to the boundary theory, the following corollary may be deduced.

The systems within the phase region PR_1 must transfer through the $(q+q')$ boundary lines or the $(q+q'-2p)$ boundary lines and p boundary points to reach the non-contact phase region, PR_k.

Since the phase region PR_1 passes through one boundary line to reach the phase region PR_2, the phase difference existing between these two phase regions $(\Phi-\phi_C)$ must be one, *i.e.* there is one non-common phase between these two phase regions. Again, the phase region PR_2 transfers through another boundary line to the phase region PR_3, the phase difference between the latter two phase regions $(\Phi-\phi_C)=1$. If counting the phase differences between the two non-contact phase regions $\mathrm{PR}_1/\mathrm{PR}_3$, $(\Phi-\phi_C)=2$ and so on. Counting the phase differences between the phase regions, PR_1/PR_k, the phase differences $\Phi - \phi_C = (q + q')$, it means that the systems in the phase region PR_1 must transfer through the $(q + q')$ boundary lines to arrive at PR_k. Recalling that "one boundary point is equivalent to two boundary lines", the system in the phase region PR_1 may also transfer through the $(q+q'-2p)$ boundary lines, plus p boundary points, to arrive at PR_k.

5.2.2 The course takes a zigzag path

If the path for the transfer of the phase regions takes a zigzag route, $2n$ (n=integer) more boundary lines must be passed. During the transfer of the phase regions from PR_1 to PR_k, if one phase common for these two phase regions disappears, then it must reappear again. An example is given in Fig. 5.2.

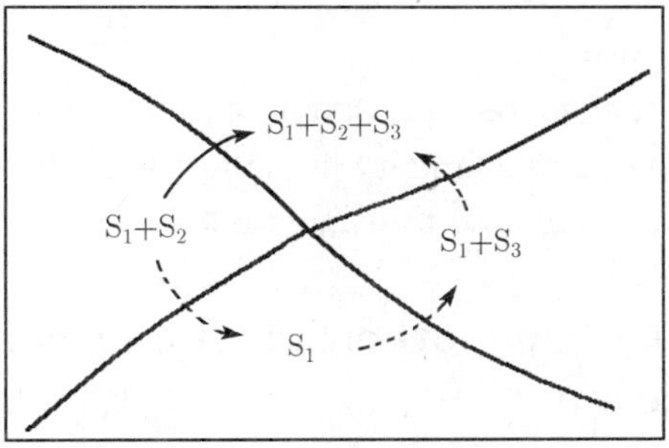

Fig. 5.2 Transfer from PR (S_1+S_2) to PR (S_1+S_2+S_3).

It is possible to transfer from the phase region (S_1+S_2) to the phase region (S_1+S_2+S_3) by passing only one boundary line separating them. If the transfer took the path as (S_1+S_2) $\rightarrow$ S_1 $\rightarrow$ (S_1+S_3) $\rightarrow$ (S_1+S_2+S_3), phase S_2 disappears at once and then reappears again. The transfer of the phase regions must pass two extra boundary lines, one for the disappearance of S_2 and another for its reappearance. On the other hand, if one phase, it being "non-existent" in both phase regions, should appear in the course of the transfer of the phase regions, it also needs to take two more boundary lines. For example, the phase region S_1 in Fig. 5.3 can transfer to the phase region (S_1+S_2) directly, by crossing only the one boundary line that separates them. There is no phase S_3 in both of the phase regions S_1 and (S_1+S_2) and thus there is no necessity for S_3 to appear. However, if the transference of the phase regions takes the path S_1 $\rightarrow$ (S_1+S_3) $\rightarrow$ (S_1+S_2+S_3) $\rightarrow$ (S_1+S_2), one "extra" phase, S_3, is created and must go, two more boundary lines for this scenario are necessary, see next page.

In summary, during the transfer course of phase region PR_1 to phase region PR_k, if λ_1 phases existing in both of phase regions PR_1 and PR_k disappear, it must cross

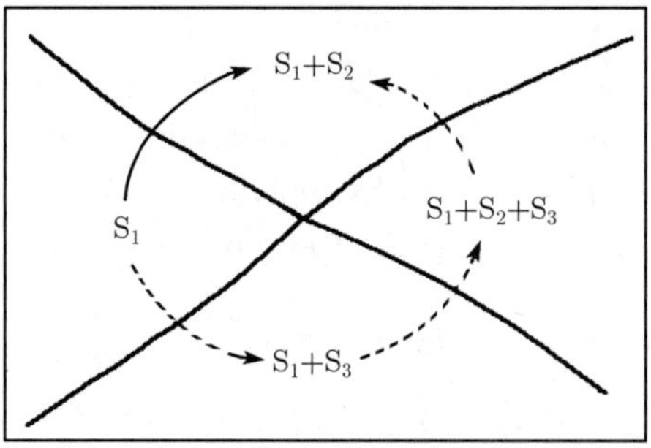

Fig. 5.3 Transfer from PR (S_1) to PR (S_1+S_2).

$2\lambda_1$ "extra" boundary lines. And if λ_2 extra phases are not existent in both phase regions PR_1 and PR_k appears, the transference of phase regions must cross $2\lambda_2$ "extra" boundary lines also.

If between the two non-contact phase regions PR_1 and PR_k, there are λ_3 new phases forming, then 2 λ_3 more boundary lines must appear between these two phase regions, the reason being similar to that mentioned above.

5.3 Construction of an Isothermal Quinary Section, with Limited Information

5.3.1 The method of the boundary theory

Let us take Fig. 5.4 to illustrate how a sketch of an isothermal section can be formed from limited experimental information.

There are five components A, B, C, D and E, in the system. The temperature and compositions of D and E are held constant in order to produce a two-dimensional, isothermal section. Five phases, namely α, β, γ, δ and ε exist in this system; they are rich in components A, B, C, D and E, respectively. Fig. 5.4 (a) demonstrates all 21 experimentally determined the phase assemblages with different compositions (The positions of the samples are shown by the identified dots in the figure. This figure was taken from Gupta's paper [Gupta *et al.*, 1986]). These experimental data are far from sufficient to depict an experimental phase diagram. On the other hand, they have been enough to enable us to delineate a prototype of the phase diagram that will help to the further investigation on this system.

With the principle of the boundary theory, some boundary lines can be drawn easily with the available information. The two NPRs $2(\alpha+\varepsilon$, or in brief, $\alpha\varepsilon)/3(\alpha+\beta+\varepsilon$, or in brief, $\alpha\beta\varepsilon)$ have the following characteristics: ϕ_2=2, ϕ_3=3, ϕ_C=2, $\Phi-\phi_C$=1, it satisfies the condition for the existence of a boundary line between the two NPRs (eq.(5-7)). One boundary line may be drawn between the two NPRs $2(\alpha\varepsilon)/3(\alpha\beta\varepsilon)$.

Around point a, there are two pairs of NPRs $2(\alpha\varepsilon)/4(\beta\varepsilon)$ and $5(\varepsilon)/3(\alpha\beta\varepsilon)$. These two pairs of NPRs satisfy the condition for the existence of a phase boundary point ($\Phi=3$, $\phi_C=1$, $\Phi-\phi_C=2$) (eq.(5-8)), point a being a phase boundary point. Similarly,

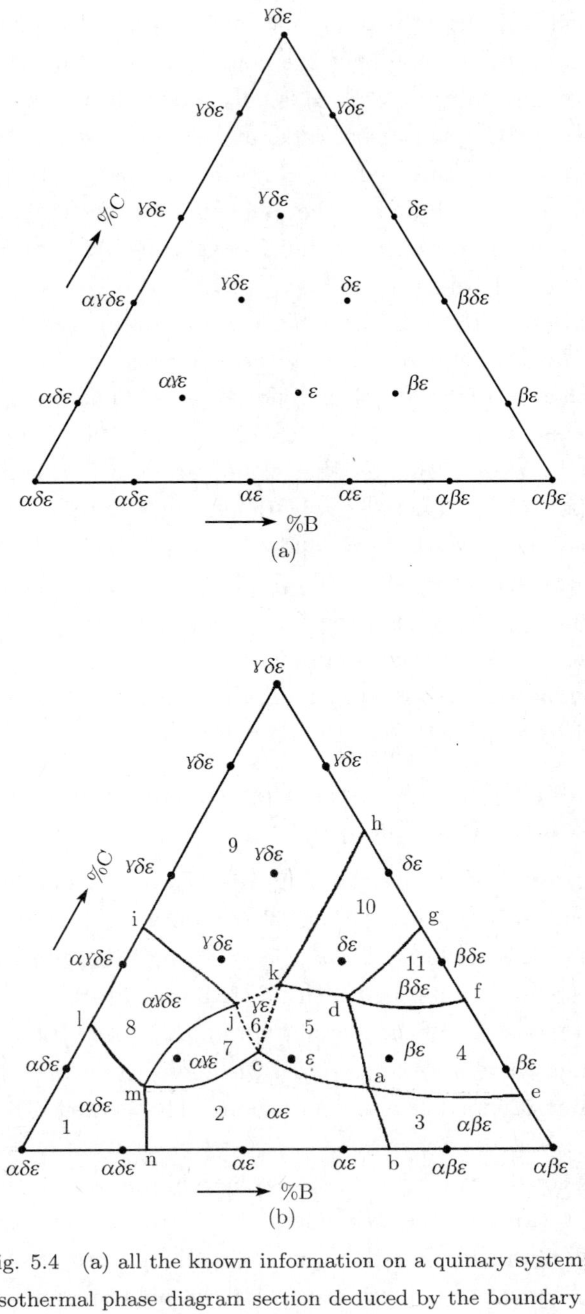

Fig. 5.4 (a) all the known information on a quinary system; (b) the isothermal phase diagram section deduced by the boundary theory.

one may also draw boundary lines ac, ad and dk, directly between the pairs of NPRs, $5(\varepsilon)/2(\alpha\varepsilon)$, $5(\varepsilon)/4(\beta\varepsilon)$ and $5(\varepsilon)/10(\delta\varepsilon)$ respectively. Since for all of these boundary lines, Φ=2, ϕ_C=1, $\Phi - \phi_C$=1, they satisfy the condition of occurring a phase boundary line. Also, boundary lines ae, df, dg, hk, lm, mn, ij and the two boundary points d and m may be obtained. As all of the NPRs around these boundary lines have $\Phi \geqslant 3$, these lines are boundary lines only. Point d (Φ=3) is a phase boundary point, point m ($\Phi > 3$) is only a boundary point.

Phase region 7 is of $(\alpha\gamma\varepsilon)$ assemblage, and lines mj and mc may be drawn to separate it from the other three NPRs. However, to finally settle the connection of the phase regions 7, 9, 10, 5 and 2, there appears a necessity of existing an extra phase region 6 in this area, which the limited experimental data failed to recognize. Our deduction is as follows.

For two pairs of NPRs $5(\varepsilon)/7(\alpha\gamma\varepsilon)$ and $5(\varepsilon)/9(\gamma\delta\varepsilon)$, they have the following characteristics: Φ=3, ϕ_C=1 and $\Phi - \phi_C$=2, the phase region 5 must be in contact with the other two NPRs with individual phase boundary points. For NPRs $7(\alpha\gamma\varepsilon)$ /$9(\gamma\delta\varepsilon)$, they have Φ=4, ϕ_C=2 and $\Phi - \phi_C$=2, therefore a single boundary point must exist between them. Further examination of the pairs of phase regions $2(\alpha\varepsilon)/9(\gamma\delta\varepsilon)$, $8(\alpha\gamma\delta\varepsilon)$/ $5(\varepsilon)$ and $7(\alpha\gamma\varepsilon)/10(\delta\varepsilon)$, indicate that they can not contact each other as they have: Φ=4, ϕ_C=1 and $\Phi - \phi_C$=3. Based on all of these assessments, we are sure that there should be a phase region 6, being delimited by the three boundary lines jc, ck, jk and the three boundary points c, j, k; and its actual phase assemblage cannot be other than $(\gamma\varepsilon)$.

Thus, all boundary lines, boundary points and phase assemblages are determined in accordance with the principles of the boundary theory.

5.3.2 Gupta's method for constructing multi-component isothermal sections [Gupta *et al.*, 1986]

Gupta *et al.* worked out an overlapping ZPF (Zero Phase Fraction) lines method to construct a multi-component isothermal section with limited information. The principle employed is as follows. First, the ZPF line, with the given phase assemblages of a few system points, is drawn. This line is drawn in such a way that a phase is located on one side of the line but not on the other. If there are ϕ phases on the phase diagram, there are therefore ϕ ZPF lines. By means of these ZPF lines, the phase diagram is divided into several regions. This is the isothermal section that is being sought.

Gupta *et al.* constructed a fictitious isothermal quinary section of the quinary system of Fig 5.4 (a) with the ZPF method. By overlapping the ZPF lines, the desired section is obtained. For this quinary section, there are 5 phases: α, β, γ, δ and ε. Since the ε phase is present in all of the phase regions, there is therefore no ZPF line for f_ε=0, 4 ZPF lines are drawn. By means of the overlapping 4 ZPF lines, the desired section is obtained in Fig. 5.5.

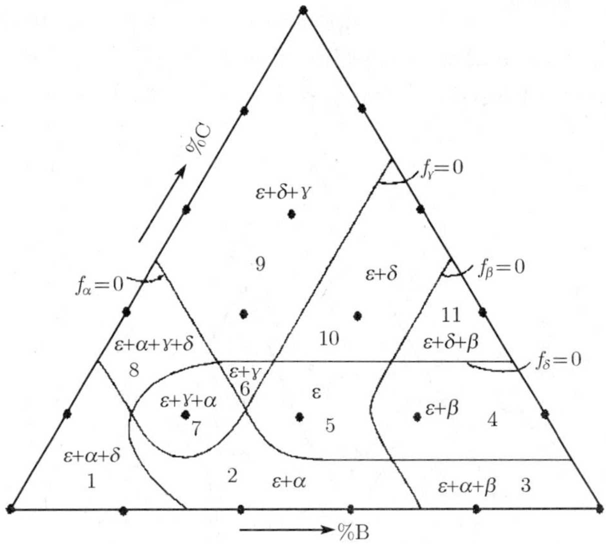

Fig.5.5 The two-dimensional section is completed by overlapping ZPF lines using 21 sample dots [Gupta *et al.*, 1986].

This method, indeed, is quick and effective to construct the phase diagram with limited data. It also successfully predicted the phase region 6, which was not confirmed by the experiments. But, on the other hand, the freedom in drawing the ZPF lines within the scarce experimental points will bring an uncertainty in resulted phase diagram. As Gupta *et al.* described, "Regions can be made to appear or disappear by the use of an arbitrary shift of the lines. For example, the ZPF lines of α, γ and δ can be shifted to cause field $(\varepsilon+\gamma)$ to disappear and a new field containing $(\alpha+\delta+\varepsilon)$ to appear." This is the situation presented in Fig. 5.6.

According to Gupta *et al.*, "Both possibilities are topologically valid ...". We have examined and confirmed that both the results show no violation of the principles of thermodynamic equilibrium and mass conservation. The situation becomes thus delicate, because in the real world, there should be only one authentic phase diagram for a system. Which one, Fig. 5.5 or Fig. 5.6, is correct? Here we see the trouble from the inherent arbitrariness in depicting the ZPF lines. The phase diagram (Fig. 5.4(b)) derived from different principle of the boundary theory conforms to the depiction of Fig. 5.5, may raise a higher odds for that section to be true.

In general cases, it is more common to see that if an i-th component increases in the system, then the quantity of the phase rich of i-th component will increase correspondently, rather than diminishing or vanishing. Compare the 5.4(b), from the phase region 7 ($\alpha\gamma\varepsilon$) to 6 ($\gamma\varepsilon$), and the Fig. 5.6, from the phase region 7 ($\alpha\gamma\varepsilon$) to 6'($\alpha\delta\varepsilon$), the former appears more probable to occur, as the component C increases in the system and γ-phase is rich of component C. However, a definitive answer relies on the further experimental work, as Gupta *et al.* had it, "... additional samples in the vicinity of the controversial region must be studied to determine its true nature."

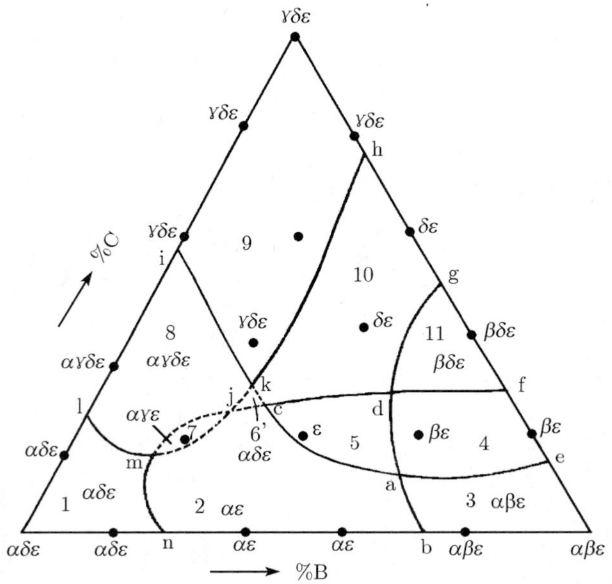

Fig. 5.6 Another possible section created by applying the ZPF method.

5.4 The Method of Constructing an Isothermal Eight-Component Section

We now treat a more complicated system to illustrate the operation of "the boundary theory" method; the system is also taken from Gupta's paper [Gupta *et al.*, 1986]. The system of this isothermal section contains eight components (Al, C, Fe, Si, Mn, Cr, Mo and Nb), eleven phases and 35 phase regions. In this isothermal section, there are also five components with fixed compositions (Fe, 62 wt%; Mn, 15 wt%; Cr, 12 wt%; Mo, 2 wt%; Nb, 1 wt%). The other three components (Al+Si+C) wt% = 8 wt%. Temperature is held at 700°C. The eleven phases in the section are α-Fe, Cr, graphite (denoted by G), β-Mn(denoted by βn), MSi(M is metal, MSi is abbreviated to $_1S$, the method of abbreviation being similar below), M_3Si($_3S$), Fe_5Si_3(F_5S_3), Mn_5Si_3(n_5S_3), M_2C($_2C$), M_3C($_3C$) and $M_{23}C_6$($_{23}C_6$) respectively. All of the phase regions contain α-Fe and Cr, and are not marked in Fig. 5.7. There are only fourteen phase regions that are determined by experiments, they are phase regions 1, 2, 3, 13, 16, 18, 24, 27, 31, 32, 34, 36, 37 and 38, denoted by a dot in each identified phase region, see Fig. 5.7.

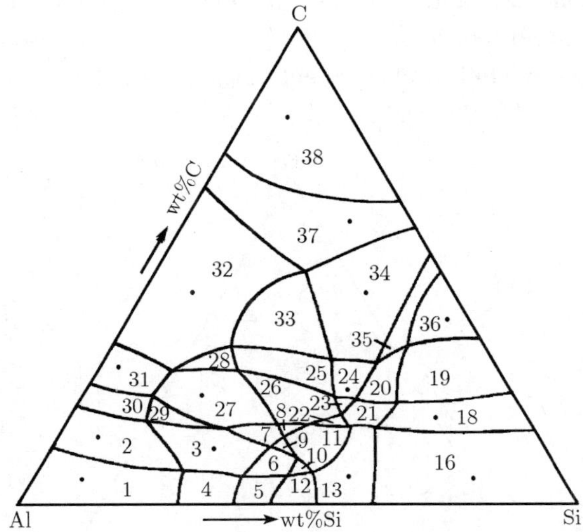

Fig. 5.7 A horizontal section of an eight-component system.

At constant temperature and pressure, the boundary theory gives $\Phi_{\max}=8$. Applying the method discussed above, we may now depict directly the boundary lines between following pairs of NPRs:

1/2, (it denotes NPRs 1/2, *i.e.* NPRs $\beta\mathrm{n}/(\beta\mathrm{n},\ \underline{{}_{23}\mathrm{C}_6})$), one more phase ${}_{23}\mathrm{C}_6$ appears in NPR 2, it is presented by an underline. This is the situation $\Phi = 2$, $\phi_C = 1$, $\Phi - \phi_C = 1$. We have been made familiar with this type of NPRs, two NPRs of this type have a phase boundary line between them. We treat other pairs using the same principle ($\Phi - \phi_C = 1$) and thence set the boundary lines between the following pairs.

2/3 $(\beta\mathrm{n},{}_{23}\mathrm{C}_6/\beta\mathrm{n},{}_{23}\mathrm{C}_6,\underline{{}_1\mathrm{S}})$

31/27 $({}_2\mathrm{C},{}_{23}\mathrm{C}_6/{}_2\mathrm{C},{}_{23}\mathrm{C}_6,\underline{{}_1\mathrm{S}})$

31/32 $({}_2\mathrm{C},{}_{23}\mathrm{C}_6/{}_2\mathrm{C},{}_{23}\mathrm{C}_6,\underline{{}_3\mathrm{C}})$

37/32 $({}_2\mathrm{C},{}_3\mathrm{C}/{}_2\mathrm{C},{}_3\mathrm{C},\underline{{}_{23}\mathrm{C}_6})$

37/34 $({}_2\mathrm{C},{}_3\mathrm{C}/{}_2\mathrm{C},{}_3\mathrm{C},\underline{\mathrm{F}_5\mathrm{S}_3})$

37/38 $(({}_2\mathrm{C},{}_3\mathrm{C}/{}_2\mathrm{C},{}_3\mathrm{C},\underline{\mathrm{G}})$

34/24 $({}_2\mathrm{C},{}_3\mathrm{C},\mathrm{F}_5\mathrm{S}_3/{}_2\mathrm{C},{}_3\mathrm{C},\mathrm{F}_5\mathrm{S}_3,\underline{{}_1\mathrm{S}})$

16/18 $({}_1\mathrm{S},{}_3\mathrm{S},\mathrm{F}_5\mathrm{S}_3,\mathrm{n}_5\mathrm{S}_3/{}_1\mathrm{S},{}_3\mathrm{S},\mathrm{F}_5\mathrm{S}_3,\mathrm{n}_5\mathrm{S}_3,\underline{{}_2\mathrm{C}})$

13/16 $({}_1\mathrm{S},{}_3\mathrm{S},\mathrm{F}_5\mathrm{S}_3/{}_1\mathrm{S},{}_3\mathrm{S},\mathrm{F}_5\mathrm{S}_3,\underline{\mathrm{n}_5\mathrm{S}_3})$

These ten lines are drawn as full lines in Fig. 5.8. This result is directly from the limited experimental information and the boundary theory. A vast vacant area remains in this section as we do not have any experimental data for the possible phase regions. The marked unknown phase regions in Fig. 5.8 are the final results when our derivation was completed. For the moment, these unknown phase regions are delineated by 44 dotted lines.

This figure was depicted by the present authors, but the system was taken from Gupta's paper [Gupta *et al.*, 1986].

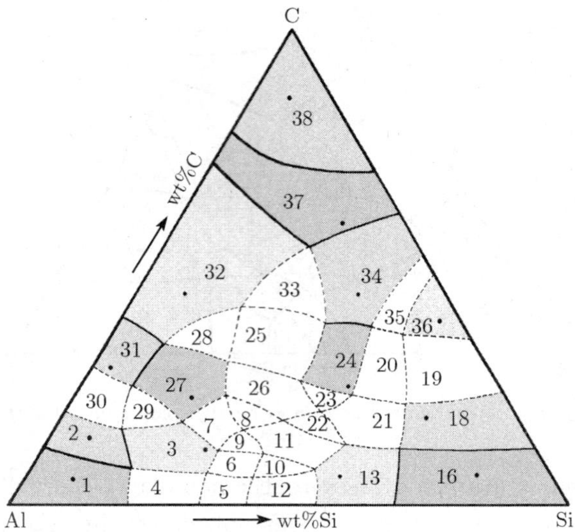

Fig. 5.8 The incomplete section for the eight component system.

(The unknown boundary lines are shown in dotted lines; □ shows the identified phase regions.)

We first find the number of boundary lines and boundary points for those non-contact phase regions(Table 5.1). Applying the principles discussed in section 5.2, the number of boundaries existing between non-contact phase regions may be obtained. A few examples, but not a complete collection, are listed in Table 5.2. In doing so, we now know how many possible boundary lines exist between these non-contact phase regions, and a tentative plot of the section could be made. For example, knowing that there are 2 lines between NPR 34 and 36, we are confident to cut out the phase region 35 from the consideration.

Table 5.1 The number of boundaries between two non-contact phase regions

Phase regions		Φ	ϕ_C	$\Phi-\phi_C$	The number of possible boundary lines or points	
No.	No.				Points	Lines
34	36	7	5	2	0	2
34	18	8	4	4	2(or0)	0(or4)
24	36	8	5	3	1(or0)	1(or3)
24	16	8	4	4	2(or0)	0(or4)
27	24	7	4	3	0(or1)	3(or1)

Table 5.2 Determination of the phases in the 4th NPR in sequence

3 known NPRs	The 4th NPR	3 known NPRs	The 4th NPR
1, 2, 3,	4	13,21,22,	11
27,31,32,	28	26,22,11,	8
32,37,34,	33	27,26,8,	7
28,32,33,	25	7, 8, 11,	9
27,28,25,	26	3, 7, 9,	6
24,25,26,	23	6, 9, 11,	10
13,16,18,	21	10,11,13,	12
21,23,24,	20	6, 10,12,	5
20,24,34,	35	3, 7, 27,	29
20,35,36,	19	2, 3, 29,	30
21,23,26,	22		

Next, we determine the phase region and its phase assemblage from the known NPRs. Inside the horizontal section, if there are three phase regions in contact at a boundary point, a fourth phase region must appear. If the phase assemblages in the three among the four NPRs are known, the fourth may be determined. Table 5.2 summarizes our deductions.

Thus, all boundary lines and phases present in the twenty-one unknown phase regions are determined, leading to the assembly of Table 5.3, and thence the whole isothermal section is constructed.

Table 5.3 The phase assemblages present in phase regions shown in Fig. 5.7

No.	Phase assemblages	No.	Phase assemblages
1	βn	20	${}_2C,{}_3C,{}_1S,{}_3S,F_5S_3$
2	$\beta n,{}_{23}C_6$	21	${}_2C,{}_1S,{}_3S,F_5S_3$
3	$\beta n,{}_{23}C_6,{}_1S$	22	${}_2C,{}_{23}C_6,{}_1S,{}_3S,F_5S_3$
4	$\beta n,{}_1S$	23	${}_2C,{}_1S,F_5S_3$
5	$\beta n,{}_1S,{}_3S$	24	${}_2C,{}_3C,{}_1S,F_5S_3$
6	$\beta n,{}_1S,{}_3S,{}_{23}C_6$	25	${}_2C,{}_3C,{}_{23}C_6,{}_1S,F_5S_3$
7	${}_1S,{}_{23}C_6$	26	${}_2C,{}_{23}C_6,{}_1S,F_5S_3$
8	${}_1S,F_5S_3,{}_{23}C_6$	27	${}_2C,{}_{23}C_6,{}_1S$
9	${}_{23}C_6,{}_1S,{}_3S$	28	${}_2C,{}_3C,{}_1S,{}_{23}C_6$
10	$\beta n,{}_1S,{}_3S,{}_{23}C_6,F_5S_3$	29	$\beta n,{}_1S,{}_2C,{}_{23}C_6$
11	${}_1S,{}_3S,{}_{23}C_6,F_5S_3$	30	${}_{23}C_6,\beta n,{}_2C$
12	$\beta n,{}_1S,{}_3S,F_5S_3$	31	${}_2C,{}_{23}C_6$
13	${}_1S,{}_3S,F_5S_3$	32	${}_2C,{}_3C,{}_{23}C_6$
14	—	33	${}_2C,{}_3C,{}_{23}C_6,F_5S_3$
15	—	34	${}_2C,{}_3C,F_5S_3$
16	${}_1S,{}_3S,F_5S_3,n_5S_3$	35	${}_2C,{}_3C,{}_3S,F_5S_3$
17	—	36	${}_2C,{}_3C,F_5S_3,{}_3S,n_5S_3$
18	${}_2C,{}_1S,{}_3S,F_5S_3,n_5S_3$	37	${}_2C,{}_3C$
19	${}_2C,{}_3C,{}_1S,{}_3S,F_5S_3,n_5S_3$	38	${}_2C,{}_3C,G$

Note: All of the phases contain the phases α-Fe and Cr which are not shown in this table.

The phase assemblages of all the phase regions presented in the isothermal section, as deduced from the different starting points, are the same, we did such work twenty years ago. We encourage our readers to try to construct this section, or to repeat some part of it, so as to become more familiar with the general method of the boundary theory applications.

Applying the overlapping ZPF lines method, Gupta *et al.* derived the isothermal section shown in Fig. 5.9. Comparing Fig. 5.9 and 5.7 (Fig.5.8 is the same as 5.7), it is seen that there is difference in number of phase regions. Our deduction does not include the phase regions 14, 15 and 17. As a matter of fact, if the middle part of ZPF line 23/6—23/6 and line Mn_5Si_3—Mn_5Si_3 retreat a little each other, *i.e.* the middle part of line 23/6-23/6 shifts to left side and the middle part of ZPF line Mn_5Si_3-Mn_5Si_3 shifts to right side, then they would not cross each other, the phase region 13 would contact phase region 21 directly and the phase regions 14 and 15 would disappear. As to the region 17, since all the MSi-containing experimental

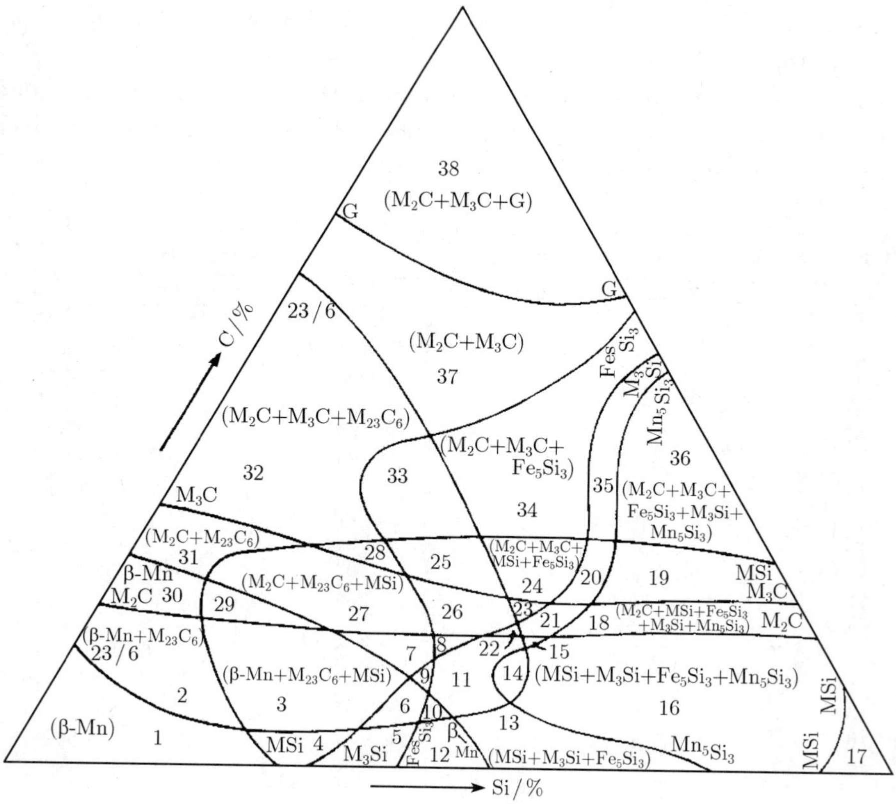

Fig. 5.9 An isothermal section of eight component system depicted by Gupta *et al.* [Gupta *et al.*, 1986].

points has been enveloped by the long ZPF line $f_{\rm MSi}=0$ (across the middle-lower part of the triangle), the short ZPF line $f_{\rm MSi}=0$ at the corner appears somehow unconvincing, as there is not any experimental data indicating that there is a phase region without MSi phase.

5.5 Summary of Using the Boundary Theory Method

In this chapter, we present a method to construct the phase diagrams of multi-component system with limited experimental data. This method employs the fundamental principle of the boundary theory to delineate the boundary line in an unknown phase diagram, and to determine the phase regions and their phase assemblages. The difficulty of this method is that it requires a good understanding of the boundary theory. Some more exercises may be necessary at the beginning with relatively simple systems. But, we suppose that to comprehend the boundary theory is not an exorbitant task for our readers.

The Gupta's method had been widely used for the same purpose. The overlapping ZPF line demonstrates certain arbitrariness in constructing the phase diagram.

Applying the boundary theory to construct the phase diagram is definitive. Moreover, the boundary theory is also able to discuss the relation existing between the non-contact phase regions in the isothermal sections. Through the parameter $(\varPhi - \phi_C)$ of the non-contact phase regions, the number of boundary lines, or the number of boundary lines and boundary points, can be calculated. Thus, the method of the boundary theory is a powerful technique for use in the construction of complex section phase diagrams. The results so derived are supported by one of the ZPF operation. Unfortunately, we have not been able to confirm the authenticity among the different ZPF results. This implies that we still have great deal to learn in the rules of phase diagram structure. Before any cogent theory available, the ultimate conclusion relies on the availability of experimental observation. The sketched phase diagrams, such as Fig. 5.4 and 5.7 may be the useful map for scientists and researchers to select the new experimental point on the isothermal phase diagrams concerned.

References-5

H. Gupta, J. E. Morral, H. Nowotny. 1986. Constructing multicomponent phase diagrams by overlapping ZPF lines. Scripta Metallurgica, 20: 889–894

M. Hillert. 1988. Constructing multicomponent phase diagrams using ZPF lines and Schreinemakers' rule. Scripta Metallurgica, 22: 1085

A. Prince. 1966. Alloy phase equilibria. New York: Elsevier

Chapter 6

The Boundary Theory of Multicomponent Isobaric Isopleth Sections

6.1 Introduction

When the temperature is varying, the equilibrium phase transitions within system of three or more components, at constant pressure, may be described by means of isobaric isopleth (or vertical) sections. Thus, isopleths have important application over a great range of the different disciplines within the various sciences and technologies. In applying the boundary theory to isopleth section, the relationship among the NPRs and their boundaries in the isobaric isopleths may be systematically clarified.

The temperature of the isopleth section is a variable, thus the isopleth section is a much more complicated component than the isothermal section. While there are differences between the isopleth section and the corresponding spatial phase diagram, from the viewpoint of phase equilibrium, both have many similarities. In the following paragraphs, the isopleth section, associated with the corresponding spatial phase diagram, is discussed.

6.1.1 General rules

The isobaric N-component phase diagram is presented here in N-dimensional space. In this phase diagram, there are variables x_i $(i = 1, 2, \cdots, N)$ and T, but $\sum x_i = 1$, the number of independent variables, in all are N. In order to present the phase equilibrium relation in a two-dimension isopleth plane, $(N-2)$ compositional variables must be fixed. So the dimensions of phase boundaries $(R_1)_\mathrm{i}$ and boundaries $(R_1')_\mathrm{i}$ (here, subscript i is the abbreviation for isopleth) in the regular isobaric isopleth section, are $(N-2)$ less than the dimensions of phase boundaries, R_1 and the boundaries, R_1' of the corresponding isobaric space phase diagrams respectively, *i.e.*

$$(R_1)_\mathrm{i} = R_1 - (N-2) \tag{6-1}$$

$$(R_1')_\mathrm{i} = R_1' - (N-2) \tag{6-2}$$

In the following paragraphs, we discuss the relation among NPRs and their boundaries, according to the different values of R_1.

6.2 The Characteristics of Boundaries in Isopleth Sections for the Case of $N \geqslant 2$ and $R_1 \geqslant 1$

When $N \geqslant 2$, $R_1 \geqslant 1$, then $\phi_C \geqslant 1$ and $R_1' = R_1 + \phi_C - 1$.

6.2.1 $N \geqslant 2$ and $R_1 \geqslant 1$, there is boundary line $(R_1')_{\rm i} = 1$ in the isopleth section

According to the boundary theory of phase diagrams, the following equations may be deduced:

$$\begin{aligned}(R_1)_{\rm i} &= R_1 - (N-2)\\ &= (N+1-\varPhi) - (N-2)\\ &= 3-\varPhi \end{aligned} \tag{6-3}$$

$$\begin{aligned}(R_1')_{\rm i} &= R_1' - (N-2)\\ &= (R_1 + \phi_C - 1) - (N-2)\\ &= (N+1-\varPhi+\phi_C-1) - (N-2)\\ &= \phi_C + 2 - \varPhi \end{aligned} \tag{6-4}$$

When $(R_1')_{\rm i} = 1$,

$$1 = \phi_C + 2 - \varPhi, \quad \varPhi - \phi_C = 1 \tag{6-5}$$

i.e. the phase difference of two NPRs is one, there is a boundary line between the two NPRs. The phase assemblages of the two NPRs are

$$(f_1 + f_2 + \cdots + f_{\phi_C})/(f_1 + f_2 + \cdots + f_{\phi_C} + f_{\phi_C+1}).$$

If

$$(R_1)_{\rm i} = (R_1')_{\rm i} = 1 \tag{6-6}$$

i.e. the boundary line is also a phase boundary line.

Since $(R_1)_{\rm i} = 3 - \varPhi$ (eq.(6-3)), if $(R_1)_{\rm i} = 1$, $\varPhi$=2.

Since $N \geqslant 2$ and $R_1 \geqslant 1$, $\phi_C \geqslant 1$, when $\varPhi = 2$, the only possibility is $\phi_C = 1$. Therefore phase assemblages of two NPRs which satisfy eq. (6-6) must be NPRs $f_i/(f_i + f_j)$, $i \neq j$.

In short, $N \geqslant 2$, $R_1 \geqslant 1$, $(R_1)_{\rm i}$=$(R_1')_{\rm i} = 1$, then $\varPhi = 2$, $\phi_C = 1$, the phase assemblages of two NPRs are $f_i/(f_i + f_j)$.

When $(R_1)_{\rm i} < 1$,

$$(R_1)_{\rm i} = 3 - \varPhi < 1, \quad \varPhi \geqslant 3 \tag{6-7}$$

That is: $N \geqslant 2, R_1 \geqslant 1$, and $\varPhi \geqslant 3$, $(R_1')_{\rm i} = 1$, then the boundary lines between the two NPRs are boundary lines only, and not phase boundary lines.

In the mean time, because $R_1 \geqslant 1$,

$$\varPhi = N + 1 - R_1 \leqslant N$$

So, $N \geqslant \varPhi \geqslant 3$, according to eq. (6-5), $\phi_C = \varPhi - 1$,
and

$$(N-1) \geqslant \phi_C \geqslant 2 \tag{6-8}$$

The ranges and regularities of the variations in $\varPhi$ and ϕ_C of these boundaries, among NPRs are wholly determined by eqs. (6-5), (6-7) and (6-8).

According to eqs. (6-1), (6-2), (6-5), (6-7) and (6-8), if the phase assemblages of two NPRs are given, the values of $\varPhi$, ϕ_C, R_1, R_1', $(R_1)_{\rm i}$ and $(R_1')_{\rm i}$ of the system of four, five and six components may be deduced logically, see Table 6.1.

Table 6.1 The characteristics of the NPRs and their boundaries when $N \geqslant 2, R_1 \geqslant 1$, $(R_1)_{\rm i} \leqslant (R_1')_{\rm i} = 1$

N	4	5	6
$\varPhi$	2, 3, 4	2, 3, 4, 5	2, 3, 4, 5, 6
$\phi_C = \varPhi - 1$	1, 2, 3	1, 2, 3, 4	1, 2, 3, 4, 5
$R_1 = N + 1 - \varPhi$	3, 2, 1	4, 3, 2, 1	5, 4, 3, 2, 1
$R_1' = R_1 + \phi_C - 1$	3, 3, 3	4, 4, 4, 4	5, 5, 5, 5, 5
$(R_1')_{\rm i} = R_1' - (N-2)$	1, 1, 1	1, 1, 1, 1	1, 1, 1, 1, 1
$(R_1)_{\rm i} = R_1 - (N-2)$	$1, 0, -1$	$1, 0, -1, -2$	$1, 0, -1, -2, -3$

In Table 6.1, when $(R_1)_{\rm i}$=$(R_1')_{\rm i}$, the boundary line is also a phase boundary line. When $(R_1)_{\rm i} < (R_1')_{\rm i} = 1$, the boundary lines are boundaries only. When $\varPhi$=3, $(R_1)_{\rm i}$=0, there may exist a phase boundary point between two NPRs. When $(R_1)_{\rm i} = -1, -2, -3$, there is no phase boundary point between two NPRs.

6.2.2 $N \geqslant 2$, $R_1 \geqslant 1$, and there are boundary points $(R_1')_{\rm i} = 0$ in the isopleth section

6.2.2.1 The case (1): the boundary point is also a phase boundary point in the isopleth section.

When $(R_1)_{\rm i}$=$(R_1')_{\rm i}$=0, by eq. (6-3)

$$(R_1)_{\rm i} = 3 - \varPhi = 0$$

$$\varPhi = 3$$

Thus, in the isobaric multicomponent phase diagram, there are three different phases in the two NPRs, $\varPhi$=3; then there is a boundary point also a phase point between the two NPRs in the isopleth section.

Since $(R_1')_{\mathrm{i}} = \phi_C + 2 - \varPhi = 0$, see eq. (6-4).

$$\phi_C = \varPhi - 2 = 1$$

$$\varPhi - \phi_C = 2$$

$\varPhi$=3, $\phi_C = 1$, the phase assemblages of the two NPRs must be NPRs of the type, $f_i/(f_i + f_j + f_k)$ or $(f_i + f_j)/(f_j + f_k)$, $i, j, k = 1, 2, 3$, $i \neq j \neq k$. There are two different phases between the two NPRs.

6.2.2.2 The case (2): in the isopleth section, there are boundary points, but not phase boundary points, i.e. $0=(R_1')_{\mathrm{i}} > (R_1)_{\mathrm{i}}$.

$$0 > (R_1)_{\mathrm{i}} = 3 - \varPhi, \varPhi > 3, i.e.$$

$$\varPhi \geqslant 4.$$

Since in the isobaric phase diagram, when $R_1 \geqslant 1$, $N \geqslant \varPhi$, then

$$N \geqslant \varPhi \geqslant 4 \tag{6-9}$$

$$0 = (R_1')_{\mathrm{i}} = \phi_C + 2 - \varPhi$$

$$\phi_C = \varPhi - 2 \tag{6-10}$$

$$\varPhi - \phi_C = 2$$

Therefore, the phase assemblages of the two NPRs are of the types NPRs $(f_1 + f_2 + \cdots + f_{\phi_C})/(f_1 + f_2 + \cdots + f_{\phi_C} + f_{\phi_C+1} + f_{\phi_C+2})$ or NPRs $(f_1 + f_2 + \cdots + f_{\phi_C} + f_{\phi_C+1})/(f_1 + f_2 + \cdots + f_{\phi_C} + f_{\phi_C+1'})$.

In the isobaric ternary phase diagram, these is no case of $R_1 \geqslant 1$ and $\varPhi \geqslant 4$, so it is impossible existing boundary point of this type. According to eqs.(6-9), (6-10) and other equations, the characteristics of the boundaries in four and more component isopleth sections may be deduced, as shown in Table 6.2.

Table 6.2 Characteristics of the boundaries in the case of $N \geqslant 2, R_1 \geqslant 1$, $0 = (R_1')_{\mathrm{i}} \geqslant (R_1)_{\mathrm{i}}$

N	4	5	6
$\varPhi$	4	4, 5	4, 5, 6
$\phi_C = \varPhi - 2$	2	2, 3	2, 3, 4
$R_1 = N + 1 - \varPhi$	1	2, 1	3, 2, 1
$R_1' = R_1 + \phi_C - 1$	2	3, 3	4, 4, 4
$(R_1')_{\mathrm{i}} = R_1' - (N-2)$	0	0, 0	0, 0, 0
$(R_1)_{\mathrm{i}} = R_1 - (N-2)$	−1	−1, −2	−1, −2, −3

When $(R_1')_{\mathrm{i}}$=0 and $(R_1')_{\mathrm{i}} > (R_1)_{\mathrm{i}}$, the boundary point is no longer a phase point.

6.3 The Characteristics of Boundaries in the Isopleth Section for the Case of $N \geqslant 2$, $R_1 = 0$, there is no Invariant Phase Transition between the two NPRs

In this case, one NPR transfers to another, only when the composition of the system changes. $R_1' = R_1 + \phi_C - 1$ still holds.

6.3.1 There is no boundary line between the two NPRs for the above mentioned case

This may be proved as follows:

Since R_1=0,

$$(R_1')_{\rm i} = R_1' - (N-2)$$
$$= (R_1 + \phi_C - 1) - (N-2)$$
$$(R_1')_{\rm i} = \phi_C - N + 1 \quad (6\text{-}11)$$

If $(R_1')_{\rm i} = 1$, $\phi_C = N$. Then, according to the phase rule, for the isobaric phase diagram, R_1=0, $\phi = N$. Now, $\phi_C = N$, the phase assemblages of the two NPRs are identical, it is meaningless.

Therefore, under the above mentioned condition, there is no boundary line with $(R_1')_{\rm i} = 1$ in the isopleth section.

6.3.2 The boundary points with $(R_1')_{\rm i} = 0$

According to eq. (6-11), if $(R_1')_{\rm i}$=0,

$$\phi_C = N - 1 \quad (6\text{-}12)$$

$$R_1 = 0$$

$$\Phi = N + 1 - R_1 = N + 1 \quad (6\text{-}13)$$

From eqs. (6-11), (6-12) and (6-13), the characteristics of the boundaries of this type are shown in Table 6.3.

Table 6.3 Characteristics of the boundaries for the case of: $N \geqslant 2, R_1 = 0$, $R_1' = R_1 + \phi_C - 1, 0 = (R_1')_{\rm i} > (R_1)_{\rm i}$

N	4	5	6
$\Phi = N+1$	5	6	7
$\phi_C = N-1$	3	4	5
R_1	0	0	0
$R_1' = R_1 + \phi_C - 1$	2	3	4
$(R_1')_{\rm i} = R_1' - (N-2)$	0	0	0
$(R_1)_{\rm i} = R_1 - (N-2)$	−2	−3	−4

Let us now discuss the phase assemblages of two NPRs. According to the phase rule, in the isobaric phase diagram, for the number of phases in any phase region, ϕ, there is $N \geqslant \phi \geqslant 1$, see eq. (2-2).

If $\phi_1 = N$

$$\begin{aligned}\phi_2 &= \Phi + \phi_C - \phi_1 \\ &= (N+1) + (N-1) - N \\ &= N\end{aligned}$$

i.e. $\phi_1 = \phi_2 = N$, $\phi_C = N - 1$.

This does not contradict the boundary theory, therefore it is possible. Also, there is only one possibility, all other phase assemblage combinations are impossible. This may be proved as follows:

If $\phi_1 < N$

$$\begin{aligned}\phi_2 &= \Phi + \phi_C - \phi_1 = (N+1) + (N-1) - \phi_1 \\ &= 2N - \phi_1 > N\end{aligned}$$

According to the phase rule, this is impossible.

Therefore, the phase assemblages of two NPRs are

$$\text{NPRs } (f_1 + f_2 + \cdots + f_{\phi_C} + f_{\phi_C+1})/(f_1 + f_2 + \cdots + f_{\phi_C} + f_{\phi_C+1'}).$$

6.4 The Case of $N \geqslant 2$, $R_1 = 0$, there is an Invariant Phase Transition between the two NPRs. In this Case, there may be a Boundary Line or a Boundary Point between two NPRs

6.4.1 In the isopleth section, boundary lines exist: $(R_1')_{\text{i}} = 1$ between the NPRs in the above condition

$$\because \ R_1 = 0$$

$$\Phi = N + 1 \tag{6-14}$$

and

$$\begin{aligned}1 = (R_1')_{\text{i}} &= R_1' - (N-2) \\ &= R_1 + \phi_C - (N-2) \\ &= \phi_C - (N-2)\end{aligned}$$

so

$$\phi_C = N - 1 \tag{6-15}$$

From the eqs.(6-14), (6-15) *etc*, the characteristics of the boundaries may be obtained, see Table 6.4.

Then, let us discuss the phase assemblages of the two NPRs.

Since $\phi_1 \leqslant N$

Table 6.4 Characteristics of boundaries for the case: $N \geqslant 2, R_1=0$, there is an invariant phase transition between NPRs, $R_1' = R_1 + \phi_C$, $1 = (R_1')_i > (R_1)_i$

N	4	5	6
$\Phi = N+1$	5	6	7
$\phi_C = N-1$	3	4	5
R_1	0	0	0
$R_1' = R_1 + \phi_C$	3	4	5
$(R_1')_i = R_1' - (N-2)$	1	1	1
$(R_1)_i = R_1 - (N-2)$	−2	−3	−4

If $\phi_1 = N$

$$\phi_2 = \Phi + \phi_C - \phi_1 = (N+1) + (N+1) - N$$
$$= N$$
$$\phi_1 = \phi_2 = N$$

There is the only one possibility. If $\phi_1 < N$,

$$\phi_2 = \Phi + \phi_C - \phi_1$$
$$= (N+1) + (N+1) - \phi_1$$
$$= 2N - \phi_1 > N$$

It is impossible.

Therefore, the phase assemblages of two NPRs are:

$$\text{NPRs}(f_1 + f_2 + \cdots + f_{\phi_C} + f_{\phi_C+1})/(f_1 + f_2 + \cdots + f_{\phi_C} + f_{\phi_C+1'}).$$

6.4.2 The boundary points $(R_1')_i = 0$ between the two NPRs in the case mentioned above

Since $R_1 = 0$, $\Phi = N+1$

and

$$0 = (R_1')_i = R_1' - (N-2)$$
$$= R_1 + \phi_C - (N-2)$$
$$= \phi_C - (N-2)$$
$$\phi_C = (N-2) \tag{6-16}$$

The characteristics of boundary points of this type are shown in Table 6.5.

Table 6.5 Characteristics of the boundary points in the case: $N \geqslant 2, R_1 \geqslant 0$, $R_1' = R_1 + \phi_C$, $0 = (R_1')_i > (R_1)_i$

N	4	5	6
$\Phi = N+1$	5	6	7
$\phi_C = N-2$	2	3	4
R_1	0	0	0
$(R_1')_i = R_1' - (N-2)$	0	0	0
$(R_1)_i = R_1 - (N-2)$	−2	−3	−4

The boundary point is no longer a phase boundary point.

Let us discuss the phase assemblages for the two NPRs.

Since $\phi \leqslant N$, if $\phi_1 = N$

$$\begin{aligned}\phi_2 &= \Phi + \phi_C - \phi_1 \\ &= (N+1) + (N-2) - N \\ &= N-1\end{aligned}$$

The only possibility is: $\phi_1 = N$ (or $N-1$), $\phi_2 = N-1$ (or N).

If $\phi_1 < (N-1)$, $\phi_2 > N$, then, according to the phase rule, it is impossible.

The above discussion clarifies the whole boundaries matter, *i.e.* there being three main types and five minor classes within the regular isobaric isopleth sections of an N-component system (in the general case, $Z = r = 0$). These are the most common types of boundaries encountered in multicomponent, isobaric isopleth sections. Even in the irregular, isobaric isopleth sections, there are only a few cases here eqs. (6-1) and (6-2) are not obeyed; in these cases, the boundary theory still holds.

The cases of $Z \neq r \neq 0$ are very rare. In these few cases, the TCR must be written in the form (see (2-6′)):

$$R_1 = (N - r - Z) - \Phi + 1$$

The boundary theory of phase diagrams still holds in these cases, where r is the number of independent reactions occurring within the system, and Z is the number of other restrictive conditions acting upon the component concentrations (exception: $\sum x_i = 1$).

6.5 Example

Let us now apply the boundary theory of isobaric, isopleth section to the analysis of one example.

A regular isobaric isopleth section of a quinary eutectic system is shown as follows:

For the quinary system,

$$R_1 = N + 1 - \Phi = 6 - \Phi$$

$$\Phi = 6 - R_1$$

$$(R_1)_{\mathrm{i}} = 6 - \Phi - 3 = 3 - \Phi$$

1. ab, bc lines, $\Phi = 2$, $\phi_C = 1$, $R_1' = R_1 + \phi_C - 1$.

$$(R_1)_{\mathrm{i}} = 3 - \Phi = 1$$

$$
\begin{aligned}
(R_1')_{\rm i} &= (R_1 + \phi_C - 1) - (N - 2) \\
&= (N - \Phi + 1 + \phi_C - 1) - (N - 2) \\
&= \phi_C - \Phi + 2 \\
&= 1
\end{aligned}
$$

Thus, they are the boundary lines and the phase boundary lines too. This case is shown in Fig. 6.1.

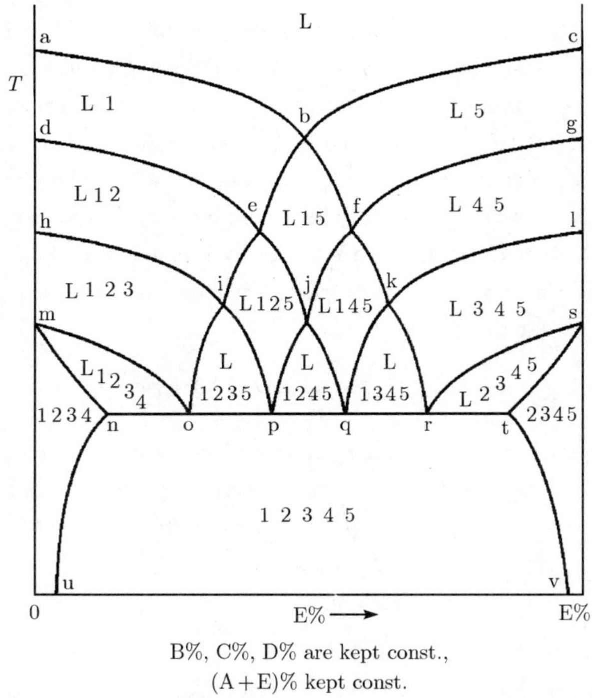

Fig. 6.1 The isopleth section of an isobaric, quinary eutectic system L liquid phase; 1, 2, 3, 4 and 5 represent $S_1 \sim S_5$ solid solution phases. [Rhines, 1956].

Point b. This is the boundary phase point between $(L+S_1)/(L+S_5)$, or between $L/(L+S_1+S_5)$, Φ=3, $\phi_C = 1$.

$$\Phi - \phi_C = 2$$

$$(R_1)_{\rm i} = 3 - \Phi = 0$$

$$
\begin{aligned}
(R_1')_{\rm i} &= (R_1 + \phi_C - 1) - (N - 2) \\
&= \phi_C - \Phi + 2 \\
&= 1 - 3 + 2 = 0
\end{aligned}
$$

$$(R_1')_{\rm i} = (R_1)_{\rm i} = 0$$

Thus, point b is both a boundary point and a phase point. It is a phase point of the common phase L, see subsection 6.2.2.1.

2. Lines de, eb, bf and fg. Φ=3, $\phi_C = 2$, $R_1' = R_1 + \phi_C - 1$

$$(R_1)_{\rm i} = 3 - \Phi = 0$$

$$(R_1')_{\rm i} = \phi_C - \Phi + 2 = 2 - 3 + 2 = 1$$

$$(R_1)_{\rm i} < (R_1')_{\rm i} = 1$$

So these lines are boundary lines only.

Point e and f. Point e is taken for discussion.

Point e is a boundary point located between NPRs $(L+S_1+S_2)/(L+S_1+S_5)$, or $(L+S_1+S_2)/(L+S_1)/(L+S_1+S_5)/(L+S_1+S_2+S_5)$; Φ=4, $\phi_C = 2$,

$$(R_1)_{\rm i} = 3 - \Phi = -1$$

$$\begin{aligned}(R_1')_{\rm i} &= (R_1 + \phi_C - 1) - (N - 2)\\ &= \phi_C - \Phi + 2 = 0\end{aligned} \tag{6-4}$$

So, point e is a boundary point only. This case is shown in Table 6.2.

3. Lines hi, ie, ej, jf, fk and kl, $\Phi = 4$, $\phi_C = 2$, $R_1' = R_1 + \phi_C - 1$.

$$(R_1)_{\rm i} = 3 - \Phi = -1$$

$$\begin{aligned}(R_1')_{\rm i} &= (R_1 + \phi_C - 1) - (N - 2)\\ &= \phi_C - \Phi + 2\\ &= 1 > (R_1)_{\rm i}\end{aligned}$$

Thus, these lines are boundary lines only. This case is set out in Table 6.1.

4. Point i, j and k. Consider point i for discussion, Φ=5, ϕ_C=3, $R_1' = R_1 + \phi_C - 1$.

$$(R_1)_{\rm i} = 3 - \Phi = -2$$

$$\begin{aligned}(R_1')_{\rm i} &= (R_1 + \phi_C - 1) - (N - 2)\\ &= \phi_C - \Phi + 2 = 0 > (R_1)_{\rm i} = -2\end{aligned}$$

Therefore, point i is a boundary point only. This case is also shown in Table 6.2.

Lines un, nm, mo, oi, ip, pj, jg, gk, kr, rs, st and tv, Φ=5, ϕ_C=4,

$$R_1' = R_1 + \phi_C - 1.$$

$$(R_1)_{\rm i} = 3 - 5 = -2$$

$$\begin{aligned}(R_1')_{\rm i} &= (R_1 + \phi_C - 1) - (N - 2)\\ &= \phi_C - \Phi + 2\\ &= 1 > (R_1)_{\rm i} = -2\end{aligned}$$

These lines are boundary lines only. This case is shown in Table 6.1.

5. Lines no, op, pg, gr and rt. Φ=6, ϕ_C=4, $R_1' = R_1 + \phi_C$ (since there is an invariant phase transition between the two NPRs, and $R_1' = R_1 + \phi_C$).

$$(R_1)_{\rm i} = 3 - \Phi = -3$$

$$\begin{aligned}(R_1')_{\rm i} =& (R_1 + \phi_C) - (N-2) = (N - \Phi + 1 + \phi_C) - (N-2)\\ =& \phi_C - \Phi + 3 = 1 > (R_1)_{\rm i} = -3\end{aligned}$$

These are boundary lines only. The case is shown in Table 6.4

6. Point n, o, p, g, r and t.

Consider point o as an example of the group. This point is the boundary point between $(L+S_1+S_2+S_3)/(S_1+S_2+S_3+S_4+S_5)$.

Φ=6, ϕ_C=3, $R_1' = R_1 + \phi_C$ (since there is an invariant phase transition between the two NPRs)

$$(R_1)_{\rm i} = 3 - \Phi = -3$$

$$\begin{aligned}(R_1')_{\rm i} =& (R_1 + \phi_C) - (N-2)\\ =& \phi_C - \Phi + 3 = 3 - 6 + 3 = 0\end{aligned}$$

$$(R_1')_{\rm i} = 0 > (R_1)_{\rm i} = -3$$

So, point o and the other points; n, p, q, r and t, are all examples of boundary points, only. This is shown in Table 6.5.

Therefore, to this point, all of the boundary points and boundary lines have been "explained" with reference to the boundary theory of isobaric, isopleths sections. Thus it may be reasonably said that the boundary theory is seen to be a useful theoretical tool with which to analyze the isobaric isopleths sections.

6.6 The Theory of Two-Dimensional Sections of Isobaric Multicomponent Phase Diagrams

The "forms" of isothermal sections and of isopleths sections are very different. We have discussed these two types of sections in separate chapters, *i.e.* Chapter 5 and Chapter 6, just for convenience of the explanations offered. We may now discuss them in a more unified manner.

The dimensions of isobaric phase diagrams of N-component systems, the dimensions of their boundaries and of the phase boundaries, are denoted by N, R_1' and R_1, respectively.

Let the N-component phase diagram be cut (horizontally or vertically) once, the dimensions of the section obtained being $(N-1)$. In order to show the phase equilibrium relation of the isobaric N-component phase diagram, on a two-dimensional plane (including the isothermal and isopleth sections), the dimensions of the section must be decreased by $(N-2)$. The compositions of $(N-2)$ components must be fixed; or the compositions of $(N-3)$ components, and the temperature, must be fixed. Their boundaries dimensions and the dimensions of their phase boundaries must be deduced by minus $(N-2)$. That is:

$$(R_1')_{\mathrm{s}} = R_1' - (N-2) \tag{6-17}$$

$$(R_1)_{\mathrm{s}} = R_1 - (N-2) \tag{6-18}$$

The subscript "s" means "section".

If all boundaries in the two-dimensional sections obey eqs.(6-17) and (6-18), they are called regular sections. Even in irregular sections, only few boundaries do not obey eqs. (6-17) and (6-18). In these cases, one must treat the problem starting from the corresponding spatial phase diagram, and applying eqs.(2-6), (2-12) and (2-13) to solve these problems.

Applying equations:

$$R_1 = N - \Phi + 1 \tag{2-6}$$

$$R_1' = R_1 + \phi_C \tag{2-12}$$

$$R_1' = R_1 + \phi_C - 1 \tag{2-13}$$

and eqs.(6-17) and (6-18), to the two-dimensional sections of the ternary and quaternary systems, then, Table 6.6 and 6.7 are obtained.

Table 6.6 Regularities of variations of Φ, ϕ_C, R_1, R_1', $(R_1')_{\mathrm{s}}$ and $(R_1)_{\mathrm{s}}$ of the two-dimensional sections of ternary systems

Φ	2	3	4
R_1	2	1	0
ϕ_C	1	$2 \geqslant \phi_C \geqslant 1$	$2 \geqslant \phi_C \geqslant 0$
R_1'	2	$R_1 + \phi_C - 1 = \phi_C$	$R_1 + \phi_C = \phi_C$
$(R_1)_{\mathrm{s}} = R_1 - 1$	1	0	-1
$(R_1')_{\mathrm{s}} = R_1' - 1$	1	$\phi_C - 1$	$\phi_C - 1$
Phase assemblages of two NPRs $i, j, k, m = 1, 2, 3, 4$ $i \neq j \neq k \neq m$	$f_i/(f_i + f_j)$	$\phi_C = 2$, $(R_1')_{\mathrm{S}} = 1$ $(f_i + f_j)/$ $(f_i + f_j + f_m)$ $\phi_C = 1$, $(R_1')_{\mathrm{S}}=0$ $f_j/(f_i + f_j + f_k)$ $(f_i + f_j)/(f_j + f_k)$	$\phi_C = 2$, $(R_1')_{\mathrm{v}} = 1$ $(f_i + f_j + f_k)/$ $(f_j + f_k + f_m)$ $\phi_C = 1$, $(R_1')_{\mathrm{v}}=0$ $(f_i + f_j)/$ $(f_j + f_k + f_m)$

Note: There is no case for $\Phi = 4$ in the regular isobaric section of the ternary system. The cases within the black line square only exit in the vertical section. The dimension of the boundary in the vertical section is denoted by $(R_1')_{\mathrm{v}}$.

Table 6.7 Regularities of variations of Φ, R_1, ϕ_C, R_1', $(R_1)_s$ and $(R_1')_s$ of the two-dimensional sections of the quaternary systems

Φ	2	3	4	5
R_1	3	2	1	0
ϕ_C	1	$2 \geqslant \phi_C \geqslant 1$	$3 \geqslant \phi_C \geqslant 1$	$3 \geqslant \phi_C \geqslant 0$
R_1'	3	$R_1 + \phi_C - 1 =$ $\phi_C + 1$	$R_1 + \phi_C - 1 = \phi_C$	$R_1 + \phi_C = \phi_C$
$(R_1)_s = R_1 - 2$	1	0	-1	-2
$(R_1')_s = R_1' - 2$	1	$\phi_C - 1$	$\phi_C - 2$	$\phi_C - 2$
The phase assemblages in two NPRs $i, j, k, m, n =$ 1,2,3,4,5, $i \neq j \neq k \neq m \neq n$	$f_i/(f_i + f_j)$	$\phi_C = 2$ $(R_1')_s = 1$ $(f_i + f_j)/$ $(f_i + f_j + f_k)$	$\phi_C = 3$ $(R_1')_s = 1$ $(f_j + f_k + f_m)/$ $(f_j + f_k + f_m + f_n)$	$\phi_C = 3$ $(R_1')_v = 1$ $(f_i + f_j + f_k + f_m)/$ $(f_j + f_k + f_m + f_n)$
		$\phi_C = 1$ $(R_1)_s = 0$ $(f_i)/(f_i + f_j + f_k)$ $(f_i + f_j)/(f_j + f_k)$	$\phi_C = 2$ $(R_1')_s = 0$ $(f_i + f_j + f_k)/$ $(f_j + f_k + f_m)$	$\phi_C = 2$ $(R_1')_v = 0$ $(f_i + f_j + f_k)/$ $(f_j + f_k + f_m + f_n)$

The forms of the horizontal sections and vertical (isopleth) sections are very different. But Table 6.6 shows that the relationship among NPRs and their boundaries, in the regular isothermal and vertical (isopleth) sections, is similar. The difference between the horizontal and vertical sections of the ternary phase diagrams is that the case of Φ=4 and R_1=0 only exists in the ternary vertical (isopleth) sections.

Through Table 6.7, all of the relationship among the NPRs and their boundaries, for the two-dimensional sections of the quaternary systems, can be well explained.

The phase assemblages shown in the black lined square only exist in the quaternary vertical sections.

Tables 6.6 and 6.7 show that both the regularities of the relationship among the NPRs and their boundaries, for the vertical and isopleth sections, are similar. Since the influences of the parameters: p, T and x_i, to the relationship among NPRs, and their boundaries in the phase diagrams are essentially similar. Our deductions therefore, are both an important and an interesting result.

References-6

F. N. Rhines. 1956. Phase diagram in metallurgy. New York: McGraw-Hill

Chapter 7

The Application of the Boundary Theory to Isobaric Phase Diagrams

7.1 Brief Review of the Application for the Boundary Theory

Through application of the boundary theory, Palatnik-Landau's contact rule for phase regions is deduced. Then, and in accord with the course of deduction of this rule, its limitations in some of it application have been examined. Comparison of the Palatnik-Landau's contact rule with the boundary theory, has been discussed in detail.

The relationship among the NPRs and their boundaries, for both simple and complex phase diagrams, has been discussed. Rhines' ten empirical rules for the construction of complicated ternary phase diagrams, from corresponding phase diagram units, have been explained. The boundary theory, dealing as it does with the isothermal and isopleth sections of multicomponent systems, has been well worked out.

In the practice of applying boundary theory, isothermal multi-component sections may be constructed with the presently limited information.

7.2 The Analysis of the Fe-Cr-C Isopleth Section

The Fe-Cr-C ternary phase diagram is a very important tool in the research and development of stainless steel compositions. Fig. 7.1 is an isopleth section of the Fe-Cr-C system, located at the 0.2 mass% carbon content [Perkner, 1977].

What is the meaning of each of the boundary lines displayed in the figure? Can the equilibrium compositions of the phases present be read from the boundary lines in the diagram? The answers to these and other related questions may be obtained with the application of the boundary theory.

There are boundary lines for three different types in the section.

1. The NPRs type with parameters: $\Phi = 2$ and $\phi_C = 1$

NPRs $\delta/(\delta+\alpha)$, $\gamma/(\alpha+\gamma)$ and $\gamma/(\gamma+\kappa_1)$ are all able to satisfy the conditions: $\Phi = 2$, $\phi_C = 1$.

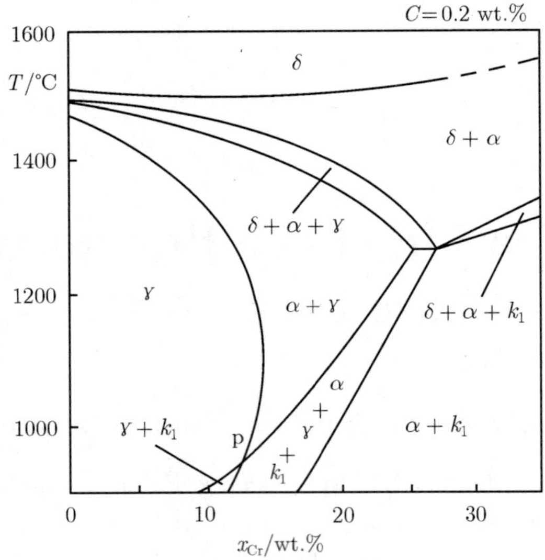

Fig. 7.1 The Fe-Cr-C isopleth section [Perkner, 1977].

The characteristics of the boundary between these pairs of NPRs, in the corresponding spatial phase diagram, are:

$$R_1 = N - \Phi + 1 = 4 - \Phi = 4 - 2 = 2$$

$$R_1' = R_1 + \phi_C - 1 = 2 + 1 - 1 = 2$$

And the dimensions of the boundaries and phase boundaries in the isopleth section, are as follows:

$$(R_1)_\mathrm{i} = R_1 - 1 = 2 - 1 = 1, \quad (R_1')_\mathrm{i} = R_1' - 1 = 2 - 1 = 1$$

$$(R_1)_\mathrm{i} = (R_1')_\mathrm{i} = 1$$

Thus, boundary lines of this type in the isopleth section are also phase boundary lines. They consist not only of the system points, but also of the phase points. At a given temperature, the equilibrium compositions of common phases (*e.g.* phases δ and γ) may be read from these phase boundary lines.

2. The type of NPRs with parameters: Φ=3 and ϕ_C=2.

The NPRs $(\alpha + \gamma)/(\alpha + \gamma + \delta)$, $(\delta + \alpha)/(\delta + \alpha + \gamma)$, $(\delta + \alpha)/(\delta + \alpha + \kappa_1)$, $(\alpha+\kappa_1)/(\delta+\kappa_1+\alpha)$, $(\alpha+\kappa_1)/(\gamma+\kappa_1+\alpha)$, $(\alpha+\gamma)/(\alpha+\gamma+\kappa_1)$ and $(\gamma+\kappa_1)/(\alpha+\gamma+\kappa_1)$ satisfy the conditions of Φ=3 and ϕ_C=2, so the dimensions of the phase boundaries and the boundaries in the corresponding spatial phase diagram, are as follows:

$$R_1 = 4 - \Phi = 4 - 3 = 1$$

$$R_1' = R_1 + \phi_C - 1 = 1 + 2 - 1 = 2$$

The dimensions of the corresponding boundaries and phase boundaries in the isopleth are

$$(R_1)_{\rm i} = R_1 - 1 = 1 - 1 = 0$$

$$(R_1')_{\rm i} = R_1' - 1 = 2 - 1 = 1$$

The boundary lines therefore consist of system points only, and phase compositions can not be read from these boundary lines.

3. The type of NPRs with conditions Φ=4 and ϕ_C=2.

The NPRs, $(\delta + \alpha + \gamma)/(\alpha + \gamma + \kappa_1)$ and $(\delta + \alpha + \kappa_1)/(\alpha + \gamma + \kappa_1)$, satisfy the conditions of Φ=4 and ϕ_C=2, the temperature being the eutectic temperature, and an invariant phase transition being placed between the two NPRs. The dimensions of the phase boundaries, and the boundaries in the corresponding spatial phase diagram are

$$R_1 = 4 - \Phi = 0$$

$$R_1' = R_1 + \phi_C = 2$$

Thus, the phase boundary in the spatial phase diagram consists of four such invariant phase points, the boundary being a plane which is a triangle formed by connecting three phase points (as vertexes of the triangle), one phase boundary point in the center of the triangle. All of these four phase points are not shown in the isopleth section, please refer Fig. 2.5 in subsection 2.6.1.

For this type of NPRs in the isopleth section:

$$(R_1)_{\rm i} = R_1 - 1 = -1$$

$$(R_1')_{\rm i} = R_1' - 1 = 2 - 1 = 1$$

$$(R_1')_{\rm i} \neq (R_1)_{\rm i}$$

Since $(R_1)_{\rm i} = -1$, the boundary lines in the isopleth section consist of system points only. Also, R_1=0, and the temperature is the eutectic temperature. Therefore, these two boundary lines must lie on the same horizontal line. The NPRs around the three boundary points on this line are the NPRs: $(\delta + \alpha)/(\alpha + \gamma + \kappa_1)$, $(\alpha + \gamma)/(\delta + \alpha + \gamma)/(\alpha + \gamma + \kappa_1)$, $(\delta + \alpha + \kappa_1)/(\alpha + \kappa_1)/(\alpha + \gamma + \kappa_1)$, all of these NPRs satisfying the conditions of Φ=4, ϕ_C=1. Thence, the characteristics of the three boundary points in the isopleth section are

$$R_1 = 4 - \Phi = 4 - 4 = 0$$

$$R_1' = 0 + 1 = 1$$

$$(R_1)_\mathrm{i} = R_1 - 1 = 0 - 1 = -1$$

$$(R_1')_\mathrm{i} = R_1' - 1 = 1 - 1 = 0$$

These particular points are only system points.

There is a point, p, in the section, the NPRs around this point being either two NPRs $(\alpha+\gamma)/(\gamma+\kappa_1)$ or four NPRs $(\alpha+\gamma)/\gamma/(\gamma+\kappa_1)/(\alpha+\gamma+\kappa_1)$. Both of these configurations satisfy the conditions: Φ=3, ϕ_C=1, thus, the characteristics of this point are

$$R_1 = 4 - \Phi = 4 - 3 = 1$$

$$R_1' = R_1 + \phi_C - 1 = 1 + 1 - 1 = 1$$

$$(R_1)_\mathrm{i} = R_1 - 1 = 0$$

$$(R_1')_\mathrm{i} = R_1' - 1 = 1 - 1 = 0$$

Therefore, this point is a common boundary point, it being a common phase boundary point also. The phase composition of the common phase γ, may be read directly from this point, p. The characteristics of the point p(Φ=3)and those of the three points at the boundary line with Φ=4 are different.

7.3 The Application of the Boundary Theory to Phase Diagram Calculation

7.3.1 The general principles are now discussed for the phase diagram calculation with the aid of the boundary theory

According to the boundary theory, the calculation of phase diagrams is no other than calculating the boundaries between NPRs. Thus, our way is different from those "traditional" methods. From the viewpoint of boundary theory, the boundaries lying between NPRs may be divided into two types: the phase boundary and the boundary. If the dimensions of a given boundary between NPRs, R_1', are equal to the dimensions of the phase boundary R_1, *i.e.* $R_1 = R_1'$. The boundary lines are also phase boundary lines. A boundary of this type is called the "boundary of the first type". If $R_1' > R_1$, this boundary is composed of system points only. The boundary of this type is called the boundary of the second type. Determining the characteristics of the boundary is beneficial for the calculation method design. For a boundary of the first type – the phase boundary, it is only needs to set the phase equilibrium equations of the relevant phase points of the system at a given temperature, then, these equations are solved and the compositions of the equilibrium phase points obtained. By calculating a series of phase points for the system at a series of different temperatures, the corresponding phase boundary may then be obtained. For a boundary of the second type, the compositions of the phase equilibrium points, at a given temperature, are the first to be calculated. Then, by means of the mass balance equations, the compositions of the corresponding system points are calculated, using the values of the equilibrium phase point compositions of the system. By calculating the equilibrium phase points, and the corresponding system points, under given conditions and at a series of temperatures, the calculated boundary line is obtained. Through calculation of all the boundary lines and the phase boundary lines, the full phase diagram, or its pre-selected section, may be constructed. The principles of this calculation process are discussed in the next section.

7.3.2 Direct calculation of isopleth sections of the Bi-Sn-Zn ternary system

As an example of phase diagram calculation through the application of the boundary theory, the calculation of isopleth sections, of the Bi-Sn-Zn system, is now presented [Zhao *et al.*, 1986].

According to the boundary theory, for this ternary system, those boundaries with $\Phi=2$ are phase boundaries, or boundaries of the first type. The equilibrium phase points may be now calculated using a set of phase equilibrium equations, at a given temperature. When $\Phi \geqslant 3$, the boundaries are composed of system points only. For these boundaries, the compositions of the relevant equilibrium phase points must initially be calculated, the compositions of system points of the system are then calculated, using the mass balance equations and the calculated values of the compositions of equilibrium phase points.

7.3.2.1 The calculation of a regular section

Fig. 7.2 is an illustration of such an example.

For this system, since $x_{\mathrm{Zn}} = x_1$=0.05(x_1 is the mole fraction of Zn of the system present; the notation used below is similar),

$$x_2 + x_3 = 0.95$$

(1) From the Fig. 7.2, the NPRs L/(L+S_j) (j=1, 2, 3) around lines de, ef and fg satisfy the conditions of Φ=2, ϕ_C=1, so the characteristics of these boundaries are

$$R_1 = 2, R_1' = 2$$

$$(R_1)_{\mathrm{i}} = 1, (R_1')_{\mathrm{i}} = 1$$

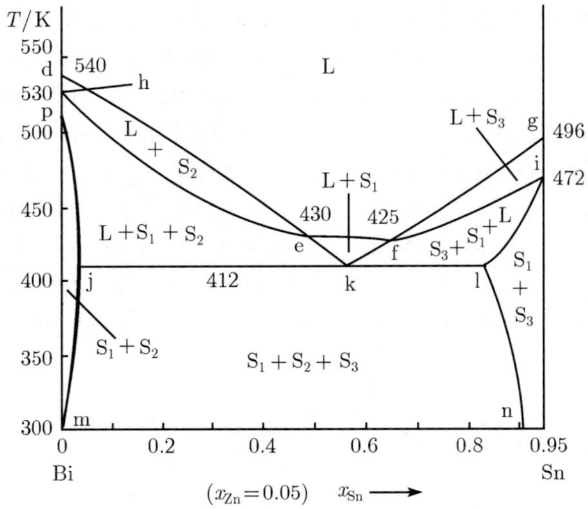

Fig. 7.2 A regular isopleth section of the Bi-Sn-Zn system. S_1-pure Zn phase; S_2-phase rich in Bi; S_3-phase rich in Sn.

All of these lines are phase boundary lines – the phase boundary lines of the common phase, L. In taking line de as an example, on this line, the system point coincides with the phase point of phase L, thus the phase composition $x_{1,L}$ of phase L satisfies the following equation:

$$x_{1,\mathrm{L}} = x_1 = 0.05$$

On line de, phases L and S_2 are coexisting in equilibrium, therefore, in accord with general thermodynamic principles, the following equations may be written:

$$\frac{a_{i,\mathrm{L}}}{a_{i,\mathrm{S}_2}} = K_i, \quad (i = 1, 2, 3) \tag{7-1}$$

Where, $a_{i,\mathrm{L}}$ and a_{i,S_2} are activities, K, the coefficient of distribution, $x_{i,j}$ the mole fraction of the i-th component in the j-th phase (i=1(Zn), 2(Bi), 3(Sn); j=1(L), 2(S_2)). Owing to $x_{1,\mathrm{L}}$=0.05,

$$\begin{aligned} x_{3,\mathrm{L}} &= 1 - x_{2,\mathrm{L}} - 0.05 \\ &= 0.95 - x_{2,\mathrm{L}} \end{aligned}$$

Thus, the mole fractions of the three component liquid phase have only one independent variable. For the solid solution S_2,

$$x_{3,\mathrm{S}_2} = 1 - x_{1,\mathrm{S}_2} - x_{2,\mathrm{S}_2}$$

Therefore, the independent composition variables of the two equilibrium phases on the boundary line, de, are: $x_{1,\mathrm{S}_2}, x_{2,\mathrm{S}_2}$ and $x_{2,\mathrm{L}}$ only. According to the thermodynamic principle, for a given temperature, x_{1,S_2}, x_{2,S_2} and $x_{2,\mathrm{L}}$ may be calculated using the phase equilibrium equations (7-1), and thus, the compositions of the equilibrium phase points are obtained. Through calculation of the equilibrium phase points over a series of temperatures, line "de" may be obtained. Lines ef and fg may be calculated in a similar fashion. Points e and f are the crossing points of the two sets of liquid phase lines, (de, ef) and (ef, fg), respectively.

(2) The pairs of NPRs around the eight boundary lines; he, ek, kf, fi, il, ln, mj and jp; satisfy the conditions of Φ=3 and ϕ_C=2. For these lines,

$$(R_1)_{\mathrm{i}} = R_1 - 1 = (N - \Phi + 1) - 1 = 0$$

$$(R_1')_{\mathrm{i}} = R_1' - 1 = (R_1 + \phi_C - 1) - 1 = (1 + 2 - 1) - 1 = 1$$

$$(R_1')_{\mathrm{i}} > (R_1)_{\mathrm{i}}$$

i.e., they are boundary lines only. Consider line "he" between ($L+S_2$)/($L+S_1+S_2$) as an example, the method of calculation for this line is now set out, as follows.

Initially, the relevant equilibrium phase points are calculated. There are three phase: L, S_1 and S_2, coexisting in equilibrium, for which one may write the following phase equilibrium equations:

$$\frac{a_{i,\mathrm{L}}}{a_{i,\mathrm{S_1}}} = K_{i,\mathrm{S_1}}, \quad (i = 1, 2, 3) \tag{7-2}$$

$$\frac{a_{i,\mathrm{L}}}{a_{i,\mathrm{S_2}}} = K_{i,\mathrm{S_2}}, \quad (i = 1, 2, 3) \tag{7-3}$$

Because the system points do not coincide with the phase points, the condition of $x_{1,\mathrm{L}}$=0.05 does not hold; 3 components in the three coexisting phases have six independent equilibrium phase compositions. When the temperature is kept constant, K_{i,S_j} is also constant. By solution of the six independent equations, (7-2) and (7-3), the compositions of a set of equilibrium phase points, at the given temperature, are thus obtained.

When the system point occurs on line he, according to the level rule, all masses of components in the system are distributed in the common phases, L and S_2. By writing a set of mass balance equations, with the compositions of the corresponding equilibrium phase points, the composition of one system point on the line, he, at the given temperature, may be calculated.

By a similar method, in calculating the equilibrium phase points and the corresponding system points at a series of temperatures, the line, he, may be obtained. Using a similar method, line ek and other boundary lines, may be calculated.

(3) The 3 points, j, k and l, are the crossing points for the three sets of boundary lines: (jm, pj), (ek, kf) and (il, ln); with Φ=3, respectively.

Therefore, the isopleth section, as shown in Fig. 7.2, can be constructed, it is a regular section.

7.3.2.2 Calculation of an irregular isopleth section

Most boundary lines in the irregular isopleth section satisfy the conditions of:

$$(R_1)_{\rm i} = R_1 - 1$$

$$(R_1')_{\rm i} = R_1' - 1$$

They may be calculated in a similar manner, as set out above. Only a few "special points" in the irregular section have the dimensions of their boundaries and phase boundaries equal to the dimensions of those corresponding boundaries and phase boundaries, as shown in the space phase diagram. For these irregular boundary points, and according to the phase assemblages of their NPRs, one may thus analyze and determine the characteristics of these special points. Subsequently, they may be calculated with the aid of general thermodynamic principles.

Fig. 7.3 is a calculated, irregular isopleth section. This particular section just crosses the ternary eutectic point. Thus, this point occurs in the form of a boundary point, seen in Fig. 7.3, it being the only one boundary point lying between NPRs L/(S_1+S_2+S_3).

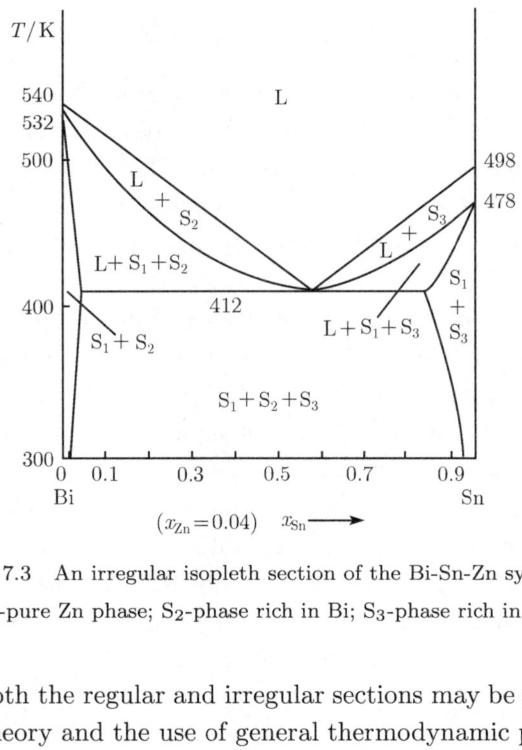

Fig. 7.3 An irregular isopleth section of the Bi-Sn-Zn system. S_1-pure Zn phase; S_2-phase rich in Bi; S_3-phase rich in Sn.

In summary, both the regular and irregular sections may be calculated, with the aid of boundary theory and the use of general thermodynamic principles.

7.3.2.3 *Further discussions*

The author and his students have calculated a series of isopleth sections with constant x_{Zn}, the positions of these sections being shown in Fig. 7.4. By combining these ternary sections, and the three experimental phase diagrams of the Bi-Sn, Sn-Zn and Zn-Bi binary systems, we were able to construct a spatial Bi-Sn-Zn ternary phase diagram, with the use of transparent materials and other materials. This transparent, spatial phase diagram is a useful tool for the teaching of phase diagrams.

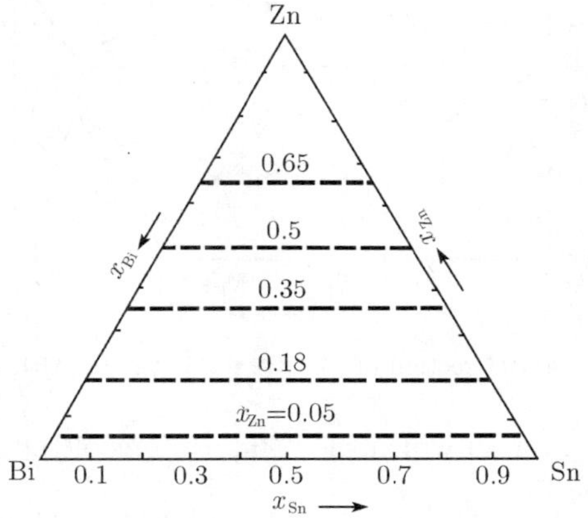

Fig. 7.4 The positions of the composition lines, with x_{Zn}=const.

Besides the isopleth sections with fixed x_{Zn} values, the following two types of isopleth sections have been calculated:

(1) The isopleth section crosses a vertex (for example, point pure Sn), of the Bi-Sn-Zn composition triangle and the line of $x_{\mathrm{Zn}}/x_{\mathrm{Bi}}$=const. on this triangle, see Fig. 7.5.

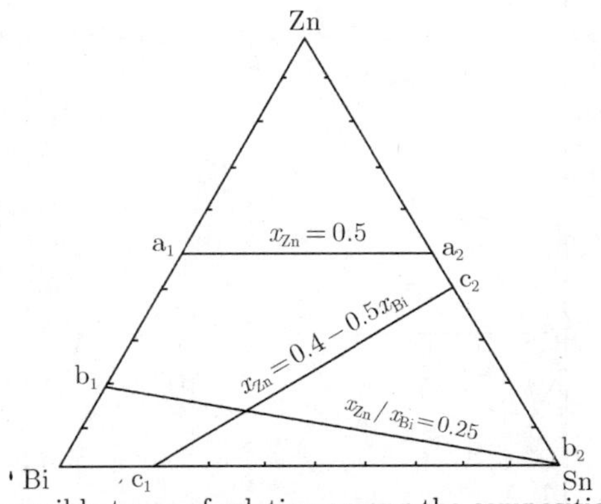

Fig. 7.5 Three possible types of relation among the compositions of the ternary system's three components.

Fig. 7.6 is a calculated isopleth section with $x_{\mathrm{Zn}}/x_{\mathrm{Bi}}$=0.25.

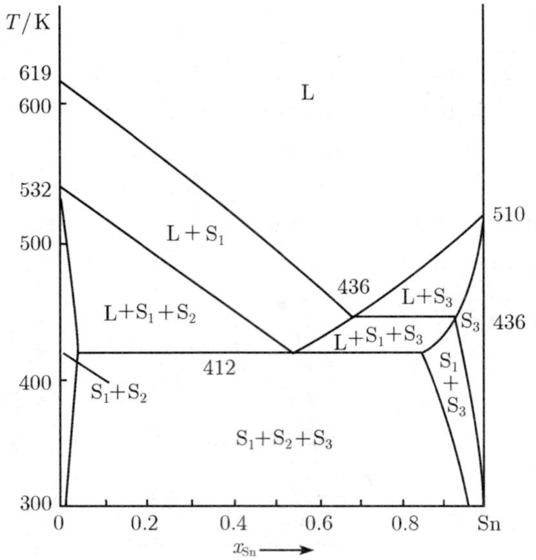

Fig. 7.6 The vertical section of the Bi-Sn-Zn system, with $x_{\mathrm{Zn}}/x_{\mathrm{Bi}}$=0.25.

(2) The vertical section, in which the compositions of the two components maintain linear relation, see Fig. 7.6.

Fig. 7.7 shows the calculated vertical section, in which the compositions of the two components retain the following relation

$$x_{\mathrm{Zn}} = 0.4 - 0.5x_{\mathrm{Bi}}$$

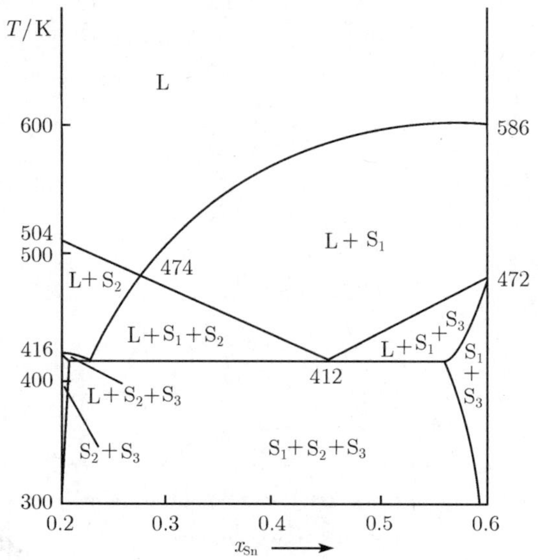

Fig. 7.7 Ternary vertical section, with $x_{\mathrm{Zn}} = 0.4 - 0.5x_{\mathrm{Bi}}$.

The three types of composition lines, as shown in Fig. 7.5, may be the basic composition lines of the ternary composition triangle. All of the vertical sections which cut across one of these composition lines, can be calculated with the aid of the boundary theory well.

7.4 Application of the Boundary Theory to Phase Diagram Assessment

Most of the "published" experimental phase diagrams are correct. However, a few of the numerous published phase diagrams do conceal some errors within their boundaries, *e.g.* between the NPRs where the invariant transition occurs and within other boundaries, also. By applying the just described "The boundary theory" to such examples, the errors are easy to reveal. Some examples of faulty phase diagrams are now discussed.

7.4.1 In-Zr binary phase diagram

The In-Zr phase diagram, shown in Fig. 7.8 [Brandes, 1983], contains some errors.

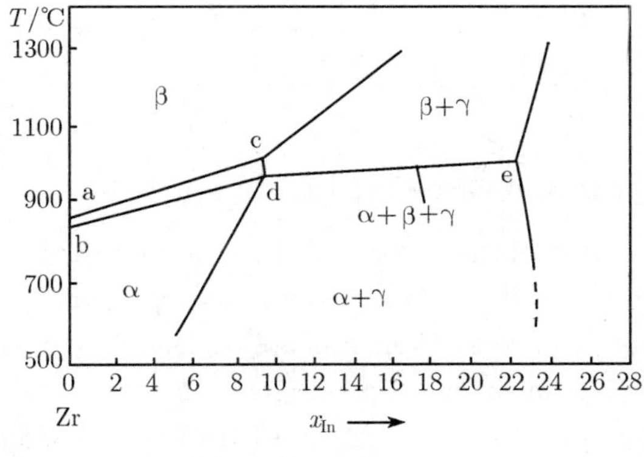

Fig. 7.8 In-Zr phase diagram.

(1) At the pure Zr component end, the split in the point a and b is in error. Since for pure Zr, N=1, Φ=2 (phases α and β are coexisting), so

$$R_1 = N - \Phi + 1 = 1 - 2 + 1 = 0$$

Thus, point a, b must be combined to a single point only.

(2) The boundaries of two pairs of NPRs $(\alpha+\beta)/(\beta+\gamma)$ and $(\beta+\gamma)/(\alpha+\gamma)$ have some errors.

Since the different phases in both pairs of the NPRs are the phases, α, β and γ, the characteristics of these two pairs of NPRs are the same; *i.e.* Φ=3, N=2, ϕ_C=1, thus, the characteristics of the boundaries are

$$R_1 = N - \Phi + 1 = 2 - 3 + 1 = 0$$

$$R_1' = R_1 + \phi_C = 0 + 1 = 1$$

Therefore, lines cd and de must be combined to form one horizontal boundary line only (since R_1=0). But both of the lines, cd and de, in the figure, are not horizontal, thus they are mistaken.

The correct phase diagram must be a peritectic phase diagram. Fig. 7.9 shows the phase diagram, correct in principle; it is depicted by applying the boundary theory.

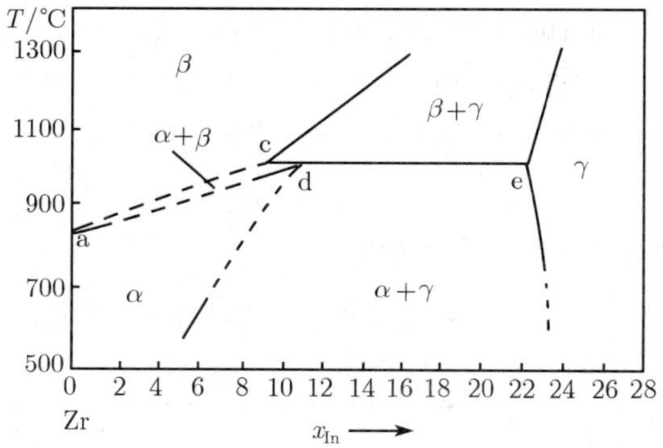

Fig. 7.9 Sketch figure of the Zr-In phase system diagram, but correct "in principle".

7.4.2 Phase diagrams of rare-earth metals

Owing to the similarity of the properties of the rare-earth metals, their separation and purification are generally rather difficult, and the differences in the melting points of some "pairs" of rare-earth metals are also small. Thus, the determination of their alloy phase diagrams is not a precise exercise.

Er-Ho phase diagram, shown in Fig. 7.10 [Brandes, 1983], is not sufficiently accurate.

According to the boundary theory and to Rhines' empirical rules, "single phase regions can only meet each other at single points." Thus, two single phases, L and HCP can not meet each other on a phase boundary line. Therefore, there must exist one two-phase region (L+HCP) between them and exist one-dimensional phase boundaries between NPRs L/(L+HCP) and (L+HCP)/HCP, respectively. These pairs of NPRs satisfy the conditions of Φ=2, ϕ_C=1,

$$R_1 = N - \Phi + 1 = 2 - 2 + 1 = 1$$

$$R_1' = R_1 + \phi_C - 1 = 1 + 1 - 1 = 1$$

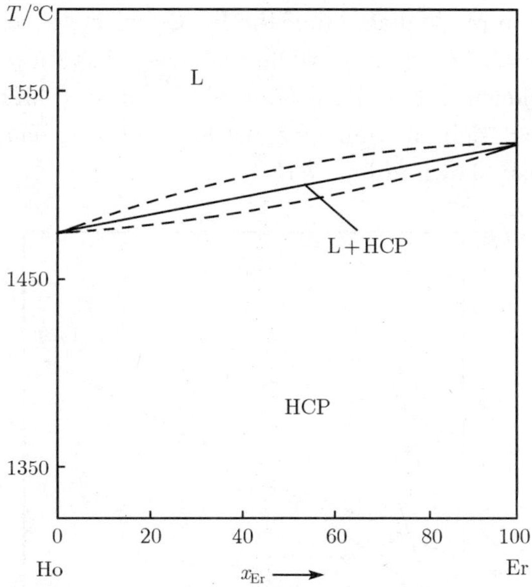

Fig. 7.10 Er-Ho phase diagram (N.B. The "width" of the two-phase region between the dotted lines is "exaggerated").

Therefore, their boundary lines and phase boundary lines are all single-dimensional lines, as shown in the dotted lines in Fig. 7.10.

By applying a similar method of deduction, the Dy-Er phase diagram, shown in Fig. 7.11 [Brandes, 1983], and the Dy-Ho phase diagram, shown in Fig. 7.12 [Brandes, 1983], are again not precise enough. These two phase diagrams are similar to each other in form. For both of the two phase diagrams, there must exist one two-phase region, between the three pairs of two NPRs of single phases L and BCC, L and HCP, BCC and HCP, respectively. These two-phase regions are (L+BCC), (L+HCP) and (BCC+HCP). Further, all of the different phases existing in two pairs of NPRs, (L+HCP)/(L+BCC) and (L+HCP)/(BCC+HCP), are the same phases: L, BCC and HCP, so Φ=3, ϕ_C=1, and there is an invariant phase transition between two NPRs,

$$R_1 = N - \Phi + 1 = 2 - 3 + 1 = 0$$

$$R_1' = R_1 + \phi_C = 0 + 1 = 1$$

There has to occur only one isothermal boundary line, composed of system points, between these two pairs of NPRs. According to this deduction, we may depict in an exaggerated fashion, the phase diagram of the Dy-Er system, as in Fig. 7.13. Based on thermodynamic principles, Muyu Zhao has calculated the phase diagrams for the Ho-Er and Dy-Er systems twenty years ago. The unpublished calculation results show that the phase diagram of the Ho-Er system is really quite similar to the dotted lines shown in Fig. 7.10, while the phase diagram for the Dy-Er system is similar to that shown in Fig. 7.13. G. J. Shiflet *et al.* [Shiflet *et al.*, 1979] have made a similar calculation, obtaining a figure for the Dy-Er phase diagram, its form is also similar to that shown in Fig. 7.13.

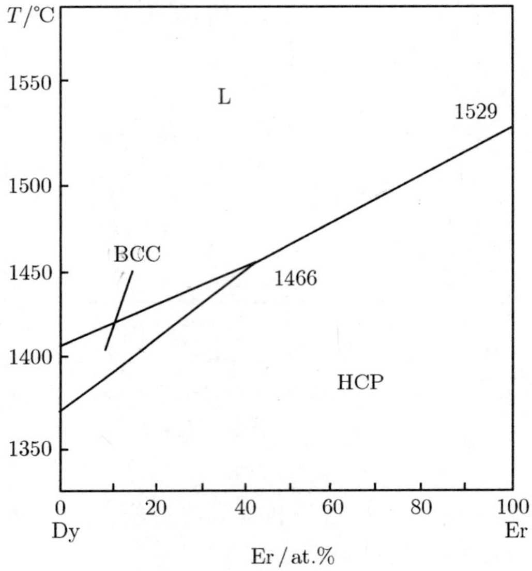

Fig. 7.11 Dy-Er phase diagram.

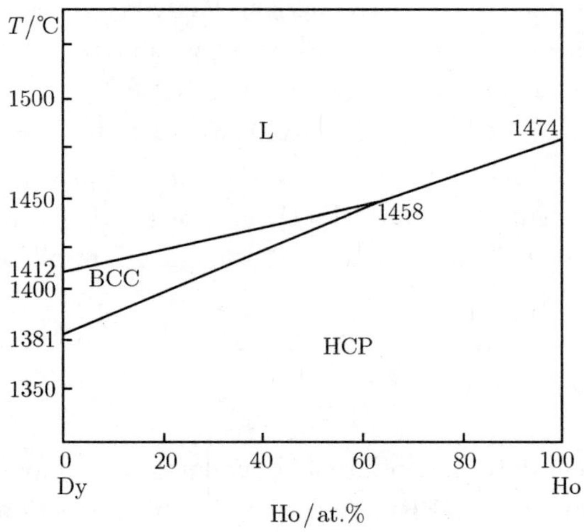

Fig. 7.12 Dy-Ho phase diagram.

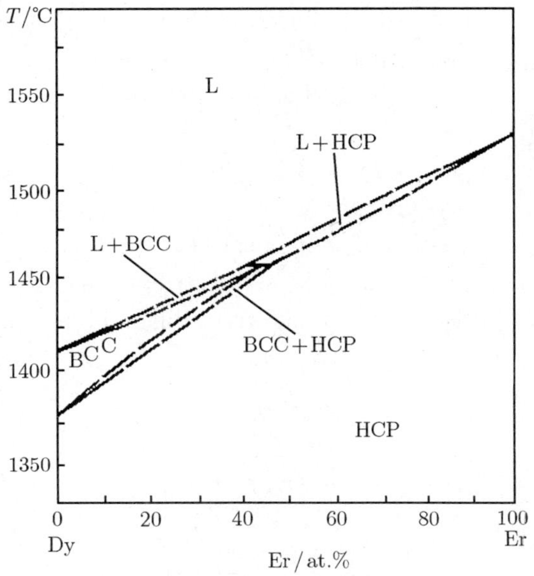

Fig. 7.13 The Dy-Er "exaggerated" phase diagram (It is correct in principle).

Other authors have found several other published phase diagrams with similar errors. According to our experience, these errors usually occur in the NPRs with invariant phase transitions (R_1=0). These errors are easily corrected with the aid of the boundary theory.

7.5 Application of the Boundary Theory to Phase Diagram Determination

(1) In the "determination" of phase diagrams, when the experimental data are insufficient, the boundary theory is both useful to aid connecting experimental points to generate boundary lines and to construct the "sketch" of the phase diagram. Or it may be utilized to "sample" the samples to being assayed.

When experimental results can generate false appearances, the application of the boundary theory may act to both check and then correct the results.

In all of the cases mentioned above, the use of the above mentioned technique(s) may improve the efficiency of the experimental work and to shorten the experimental duration.

(2) According to the boundary theory, the present authors have designed an experimental scheme to determine a quaternary isothermal section, with fixed compositions for one component. The expected experimental results will yield the fol-

lowing information from the "determined" isothermal section: *i.e.* the phases, the phase regions, the phase assemblage for each phase region, the boundary lines and the boundary points between the NPRs, and their precise positions within the determined horizontal section.

We chose a general quaternary A-B-C-D alloy system to study.

The experimental procedures are as follows:

(a) At first, the composition of component D of the A-B-C-D quaternary system is fixed, then sufficient (for example 28) well-distributed samples, within the A-B-C composition triangle (D%=const.), as shown in Fig. 7.14, are chosen.

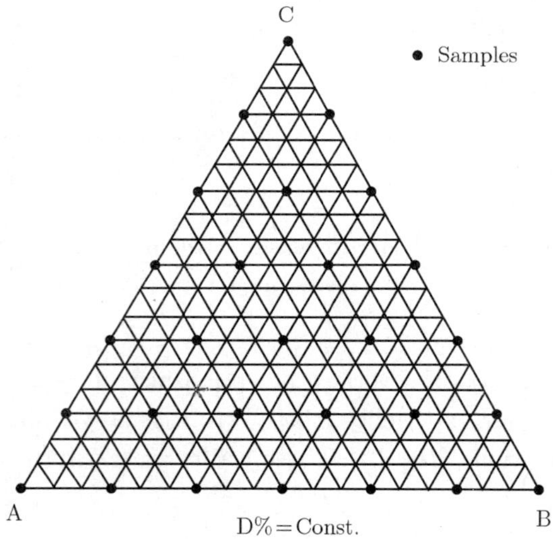

Fig. 7.14 The distribution figure for the different samples.

(b) Determine only the phase assemblage of each sample by the X-ray diffraction method or another powerful technique, determining only the phases (not including their compositions) present in each sample.

(c) Construct a "sketch" of the isothermal quaternary section with the aid of the boundary theory.

The method of constructing the sketch of this section is similar to the method discussed in section 5.3 and section 5.4 of Chapter 5. It is therefore omitted here.

When depicting the sketch, other thermodynamic principles must be obeyed. For example, the solubility of metastable phases in a solid solution must be higher than the solubility of stable phases in the same solid solution.

Consider a binary, eutectic phase diagram, shown in Fig. 7.15, as an example.

In Fig. 7.15, the boundary line "ce", would be extended into the two-phase region (S_1+L).

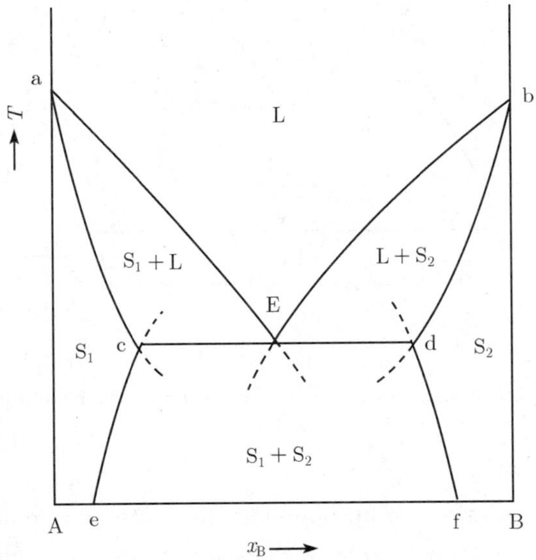

Fig. 7.15 The correct binary phase diagram.

Surely, the phase rule must be the first to be obeyed.

(d) Assuming that we have obtained the "sketch" of this section, only the phase regions, and the phase assemblages of each phase region, are already known; the exact position of the boundary lines and boundary points still have to be determined.

(e) Assuming the partial section near the corner A, as shown in Fig. 7.16(a), while the experimental point to be determined for plotting the boundary line, mn, are shown in Fig. 7.16(b).

The method for the determination of the exact boundary line position between the two NPRs, by X-ray diffraction, is a well-known technique. It is therefore omitted here.

At first, we determine the exact position of the boundary line, mn, between $\alpha/(\alpha+\beta)$ (see Fig. 7.16(b)). Other boundary lines may be determined in a similar

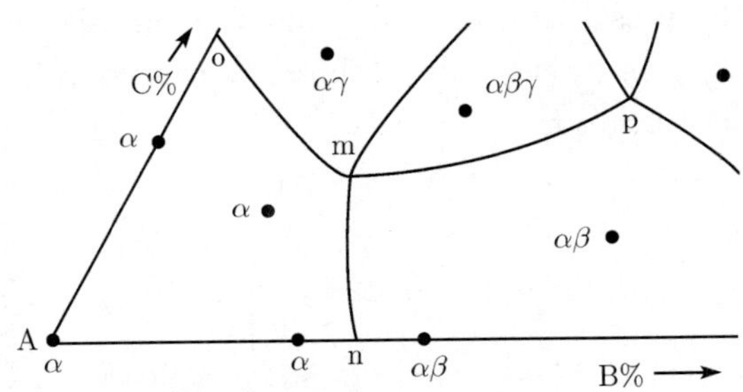

(a)

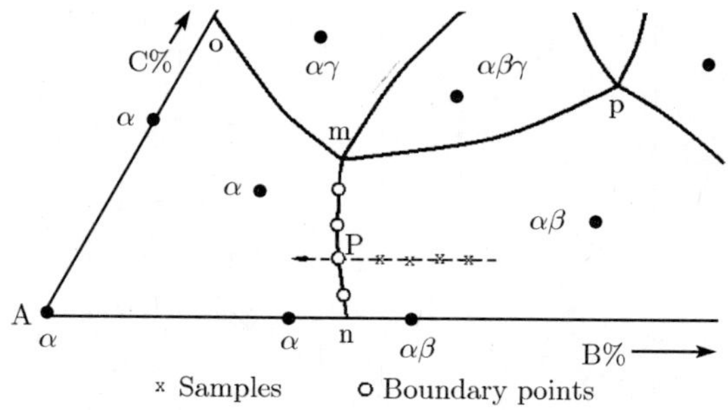

(b)

Fig. 7.16

(a) The partial section near corner A; (b) The sketch of the experimental procedure

fashion.

When the exact positions of all boundary lines are determined, then the whole of the isothermal quaternary section can be said to have been obtained.

The distinguishing feature of our method lies in the procedures (a), (b) and (c).

7.6 The Application of the Boundary Theory to Phase Diagram Education

Since phase diagrams consist of phase regions and their boundaries, the boundary theory discusses the relationship among the NPRs and their boundaries. It will be of some benefit to students to understand the full "meaning" of phase diagrams, especially the more complicated phase diagrams.

There are presently three universities in China teaching "the boundary theory" in their courses, concerning the production and utilization of phase diagrams. Students are known to be interested in the content of the boundary theory. Having acquired basic knowledge of the boundary theory, further study of these complicated ternary and multi-component systems, will be both a pleasant inquiry and task for students to perform.

The authors of this present document consider that the teaching of "the boundary theory" is both a very useful adjunct to those courses concerning phase diagrams and to their ongoing utilization.

References-7

E. A. Brandes. 1998. Smithells metals reference book. 7th ed. London: Butterworth-Heinemann

D. Perkner, I. M. Berstein. 1977. Handbook of Stainless Steels. New York: McGraw-Hill Inc.

G. I. Shiflet *et al.* 1979. CALPHAD, 3(2): 129

Muyu Zhao, Zezhong Fu, Baokun Xu. 1986. Method of the direct calculation of vertical sections in isobaric phase diagrams. High Temperature Science, 22(2): 15-22

Muyu Zhao, Baokun Xu, Xiaobao Fan, Zezhong Fu. 1986. Progress in the theorem of the corresponding relation in isobaric phase diagrams and its application. High Temperature Science, 22(2): 1-14

Muyu Zhao. 1983. The theorem of corresponding relation between neighboring phase regions and their boundaries in phase diagrams. CALPHAD, 7(3): 185-199

Summary of Part Two

The recognition of the difference of the "phase boundary" and the "boundary" in the phase diagrams, leads to the Theorem of the Corresponding Relationship (TCR), between the total number of all the different phases in neighboring phase regions and the dimensions of the phase boundary in phase diagrams. For p-T-x_i phase diagrams in the general case

$$R_1 = (N - Z - r) - \Phi + 2$$

We demonstrated that TCR is an independent theorem. TCR and its corollaries revealed the regularities in phase regions, which govern and determine the fundamental structure and the outlook of phase diagrams.

Based on TCR, the relationship between the dimensions of the phase boundary and the dimensions of the boundary are derived. This is the "boundary theory", the very core of this present monograph, which explains well the different types of phase transitions within phase diagram. Thence, the rule of how the phase regions compose a phase diagram has been expounded.

$$R_1' = R_1 + \phi_C \quad \text{or} \quad R_1' = R_1 + \phi_C - 1$$

The comparison of the boundary theory and P-L'S contact rule of phase regions is given in details. It successfully shows the merits of the boundary theory and the shortcoming of the contact rule.

With the aid of the "boundary theory", we are able to analyze the complicated phase diagrams. We give the phase regions' structure and the boundary properties in tabulated form for the unary, binary, $\cdots$, quinary phase diagrams, both isothermal and isopleth sections included. This "analyzing" function can easily be used to discriminate the "faulty" phase diagrams, resulted from the difficulty in experimental measurements.

An interesting application of the boundary theory is to "sketch" phase diagram with limited data. Previously, there is only Gupta's method available for such purpose. Since boundary method can "sketch", or predict the structure of unknown phase diagram also. And a unique determination technique was thus developed. An example of determination of isopleth sections of the A-B-C-D (quarternary) system was presented in the text.

The "boundary theory" is generally valid for different types of phase diagram. It conforms to and/or embraces those well-established theories in phase diagram science, for example, Rhines' "ten rules", Palatnik-Landau's "contact rule", the "cross rule" *etc.* However, the "boundary theory" is more "powerful" in application, exempted many prerequisites, which some theories had to rely on. This is because the "boundary theory" is based on a deeper grasp of the nature of phase diagram, thus, it reflects properly the features and characters of various phase diagrams.

Limited by the volume, we didn't show much examples of the application of the boundary theory in p-T diagrams (may also see Section 9.3) and multiply molar axes phase diagrams, which is important in geology science and alloy engineering. The principle and method of boundary theory surely can do more in these fields.

Part Three

The Boundary Theory and Calculation of High Pressure Phase Diagrams

Chapter 8

The Boundary Theory for p-T-x_i Multicomponent Phase Diagrams

8.1 Introduction

The multicomponent phase equilibrium, in which p-T-x_i are independent variables, is one of the key problems studied in geology, high-pressure physics and high-pressure chemistry. The equilibrium, as applied to geology, are usually presented in p-T phase diagrams, with invariant composition parameters or temperature-composition phase diagrams, set at different given pressures. We now discuss the p-T-x_i multicomponent phase diagrams in this text; such analyses may be more comprehensive, and if so, then they are useful for the researches in geology and applied high-pressure physics. When compared with "isobaric" phase diagrams, there is one additional parameter to be considered. Even for the p-T-x binary phase diagrams, they must be depicted into three-dimensional space, therefore, the problem becomes much more complicated.

The study of the boundary theory of p-T-x_i multicomponent phase diagrams may apply the boundary theory of isobaric phase diagrams, as its basis. The train of thought, method of study and the technical terms employed are the same as those used in the boundary theory of isobaric phase diagrams. And the theorem of corresponding relationship (TCR), for p-T-x_i multi-component phase diagrams, has already been deduced, see eq. (2-7). In this chapter, we discuss directly the corollaries of this theorem, the relationship among the dimensions of the boundary, R'_1 and the dimensions of the phase boundary, R_1.

The influence of pressure on phase transitions is much less than the corresponding temperature influence. For phase diagrams, with phase transitions between solid and liquid or between solids only, the pressure must be as high as several GPa, then, the difference between the phase diagram at high pressure and that at an ordinary pressure may well be manifest. The experimental equipment required for phase transition research at such high pressures is expensive and very complicated. Thus, such research is rare, and the resulting number of phase diagrams produced at high pressures is very much less than the number of phase diagrams generated at ordinary pressures. There is either little or no systematic work for discussions concerning the relationship among NPRs and their boundaries, as displayed in high pressure and multicomponent phase diagrams. Therefore, the discussion contained within this Chapter is of a quite important note.

At the outset, let us present some basic concepts for p-T-x_i multicomponent phase diagrams, *e.g.* if the number of components is N, then the dimensions of such phase diagrams are $(N-1)+2=(N+1)$. The dimensions of the defined phase regions still equal the dimensions of these phase diagrams. So, for these phase regions, the temperature and the pressure may vary independently, *i.e.* $f \geqslant 2$. If one of these two parameters is kept constant, then the phase regions exist only over the isothermal or isobaric sections, its dimensions being equal to $(N+1)-1=N$. For those phase regions in which T and p are independent variables, then $f \geqslant 2$, $\phi = N+2-f$, $\phi \leqslant N$, or $N \geqslant \phi \geqslant 1$.

For p-T-x_i multicomponent phase diagrams, the equation $\phi_C = \phi_1 + \phi_2 - \Phi$ still holds.

8.2 The Theorem of Corresponding Relationship for p-T-x_i Multicomponent Phase Diagrams and Its Corollaries

8.2.1 The theorem of corresponding relationship

The Theorem of Corresponding Relationship (TCR) between the dimensions of the phase boundary, R_1, and the total number of different phases existing within all of the NPRs, Φ, is

$$R_1 = N - \Phi + 2 \tag{8-1}$$

Usually $Z = r$=0. This formula was proved earlier in Chapter 2.

8.2.2 The corollaries of TCR

The corollaries were derived from the TCR for p-T-x_i multicomponent phase diagrams, with $N \geqslant 2$ and $Z = r = 0$, by Muyu Zhao [Zhao, 1983]. They are as follows:

(1) The variation range of Φ. By TCR, $\Phi = N+2-R_1$, and $R_1 \geqslant 0$, $N+2 \geqslant \Phi$. On the other hand, there are at least two phases in any two NPRs, *i.e.*, $\Phi \geqslant 2$,

$$(N+2) \geqslant \Phi \geqslant 2 \tag{8-2}$$

(2) The variation range of R_1. For $\Phi \geqslant 2$, by TCR, $R_1 = N+2-\Phi$, $N \geqslant R_1$. And by definition, $R_1 \geqslant 0$, so

$$N \geqslant R_1 \geqslant 0 \tag{8-3}$$

(3) All of the single-phase regions contact one another only along the curved line of a common phase boundary of a single dimension.

The proof is as follows. If there are two single-phase regions contacting each other with certain, common phase boundary, every common phase point on the phase boundary has

$$x_{1i} = x_{1j}, x_{2i} = x_{2j}, \cdots, x_{Ni} = x_{Nj} \tag{8-4}$$

x_{Nj} denotes the mole fraction of the N-th component in the j-th phase, and the other items are defined similarly. In any phase, there exists such a condition that the sum of the mole fractions of each component is equal to 1, so eq.(8-4) offers only $(N-1)$ independent constraining conditions, *i.e.* $Z = N-1$, $\Phi = 2$, then

$$R_1 = N - (N-1) + 2 - 2 = 1$$

i.e., all the single-phase regions can be in contact with each other only along the curved phase boundary lines of one dimension, in the particular phase diagram mentioned above.

(4) In the phase diagram mentioned above, there is a common phase boundary, with dimensions $R_1 \geqslant 2$ between two NPRs, then

$$(\Phi - 1) \geqslant \phi_C \geqslant 1 \tag{8-5}$$

Firstly, prove that $\phi_C \geqslant 1$ by application of the reduction to absurdity concept.

In the phase diagram mentioned above, if both NPRs do not have a common phase, *i.e.*, $\phi_C = 0$, but there is a common phase boundary, with dimensions $R_1 \geqslant 2$ between the NPRs, then, there must be two phases, each of which belongs to either of the two NPRs, contacting on the common phase boundary with dimension $R_1 \geqslant 2$. According to the 3rd Corollary in this chapter, all single-phase regions can be in contact with each other, but only along curved, phase boundary lines, of one dimension. It is impossible for them to be in contact with each other on the common phase boundary, with the dimension, $R_1 \geqslant 2$, in the phase diagrams mentioned above. Therefore, the above case is false and $R_1 \geqslant 2$, $\phi_C \geqslant 1$ is true. Secondly, if $\phi_C = \Phi$, then both NPRs are identical, the result is meaningless. By combining these two cases, the formula (8-5) is obtained.

(5) In the phase diagram mentioned above, if R_1=1

$$(\Phi - 2) \geqslant \phi_C \geqslant 0 \tag{8-6}$$

For R_1=1, $\Phi = N+2-1 = N+1$, the maximum phase number in any phase region $\phi_{\max} \leqslant N = \Phi - 1$ and $\phi_C \leqslant (\phi_{\max} - 1) \leqslant (\Phi - 2)$. Secondly, under the conditions in question, the maximum for ϕ_1 in the first phase region is $(\Phi - 1)$, the minimum of ϕ_2 is 1 in the second NPR, and the sum of them is equal to Φ, so the minimum of ϕ_C may be zero, *i.e.* $\phi_C \geqslant 0$ and the relation (8-6) is thus established.

(6) When R_1=0, and there is an invariant phase transition between the two NPRs, then

$$(\Phi - 4) \geqslant \phi_C \geqslant 0 \tag{8-7}$$

For $R_1 = 0$, $\Phi = N + 2$ and $\Phi > N$, by the phase rule, $\phi_{\max} \leqslant N$. In this case, the maximum phase number in both NPRs may be N, and the two NPRs may not be identical. For $\phi_C = \phi_1 + \phi_2 - \Phi$, one has

$$(\phi_C)_{\max} = 2N - \Phi = 2(\Phi - 2) - \Phi = \Phi - 4$$

i.e.,

$$\Phi - 4 \geqslant \phi_C$$

Since R_1=0, $\Phi = N + 2$. If the maximum of ϕ_1 in the first phase region is N, the minimum of ϕ_2 in the second NPR is 2. The sum of them is equal to Φ, so the minimum of ϕ_C may be zero, $\phi_C \geqslant 0$. On the basis of these aspects, the relation (8-7) is obtained.

8.3 The Relationship between R_1' and R_1 in p-T-x_i Multicomponent Phase Diagrams [Zhao, 1985]

In p-T-x_i multicomponent phase diagrams, with $r = Z$=0 and $N \geqslant 2$, there are three cases for the relationship between R_1' and R_1.

1. When the two NPRs with phase boundary of $R_1 \geqslant 2$, then $\phi_C \geqslant 1$ and when the system existing on the boundary, the components of the system are distributed over the common phases only. The following equation holds:

$$R_1' = R_1 + \phi_C - 1 \tag{8-8}$$

2. In the process of temperature or pressure change, there is a phase transition between the two NPRs with $R_1 = 1$ or 0; and the system exists on the boundary with $\Phi = (\phi_{\max} + 1)$ or $(\phi_{\max}+2)$ coexisting phases, the components of the system are distributed over the common phases and one or two non-common phases, then there exists $\phi_C \geqslant 0$ and

$$R_1' = R_1 + \phi_C \qquad (R_1 = 1) \tag{8-9}$$

or

$$R_1' = R_1 + \phi_C + 1 \qquad (R_1 = 0) \tag{8-10}$$

3. When R_1=1 or 0, but there is no univariant or an invariant region comprising $\Phi = (\phi_{\max}+1)$ or $(\phi_{\max}+2)$ co-existing phases between the two NPRs, the components of the system are distributed over the common phases only. Then, $\phi_C \geqslant 1$ and transference from one NPR to another may occur, only when the composition of the system varies. This is not a really "true" phase transition, and nor is it important. In this case, the following equation

$$R_1' = R_1 + \phi_C - 1 \tag{8-8}$$

still holds.

These formulae can be proved, respectively, as follow

1. When the two NPRs with $R_1 \geqslant 2$, then $\phi_C \geqslant 1$ and when the system existing on the boundary, the components of the system are distributed in the common phases, only.

$$R_1' = R_1 + \phi_C - 1 \tag{8-8}$$

At first, let us discuss this equation in a comprehensive way.

In the T-x_i phase diagram for different pressures, in the case of $R_1 \geqslant 1$ and $\phi_C \geqslant 1$, a phase transition occurs in the system and makes the system transfer from a phase region to another. According to the lever rule (for binary phase diagrams), the center-of-gravity rule (for ternary phase diagrams) and the "extended" center-of-gravity rule for multicomponent phase diagrams [Palatnik and Landau, 1964], the system existing on the boundary has such characteristics that the components of the system are almost completely distributed over the common phases of the two NPRs, the amounts of the phases belonging to one, or the other phase regions only, are infinitesimal. As shown in Fig. 8.1, no matter whether the system transfers from L→ (L+S_1) or (L+S_1) →L, when the system is located on the boundary line, aE, according to the lever rule, all components of the system are distributed over the common phase, L. The amount of the phase belonging only to either one phase region (in this case, it is S_1) is infinitesimal. Any T-x_i phase diagram obviously has the same characteristics at different pressures. The locus of a series of T-x_i multi-

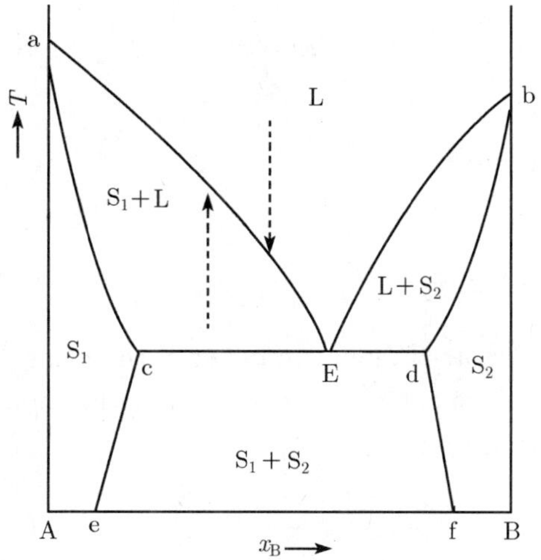

Fig. 8.1 A binary phase diagram at given pressure.
L: Liquid phase; S_1, S_2: two solid phases.

component, phase diagrams at different pressures, constructs a p-T-x_i multicomponent phase diagrams. So, in p-T-x_i multi-component phase diagrams, in the case of the phase transition with $R_1 \geqslant 2$ and $\phi_C \geqslant 1$, the system located on the boundary has the same characteristic, *i.e.*, all components of the system are distributed over the common phases, and the amounts of the phases belonging only to either single phase region, are infinitesimal.

In fact, the lever rule, the center-of-gravity rule and the extended center-of-gravity rule, are all valid for p-T-x_i multicomponent phase diagrams, so, the above conclusion may be drawn directly from them. We have explained this point more indirectly through the isobaric phase diagram simply because it is easier to understand it that way.

Let us prove eq. (8-8) theoretically, as follows.

At a given values of T and p, ϕ_C common phases of both NPRs have ϕ_C common phase points which form ϕ_C concentration vectors of N dimensions $\{x_{ij}\}$, $(i = 1, 2, \cdots, N; j = 1, 2, \cdots, \phi_C)$. It has been proved (fourth corollary in this chapter) that, if $R_1 \geqslant 2$, $\phi_C \leqslant (\Phi - 1)$. Since $\Phi = N + 2 - R_1$, and $R_1 \geqslant 2$, $\Phi \leqslant N$, $(\Phi - 1) \leqslant (N - 1)$, so $\phi_C \leqslant (N - 1)$. These concentration vectors of the common phase points are linearly independent except that they are related to one another through the phase equilibrium conditions. So, these ϕ_C common phase points comprise a hyperplane of $(\phi_C - 1)$ dimensions. Since all of the components of the system located on the boundary are distributed over the common phases, then it may be written as:

$$x_{i1}m_1 + x_{i2}m_2 + \cdots + x_{ij}m_j + \cdots + x_{i\phi_C}m_{\phi_C} = x_iM_i \quad (i = 1, 2, \cdots, N) \tag{8-11}$$

$$m_1 + m_2 + \cdots + m_j + \cdots + m_{\phi_C} = M \tag{8-12}$$

Let

$$y_j = m_j/M \quad (j = 1, 2, \cdots, \phi_C) \tag{8-13}$$

then

$$x_{i1}y_1 + x_{i2}y_2 + \cdots + x_{ij}y_j + \cdots + (x_{i\phi_C}y_{\phi_C}) = x_i \quad (i = 1, 2, \cdots, N) \tag{8-14}$$

Where M, M_i and m_j denotes the mole number of the mass in the system, the mole number of the i–th component in the system and the mole number of the j–th phase in the system, respectively.

$$\sum_{j=1}^{\phi_C} y_j = 1 \tag{8-15}$$

$$1 \geqslant y_j \geqslant 0, \quad (j = 1, 2, \cdots, \phi_C) \tag{8-16}$$

Eqs.(8-14)~(8-16), imply that under a given condition for T and p, the system points located on the boundary $\{x_i\}$ $(i = 1, 2 \cdots, N)$ must lie on the hyperplane of $(\phi_C - 1)$ dimensions, which, in turn, is composed of ϕ_C common phase points $\{x_{ij}\}$ $(i = 1, 2, \cdots, N;\ j = 1, 2, \cdots, \phi_C)$, thus filling the whole hyperplane, and not exceeding it.

With variations applied to the conditions, equilibrium phase points of the common phases, *i.e.* the vertices of the hyperplane, may move around on the space of R_1 dimensions (since the dimensions of the phase boundary is R_1); so the hyperplane of $(\phi_C - 1)$ dimensions, on which the system points lie, may move around in this space of R_1 dimensions. Therefore, the system points, existing on the boundary, may move around the space of $(R_1 + \phi_C - 1)$ dimensions as a whole, *i.e.*,

$$R_1' = R_1 + \phi_C - 1 \tag{8-8}$$

2. When phase transition occurs, from one NPR to another NPR, with R_1=1 or 0, there is either a univariant, or an invariant, phase transition between the two NPRs. The components of the system are distributed over the common phases, and one or two additional non-common phases, being $\varPhi$ phases in total. During variations of T and/or p, the components of the system may be distributed over these $\varPhi$ phases in varying proportions.

(1) When R_1=1 and there is a univariant region containing $\varPhi = (\phi_{\max} + 1)$ coexisting phases during the univariant phase transition, caused by the variation of T or p, then:

$$R_1' = R_1 + \phi_C \tag{8-9}$$

(2) During the variation process for both T and p, under special conditions: R_1=0, and an invariant region of $\varPhi = (\phi_{\max} + 2)$ phases exists between the two NPRs:

$$R_1' = R_1 + \phi_C + 1 \tag{8-10}$$

Both types of phase transitions, from the first phase region to the second, have such characteristics: when the system reaches this univariant or invariant region and the phase transition has not yet occurred or just starts to occur, all components of the system are completely distributed over the phases of the first phase region $f_1, f_2, \cdots, f_{\phi_1}$. All of these phases may be of definite amounts. As the phase transition proceeds, phases belonging only to the second phase region form and grow, while phases belonging only to the first region decline and diminish. During the process of phase transition, the $\varPhi = (\phi_{\max} + 1)$ or $(\phi_{\max} + 2)$ phases contained in the two NPRs may co-exist, and their separate amounts may vary over a wide range. When this phase transition ends, all components of the system are completely distributed over the phases of the second phase region $f_{1'}, f_{2'}, \cdots, f_{\phi_2}$.

When components of the system are entirely distributed over the phases of the first phase region, then the following relation among the total compositions of the system, $\{x_i\}$, and the phase compositions of the phases in the first phase region, $\{x_{ij}\}$(where $i = 1, 2, \cdots, N; j = 1, 2, \cdots, \phi_1$) holds:

$$x_{i1}m_1+x_{i2}m_2+\cdots+x_{ij}m_j+\cdots+x_{i\phi_1}m_{\phi_1}=x_i\sum_{j=1}^{\phi_1}m_j \quad (i=1,2,\cdots,N; N \text{ equations}) \tag{8-6}$$

When the components of the system are completely distributed over the phases of the second phase region, there are other active relation among the total compositions of the system, $\{x_i\}$ and the phase compositions of the phases in the second phase region, $\{x_{ij}\}$:

$$x_{i1'}m_{1'} + x_{i2'}m_{2'} + \cdots + x_{ij'}m_{j'} + \cdots + x_{i\phi_2}m_{\phi_2} = x_i\sum_{j=1}^{\phi_2}m_j \tag{8-17}$$

$$(i = 1, 2, \cdots, N; N \text{ equations})$$

$m_1, m_2, \cdots, m_{\phi_1}$ and $m_{1'}, m_{2'}, \cdots, m_{\phi_2}$ are the mole numbers of the phases of the first and second phase regions, respectively.

If R_1=1, the system becomes invariant at a given pressure (or temperature). If R_1=0, the system itself is in invariant. In both cases of invariant equilibrium, the phase compositions are fixed, so $\{x_{ij}\}$ and $\{x_{ij'}\}$ are known values. Since there are ϕ_C common phases between both NPRs, the common concentration vectors in both $\{x_{ij}\}$ and $\{x_{ij'}\}$ are the same. However, when these same common phases exist in different phase regions, their mole numbers may be different, so that all parameters $m_1, m_2, \cdots, m_{\phi_1}; m_{1'}, m_{2'}, \cdots, m_{\phi_2}$ may be considered as independent variables, except that there also exists:

$$\sum_{j=1}^{\phi_1}m_j = \sum_{j'=1}^{\phi_2}m_{j'}(= M) \quad (1 \text{ equation}) \tag{8-18}$$

Consider Eqs. (8-16)~(8-18) as independent equations, then

$$\sum_{i=1}^{N}x_i = 1$$

is not an independent equation. The unknowns in Eqs. (8-16)~(8-18) are N unknowns of x_i $(i = 1, 2, \cdots, N)$, ϕ_1 unknowns of $m_j(j = 1, 2, \cdots, \phi_1)$ and ϕ_2 unknowns of $m_{j'}(j' = 1, 2, \cdots, \phi_2)$. The total number of independent unknowns is

$$N + \phi_1 + \phi_2 = N + \Phi + \phi_C \tag{8-19}$$

since $\varPhi = \phi_1 + \phi_2 - \phi_C$. The number of independent equations is $(2N+1)$, so the dimensions of solutions of eqs. (8-16)~(8-18) are:

$$N + \varPhi + \phi_C - (2N+1) = (\varPhi - N - 1) + \phi_C \tag{8-20}$$

For the first case, *i.e.* $R_1 = 1$, according to the theorem of corresponding relationship;

$$\varPhi = N - R_1 + 2 = N - 1 + 2 = N + 1 \tag{8-21}$$

If the temperature or pressure is fixed, then the phase points of the system are also fixed. Substituting eq. (8-21) into eq. (8-20), the dimensions of system points $R_1' = \phi_C$. This is explained as follows. Though the unknowns, in eqs. (8-16)~(8-18) have x_i, m_j and $m_{j'}$, the parameters presented in the phase diagram are x_i $(i = 1, 2, \cdots, N)$. So, the ϕ_C unknown quantities in the solutions from x_i $(i = 1, 2, \cdots, N)$ are chosen. We may fix M arbitrarily as one mole, and then all other unknowns may be solved from eqs. (8-16)~ (8-18), *i.e.*, relative amounts of all phases may be determined. Furthermore, $\phi_C \leqslant (N-1)$, so these ϕ_C unknowns may be surely chosen from x_i $(i = 1, 2, \cdots, N)$. This is the reason why we consider the dimensions of system points, $R_1' = \phi_C$.

$R_1' = \phi_C$, that is to say, under the above mentioned conditions, if the phase points are fixed, then the system points may be distributed over the hyperplane of ϕ_C dimensions. This hyperplane is constructed in such a way: ϕ_C common phases have ϕ_C common phase points; besides, when $\phi_C = 0$, there is one common system point between the two NPRs (proof of this point will be set out below). These ϕ_C common phase points, and one common system point, comprise $(\phi_C + 1)$ common points. In taking these $(\phi_C + 1)$ common points as vertices and connecting them, a hyperplane of ϕ_C dimensions is formed. System points are distributed over this hyperplane. When the temperature or pressure varies, these ϕ_C common phase points and one common system point, may move around the space of dimension R_1 (one in this case), and so does the hyperplane of ϕ_C dimensions formed by them. Therefore, dimensions of the hyperspace, over which the system points are distributed, are

$$R_1' = R_1 + \phi_C \tag{8-9}$$

For the second case, R_1=0, according to the theorem of the corresponding relationship: $\varPhi = N + 2 - R_1 = N + 2$; substituting it into eq.(8-20), the dimensions of the solutions of the system points is

$$(\varPhi - N - 1) + \phi_C = (N + 2 - N - 1) + \phi_C = \phi_C + 1$$

That is to say, when R_1=0, the phase points are fixed, and the system points may be distributed over the hyperplane of $(\phi_C + 1)$ dimensions. This hyperplane is formed in such a way: ϕ_C common phases have ϕ_C common phase points; and when $\phi_C = 0$, there is a boundary line of one dimension which is formed by two system points (two non-common phase points) (its proof will be given below). The two ends of the boundary line – two common system points (two non-common phase points) plus ϕ_C common phase points equal $(\phi_C + 2)$ common points. It has been proved that if R_1=0, $(\phi_C)_{\max} = \Phi - 4 = N - 2$ (see subsection 8.2.2 (6th corollary in this chapter)), $(\phi_C + 2) \leqslant N$. These $(\phi_C + 2)$ common points are linearly independent in the concentration space of N dimensions and form a hyperplane of $(\phi_C + 1)$ dimensions. The system points are distributed over it, so $R_1' = \phi_C + 1$. And R_1=0, for the sake of the consistency in form with eq. (8-9), this may be rewritten as

$$R_1' = R_1 + \phi_C + 1 \tag{8-10}$$

Now, we return to the problem: R_1=1 or 0, there is a univariant or invariant phase transition between two NPRs and there exists a univariant or an invariant region, with Φ=($\phi_{\max}$+1) or ($\phi_{\max}$+2) coexisting phases between two NPRs. When $\phi_C = 0$, there is a sole common system point (non-common phase point) or a boundary line of one dimension between the two NPRs, respectively. According to eqs. (8-16)~(8-18), and similar deductions, when R_1=1, if the temperature or pressure is fixed and ϕ_C=0, the solution of the system point is zero-dimensional, *i.e.* there is only a sole common system point (non-common phase point). When R_1=0 and ϕ_C =0, the solution of the system points is one-dimensional, *i.e.* there is a common boundary line of one dimension.

3. When R_1=1 or 0, but there is no univariant or invariant phase transition between the two NPRs and there is no univariant or invariant region, with Φ= ($\phi_{\max}$+1) or ($\phi_{\max}$+2) coexisting phases between the two NPRs, *i.e.* the two NPRs are located on the same side of this univariant or invariant region. In this case, the system changes from first NPR to second only when the total composition of the system varies, *i.e.*, it is not a phase transition. In this case, $\phi_C \geqslant 1$ [Zhao, 1983] and

$$R_1' = R_1 + \phi_C - 1 \tag{8-8}$$

The relationship between R_1' and R_1 is similar to that for $R_1 \geqslant 2$ and $\phi_C \geqslant 1$. If the system changes from the first NPR to the second, while the system lies just on the boundary, the amounts of the phases belonging only to either one of the NPR are infinitesimal, and all components of the system are distributed over the common phases (for example, in Fig. 8.1, the system changes from (S_1+L) → (L+S_2); when the system is located at point E, all of the system mass is distributed over the common phase, L). ϕ_C common phases have ϕ_C common phase points, and they form a hyperplane of $(\phi_C - 1)$ dimensions. The argument is similar to the previous one, the system points must be distributed over this hyperplane. When the conditions vary, ϕ_C common phase points may move around the space of R_1 dimensions ($R_1 = 1$ or 0), so, the total dimensions of the hyperspace over which the system points are distributed are:

$$R_1' = (R_1 + \phi_C - 1)$$

i.e., eq. (8-8) is also obtained. All of the equations, (8-8)~(8-10), have thus been proven.

8.4 The Relationship among NPRs and Their Boundaries for the p-T-x Binary Phase Diagrams.

8.4.1 A simple case

A simple case is the system with two components, these being completely miscible in the liquid state and partially miscible in the solid state. Let L, S_1 and S_2 refer the liquid phase and two solid phases respectively. If $r = Z=0$, $R_1 = N+2-\Phi = 4-\Phi$, $\Phi = 4 - R_1$. The relationship between NPRs and their boundaries for this phase diagram is shown in Table 8.1.

Table 8.1 Relationship among R_1, Φ and ϕ_C of a simple binary p-T-x phase diagram

$R_1(2\geqslant R_1 \geqslant 1)$	2	1	0
$\Phi(3\geqslant\Phi \geqslant 2)$	2	3	For there are only 3 phases, the case in which Φ=4, R_1=0 does not exist.
$\phi_{\max}$	2	2	
ϕ_C	1	$1\geqslant \phi_C \geqslant 0$	
R_1'	$R_1' = R_1 + \phi_C - 1$	$R_1' = R_1 + \phi_C$	
Phase assemblages in two NPRs i, j=1,2 $i \neq j$		ϕ_C=0	
	L/(L+S_i) S_i/(S_1+S_2)	L/(S_1+S_2) (L+S_i)/S_j	
		ϕ_C=1	
	(L+S_i)/(S_1+S_2)	(L+S_i)/(S_1+S_2)	

8.4.2 Complex p-T-x binary phase diagrams

In a complex p-T-x binary phase diagram, the total number of different phases at different temperatures and pressures may be more than $N + 2$ ($N + 2$=4) in a binary system. Under certain T and p conditions, a region, $\Phi = N$+2, R_1=0, is an invariant region. The complicated p-T-x binary phase diagram consists of ($N + 2$) phases in one group, with one invariant region. Surrounding the invariant region are the corresponding uni- and bi-variant regions, comprising some phases of the (N+2) ones. The relation for one typical phase diagram unit, is shown in Table 8.2.

Table 8.2 Relationship among Φ, R_1, ϕ_C, ϕ_{max} and R_1' of a p-T-x, binary phase diagram, with $r = Z = 0$, $R_1 = 4 - \Phi$

[Suppose that there are four phases (f_1, f_2, f_3 and f_4)]

$R_1(2 \geqslant R_1 \geqslant 0)$	2	1	0
$\Phi(4 \geqslant \Phi \geqslant 2)$	2	3	4
ϕ_{max}	2	2	2
ϕ_C	1	$1 \geqslant \phi_C \geqslant 0$	0
R_1'	$R_1' = R_1 + \phi_C - 1$	$R_1' = R_1 + \phi_C$	$R_1' = R_1 + \phi_C + 1$
Phase assemblages	$\phi_C = 1$	$\phi_C = 0$	$\phi_C = 0$
in two NPRs	R_1'=2	R_1'=1	R_1' = 1
i, j, k, $m = 1, 2, 3, 4$		$f_i/(f_j + f_k)$	
$i \neq j \neq k \neq m$	$f_i/(f_i+f_j)$	ϕ_C=1	$(f_i + f_j)/(f_k + f_m)$
		R_1'=2	
		$(f_i + f_j)/(f_j + f_k)$	

Note: Here the case in which f_i/f_j, $\Phi = 2$, $\phi_C = 0$, $Z = 1$ and $R_1 = 1$, scarcely exists. It is similar to the ternary phase diagram.

It is interesting to note that, when R_1=0, Φ=4. Two, three-dimensional, two-phase regions $(f_i + f_j)/(f_k + f_m)$ meet each other only at a straight boundary line (R_1'=1), four invariant equilibrium phase points (I, J, K, M) are being distributed on this line. The following figure illustrates the form of one of the "probable" cases. The author is hopeful that some researcher will, one day, verify this conclusion experimentally in a suitable system.

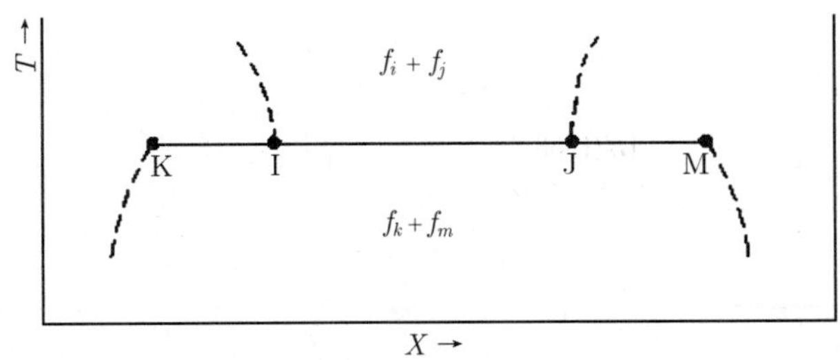

Fig. 8.2 Probable scheme of invariant reaction of a p-T-x binary phase diagram.

8.5 Relationship among NPRs and their Boundaries for the p-T-x_i Ternary Phase Diagram

8.5.1 A simple case

A simple case of the system with three components, they are completely miscible in the liquid and partially miscible in the solid state. Let L, S_1, S_2 and S_3 denote the liquid phase and three solid phases respectively. If $r = Z$=0, $R_1 = N + 2 - \Phi =$

$5-\Phi$, $\Phi=5-R_1$. The relationship among NPRs, and their boundaries for this phase diagram, is shown in Table 8.3.

Table 8.3 Relation among R_1, Φ and ϕ_C for a simple ternary p-T-x_i phase diagram

$R_1(3\geqslant R_1\geqslant 1)$	3	2	1
$\Phi(4\geqslant\Phi\geqslant 2)$	2	3	4
$\phi_{\max}$	2	3	3
ϕ_C	1	$2\geqslant\phi_C\geqslant 1$	$2\geqslant\phi_C\geqslant 0$
R_1'	$R_1+\phi_C-1$	$R_1+\phi_C-1=\phi_C+1$	$R_1+\phi_C=\phi_C+1$
Phase assemblages in two NPRs i, j, k=1, 2, 3 $i\neq j\neq k$	L/(L+S_i) S_i/(S_i+S_j) (L+S_i)/S_i	ϕ_C =1, R_1'=2 L/(L+S_i+S_j) (L+S_i)/(L+S_j) (L+S_i)/(S_i+S_j) S_i/(S_1+S_2+S_3) (S_i+S_j)/(S_j+S_k) ϕ_C = 2, R_1' = 3 (L+S_i)/(L+S_i+S_j) (S_i+S_j)/(S_1+S_2+S_3) (L+S_i+S_j)/(S_i+S_j)	ϕ_C = 0, R_1'=1 L/(S_1+S_2+S_3) (L+S_i)/(S_j+S_k) (L+S_i+S_j)/S_k ϕ_C =1, R_1'=2 (L+S_i)/(S_1+S_2+S_3) (L+S_i)/(L+S_j+S_k) ϕ_C = 2, R_1'=3 (L+S_i+S_j)/(S_1+S_2+S_3) (L+S_i+S_j)/(L+S_j+S_k)

Note: There are only four phases, the case in which $\Phi=5$, $R_1=0$ cannot occur.

8.5.2 Complicated p-T-x_i ternary phase diagrams

In a complicated, p-T-x_i ternary phase diagram, under certain T and p conditions, a region develops, that is a ternary invariant region, in which $\Phi=N+2=5$, $R_1=0$. Surrounding this invariant region are the corresponding uni-, bi- and tri-variant regions, comprising some of the five phases. The relationship among NPRs and their boundaries, within a ternary p-T-x_i phase diagram, are presented in Table 8.4. (See next page)

8.5.3 Some remarks

The isobaric phase diagram is a section of p-T-x_i phase diagram only with p=const. Thus, in the isobaric ternary phase diagram, there is no case for the column 5 (R_1=0) in Table 8.4, since the pressure chosen is an arbitrary choice. The relationship among NPRs and their boundaries in the isobaric ternary phase diagram, with Φ=2, 3 and 4, are shown in the columns 2, 3, and 4, in Table 8.4, but the numbers of R_1 and R_1' of them are one less than that shown in this table.

Table 8.4 Relationship among R_1, Φ, ϕ_C and $R_1{}'$ of a typical p-T-x_i phase diagram

($r = Z = 0$, $R_1 = 5 - \Phi$. There are five phases, f_1, f_2, f_3, f_4, f_5 in this phase diagram)

$R_1(3\geqslant R_1\geqslant 0)$	3	2	1	0
$\Phi(5\geqslant \Phi\geqslant 2)$	2	3	4	5
$\phi_{\max}$	2	3	3	3
ϕ_C	1	$(\Phi\text{-}1)\geqslant\phi_C\geqslant 1$	$(\Phi\text{-}2)\geqslant\phi_C\geqslant 0$	$(\Phi\text{-}4)\geqslant\phi_C\geqslant 0$
R_1'	3	ϕ_C+1	ϕ_C+1[1)]	ϕ_C+1[1)]
Phase assemblages in two NPRs i, j, k, m, n= 1, 2, 3, 4, 5 $i\neq j\neq k\neq m\neq n$	$f_i/\ (f_i+f_j)$	ϕ_C=1 R_1'=2 $f_i/$ $(f_i+f_j+f_k)$ $(f_i+f_j)/$ (f_j+f_k)	ϕ_C=0 R_1'=1 $f_i/(f_j+f_k+f_m)$ $(f_i+f_j)/$ (f_k+f_m)	ϕ_C=0 R_1'=1 $(f_i+f_j)/$ $(f_k+f_m+f_n)$
		ϕ_C=2 R_1'=3 $(f_i+f_j)/$ $(f_i+f_j+f_k)$	ϕ_C=1 R_1'=2 $(f_i+f_j)/$ $(f_j+f_k+f_m)$	ϕ_C=1 R_1'=2 $(f_i+f_j+f_k)/$ $(f_k+f_m+f_n)$
			ϕ_C=2 R_1'=3 $(f_i+f_j+f_k)/$ $(f_j+f_k+f_m)$	

1) Note: Without discussion of the cases; R_1'=1, or R_1'=0 and there is no univariant or invariant phase transition between two NPRs, and there does not exist $(N+1)$ or $(N+2)$ phases between two NPRs. In these cases, $R_1' = R_1 + \phi_C - 1$ still holds. Since they are not otherwise important, these cases have not been shown in the table.

8.6 The Application of Boundary Theory for Quaternary p-T-x_i Phase Diagrams

No experimental, quaternary p-T-x_i phase diagram has yet been created, so a simple table has been arranged to show the basic characteristics of the relationship among the NPRs and their boundaries, in the quaternary p-T-x_i phase diagram, see Table 8.5.

Table 8.5 Relationship among R_1, Φ, ϕ_C and R_1' of the quaternary p-T-x_i phase diagram

$\Phi(6\geqslant\Phi\geqslant 2)$	2	3	4	5	6
$R_1(4\geqslant R_1\geqslant 0)$	4	3	2	1	0
$\phi_{\max}$	2	3	4	4	4
ϕ_C	ϕ_C=1	$(\Phi-1)\geqslant$ $\phi_C\geqslant 1$ $2\geqslant\phi_C\geqslant 1$	$(\Phi-1)\geqslant$ $\phi_C\geqslant 1$ $3\geqslant\phi_C\geqslant 1$	$(\Phi-2)\geqslant$ $\phi_C\geqslant 0$ $3\geqslant\phi_C\geqslant 0$	$(\Phi-4)\geqslant$ $\phi_C\geqslant 0$ $2\geqslant\phi_C\geqslant 0$

Continued

$\Phi(6\geqslant \Phi \geqslant 2)$	2	3	4	5	6
R_1'	$R_1+\phi_C$ $-1=4$	$R_1+\phi_C-1$ $=\phi_C+2$	$R_1+\phi_C-1$ $=\phi_C+1$	$R_1+\phi_C^{1)}$ $=\phi_C+1$	$R_1+\phi_C+1^{1)}$ $=\phi_C+1$

Note: In this table, the condition of R_1=1 or R_1=0 and there is no univariant or invariant phase transition between two neither NPRs, nor does there exist $(N+1)$ or $(N+2)$ phases over the boundaries. In those cases, $R_1'=R_1+\phi_C-1$ still holds, the transference from one phase region to another phase region only occurs when the composition of the system changes, those cases are not important.

According to Table 8.5, the phase assemblages of NPRs of the quaternary p-T-x_i phase diagram may be deduced, but the cases are much more complicated. So the discussion of them is omitted here.

8.7 The Reliability of the Boundary Theory of Multicomponent p-T-x_i Phase Diagrams

For isobaric phase diagrams, there exist many experimental phase diagrams verifying the validity of the boundary theory. The verification shows that the boundary theory of isobaric phase diagrams is correct. But the circumstance of multicomponent p-T-x_i phase diagrams is different, due to the experimental difficulty, the experimental multicomponent p-T-x_i phase diagrams are rare. The correctness of the boundary theory of multicomponent p-T-x_i phase diagrams relies on the correctness of the initial premises and on rigorous logical deduction. Between year 1987 to 1993, Muyu Zhao *et al.* deduced out a thermodynamic method to calculate multicomponent p-T-x_i phase diagrams with the aid of the boundary theory [Zhao *et al.*, 1987], while his students and research colleagues calculated and determined the Cd-Sn-Zn [Song *et al.*, 1992, 1993] and Cd-Pb-Sn [Zhou *et al.*, 1988, 1990, 1992] high-pressure phase diagrams. These calculated phase diagrams "tally" well with the experimentally determined ones. These results have, at least, partially verified the boundary theory for the p-T-x_i multicomponent phase diagrams.

References-8

Lizhu Song, Hua Yang, Muyu Zhao. 1992. Determination of the phase diagrams of the Cd-Sn(0.2)-Zn ternary system at high pressure. J. Alloys and Compounds, 187: 137

Lizhu Song, Hua Yang, Ping Xiao, Muyu Zhao. 1993. Phase diagrams of ternary alloy system at high pressure. J. Alloys and Compounds, 196: 229-234

Muyu Zhao. 1983. The application of theorem of corresponding relation and its corollaries for p-T-x_i multicomponent phase diagrams. Scientia Sinica, Ser. B, 26(3): 274

Muyu Zhao. 1985. The relation between the dimensions of the boundary and phase boundary of the p-T-x_i multicomponent phase diagram. Scientia Sinica, Ser. B, 28(6): 655

Muyu Zhao, Ping Xiao, Hongye Kang. 1987. The principles of calculation of high pressure multicomponent phase diagrams. High Temperatures-High Pressures, 19: 513-518

Weiya Zhou, Zhongyi Shen, Yun Zhang, Muyu Zhao. 1988. Effects of pressure on the eutectic or eutectoid temperatures of Cd-Pb, Cd-Sn, Pb-Sn and Cd-Pb-Sn system. J. Less-Common Metals, 143: 59

Weiya Zhou, Lizhu Song, Muyu Zhao. 1990. Calculation of high-pressure phase diagrams of binary system. J. Less-Common Metals, 160: 237-245

Weiya Zhou, Lizhu Song, Fengqing Wu, Muyu Zhao. 1992. Optimization of thermodynamic properties and calculation of phase diagrams for the Cd-Sn system at high pressure. High Temperatures-High Pressures, 24: 511-518

Weiya Zhou, Zhongyi Shen, Muyu Zhao. 1988. The determination of high-pressure vertical sections of Cd-Pb-Sn ternary system. High Temperatures-High Pressures, 20: 561

Chapter 9

The Calculation of Unary High-Pressure Phase Diagrams and the Boundary Theory of *p*-*T* Phase Diagrams of Multicomponent Systems

9.1 Introduction

The determination of high-pressure phase diagrams, especially those of the multicomponent phase diagram type, is generally quite difficult. Up until now, most experimentally determined phase diagrams at high-pressure are unary in type. The number of published, high-pressure phase diagrams covering binary alloy systems has been rather small. *COMPOUND AND ALLOY UNDER HIGH PRESSURE: A HANDBOOK* [Tonkov, 1998] has presented information on about 890 binary systems, along with some data on the behavior of 1153 "pseudo" binary and ternary systems, "revealed" up to 1995. This book is the most complete reference work concerning the behavior and related data on alloys exposed to high pressures up till now. Besides the alloy systems, there are also many experimental results now available on the high-pressure, phase equilibrium of other multicomponent systems, mostly on the oxide systems as studied in geology *etc.*

Theoretical calculations offer a useful supplementary means for the study of the phase diagrams of materials at very high pressures. The use of this technique has the potential to yield more information about phase equilibrium, at high pressures within a shorter period, than many more complicated experiments could provide.

As is now well known, much work has been performed on the "calculation of phase diagrams" at atmospheric pressure. Many calculation methods have been established, resulting in the reporting of many excellent calculated findings (Ref. CALPHAD). Based of these calculation methods, as used for phase diagrams at around atmospheric pressure, "volumetric terms" can be introduced and used to calculate the high-pressure phase diagrams. However, various problems may be encountered in this application. One of the main troubles is the "scarceness" or indeed, the total lack of thermodynamic date at elevated pressures, especially for multicomponent systems. If, however, some acceptable assumptions are made for the approximate calculation of high pressure thermodynamic parameters, in addition to applying some available high pressure and other parameters at atmospheric pressure, calculation work for high-pressure phase diagrams can be performed and useful phase diagrams obtained.

In this chapter, the application of the boundary theory to p-T multicomponent phase diagram is also discussed.

9.2 Calculation of Unary p-T Diagrams

The boundary theory of unary system has been discussed in section 3.2. Now the calculation of unary p-T diagrams is discussed.

The principles, for the thermodynamic calculation of unary p-T phase diagrams, are rather simple. From thermodynamic principle

$$dG = -SdT + Vdp \tag{9-1}$$

G, S and V are the Gibbs free energy, entropy and volume of a closed system, respectively. When one mole of an element or compound changes from the solid state to the liquid state, one has the relationship

$$d\Delta G = -\Delta SdT + \Delta Vdp \tag{9-2}$$

While the system remains in a state of equilibrium at constant temperature and pressure, it follows that

$$\Delta G = 0 \tag{9-3}$$

$$\frac{dp}{dT} = \frac{\Delta S}{\Delta V} = \frac{\Delta H}{T\Delta V} \tag{9-4}$$

ΔG, ΔH, ΔS and ΔV are the changes in the molar Gibbs free energy, enthalpy, entropy and volume, for the phase transition from a solid state to the liquid state at equilibrium, respectively.

For each phase, for example the liquid phase, when the temperature of this phase, T_0, changes to T, at constant pressure p_0, one has

$$dH_L = C_{p_L}dT \tag{9-5}$$

$$\Delta H_L = H_L(T, p_0) - H_L(T_0, p_0) = \int_{T_0}^{T} C_{p_L}dT \tag{9-6}$$

Similarly, when the pressure changes at constant T, by thermodynamic principles, one has

$$d(H_L) = \left(\frac{\partial H_L}{\partial p}\right)_T dp \tag{9-7}$$

and

$$d(H_\mathrm{L}) = TdS_\mathrm{L} + V_\mathrm{L}dp \tag{9-8}$$

$$\left(\frac{\partial H_\mathrm{L}}{\partial p}\right)_T = T\left(\frac{\partial S_\mathrm{L}}{\partial p}\right)_T + V_\mathrm{L} \tag{9-9}$$

By Maxwell's relation,

$$\left(\frac{\partial S_\mathrm{L}}{\partial p}\right)_T = -\left(\frac{\partial V_\mathrm{L}}{\partial T}\right)_p \tag{9-10}$$

Therefore, $\Delta H(p,\,T)$ in eq. (9-4) may be expressed as

$$\begin{aligned}\left(\frac{\partial H_\mathrm{L}}{\partial p}\right)_T &= -T\left(\frac{\partial V_\mathrm{L}}{\partial T}\right)_p + V_\mathrm{L}\\ &= -T\alpha_\mathrm{L}V_\mathrm{L} + V_\mathrm{L} = V_\mathrm{L}(1-\alpha_\mathrm{L}T)\end{aligned} \tag{9-11}$$

$$\Delta H = \int_{p_0}^{p} V_\mathrm{L}(1-\alpha_\mathrm{L}T)dp \tag{9-12}$$

α_L is the thermal expansion coefficients of the liquid. Thus, it follows that

$$H_\mathrm{L}(p,T) = H_\mathrm{L}(p_0,T_0) + \int_{T_0}^{T} C_{p\mathrm{L}}dT + \int_{p_0}^{p} V_\mathrm{L}(1-\alpha_\mathrm{L}T)dp \tag{9-13}$$

Similarly, for the solid phase, one has

$$H_\mathrm{S}(p,T) = H_\mathrm{S}(p_0,T_0) + \int_{T_0}^{T} C_{p\mathrm{S}}dT + \int_{p_0}^{p} V_\mathrm{S}(1-\alpha_\mathrm{S}T)dp \tag{9-14}$$

Therefore:

$$\begin{aligned}\Delta H(p,T) &= H_\mathrm{L}(p,T) - H_\mathrm{S}(p,T)\\ &= [H_\mathrm{L}(p_0,T_0) - H_\mathrm{S}(p_0,T_0)] + \int_{T_0}^{T}\Delta C_p dT\\ &\quad + \int_{p_0}^{p}[V_\mathrm{L}(1-\alpha_\mathrm{L}T) - V_\mathrm{S}(1-\alpha_\mathrm{S}T)]dp\\ &= \Delta H_0(p_0,T_0) + \int_{T_0}^{T}\Delta C_p dT + \int_{p_0}^{p}[V_\mathrm{L}(1-\alpha_\mathrm{L}T) - V_\mathrm{S}(1-\alpha_\mathrm{S}T)]\mathrm{d}p\end{aligned} \tag{9-15}$$

$$\Delta C_p = C_{p\mathrm{L}} - C_{p\mathrm{S}}$$

$$C_{p\mathrm{L}} = a_\mathrm{L} + b_\mathrm{L}T + c_\mathrm{L}T^{-2} + d_\mathrm{L}T^2 \tag{9-16}$$

$$C_{p\mathrm{S}} = a_\mathrm{S} + b_\mathrm{S}T + c_\mathrm{S}T^{-2} + d_\mathrm{S}T^2 \tag{9-16$'$}$$

The volume change, ΔV in eq. (9-4) may be expressed as

$$\Delta V(p,T) = V_\mathrm{L}(p,T) - V_\mathrm{S}(p,T) \tag{9-17}$$

While

$$V_{\rm L}(T,p) = V_{\rm L}(T_0,p_0)\exp[\alpha_{\rm L}(T-T_0) - \beta_{\rm L}(p-p_0)] \tag{9-18}$$

$$V_{\rm S}(T,p) = V_{\rm S}(T_0,p_0)\exp[\alpha_{\rm S}(T-T_0) - \beta_{\rm S}(p-p_0)] \tag{9-19}$$

where $\alpha_{\rm L}$ and $\alpha_{\rm S}$ are the thermal expansion coefficients of the liquid and the solid phases, respectively, and may be assumed to be approximately independent of pressure; while $\beta_{\rm L}$ and $\beta_{\rm S}$ are the compressibility of the liquid and the solid phases, respectively. These parameters may also be assumed to be approximately independent of temperature.

Since the thermodynamic parameters of elements and compounds, at the melting temperature and at normal pressure, are easier to obtain, T_0 is usually chosen as T_m (the melting point at the normal pressure), p_0 is chosen as the normal pressure.

Thus, the terms, ΔH and ΔV in eq. (9-4), have been expressed, and the values of dp/dT may be calculated.

In some cases, not all of the desired thermodynamic parameters are obtainable, thus one has to make an assumption:

1. α and β may be assumed to be constant.
2. or $C_{p_{\rm L}}, C_{p_{\rm S}}$ be assumed to be constant.
3. ΔH and ΔV in eq. (9-4) may also be assumed to be constant. In this case, the results obtained are not very accurate.

For solid-solid transitions, $\alpha \to \beta$, *etc*, at high temperatures and pressures, if the structural parameters and the number of atoms packed in the unit cell for each phase are known, then the molar volumes V_α, V_β and ΔV may be calculated. However, the value of ΔH is usually not known. Then, one has to use some other methods to estimate ΔH, based on the microscopic viewpoint, for example, the molecular dynamics method, the Monte Carlo method, and the "first principles" method *etc.*

9.3 The Boundary Theory of *p*-*T* Phase Diagrams of Multicomponent Systems without Composition Variable

For p-T phase diagrams of a multicomponent equilibrium system, there is no way to present any variation of composition. The phase rule is the convenient tool to investigate the diagram, and now the boundary theory is also available for such assessment.

As mentioned in earlier section 2.4, the difference between the application of the phase rule and the boundary theory is that the phase rule considers the number of equilibrium phases (ϕ) in the system and the degrees of freedom of the system (f); while the boundary theory underlines the total number of different phases in NPRs (Φ) and the dimensions of phase boundaries between NPRs (R_1). The conclusions should be the same.

Let us discuss the following p-T phase diagram in Fig. 9.1. Using the phase rule, on the boundary line, we have

N=4 ($CaCO_3$-calcite, $CaSiO_3$-wollastonite, SiO_2-quartz, CO_2)

ϕ=4 ($CaCO_3$, CO_2, $CaSiO_3$, SiO_2)

r =1 ($CaCO_3+SiO_2=CaSiO_3+CO_2$)

Z=0

Then, the phase rule tells that the boundary has the freedom of 1.

$$f = (N - r - Z) - \phi + 2 = (4 - 1 - 0) - 4 + 2 = 1$$

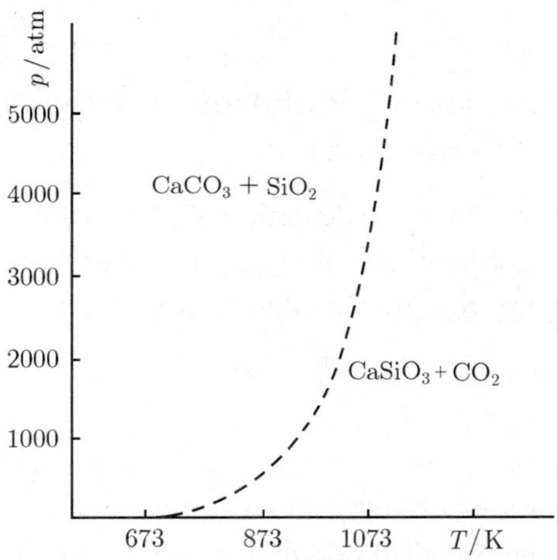

Fig. 9.1 p-T diagram for reaction $CaCO_3+SiO_2=CaSiO_3+CO_2$ [Brownlow, 1979].

With the boundary theory:

N=4 ($CaCO_3$-calcite, $CaSiO_3$-wollastonite, SiO_2-quartz, CO_2)

Φ=4 ($CaCO_3$, CO_2, $CaSiO_3$, SiO_2)

r = 1 ($CaCO_3+SiO_2 = CaSiO_3+CO_2$)

Z=0

then

$$R_1 = (N - r - Z) - \Phi + 2 = (4 - 1 - 0) - 4 + 2 = 1 \quad (2\text{-}5')$$

So the dimension of the phase boundary between NPRs ($CaCO_3+SiO_2$)/($CaSiO_3+CO_2$) is one, and we underline this boundary is also a phase boundary line.

That is to say: the boundary theory can treat p-T phase diagrams of multi component system without composition variable. It is a very important conclusion.

References-9

Arthur H. Brownlow. 1979. Geochemisty. Englewood Cliffs: Prentice-Hall, Inc.

E. Yu. Tonkov. 1998. Compound and alloy under high pressure: A handbook. NY: CRC Press

Chapter 10

Calculation of Binary High-Pressure Phase Diagrams

10.1 Principles for the Calculation of Binary Phase Diagrams at Elevated Pressures

The basic principle utilized for the calculation of phase diagrams at high pressures is: when a closed system is at equilibrium at the prescribed temperature and pressure, its total Gibbs free energy reaches the minimum value, *i.e.*

$$G = G_{\text{min}} \tag{10-1}$$

According to the above principle, the equilibrium criteria can be deduced in terms of intensive properties: when a closed system reaches an equilibrium state, at given T and p values, the chemical potentials of any component, i, in all the phases are equal to one another

$$\mu_{ij} = \mu_i \quad (i = 1, 2, \cdots, N;\ j = 1, 2, \cdots, \phi) \tag{10-2}$$

So, there are two ways available to calculate the high-pressure phase diagram. When the system is rather simple, and there are no intermediate phases or compounds in the system, it is then convenient to use the method of equalization of chemical potentials. If the system is more complicated, one has to use the method of Gibbs free energy minimization of the system. In general, it is difficult to obtain thermochemical data for intermediate phases or compounds at high pressures, thereby inhibiting the calculation of complicated phase diagrams at high pressures. Therefore the method of equalization of chemical potentials exclusively will be discussed.

Usually, the T-x binary phase diagrams are calculated for different pressure regimes. It is more convenient to calculate the boundaries of a phase region. We take a eutectic system as the example (Fig. 10.1). For the equilibrium phase regions $(\text{L+S}_j)(j = 1, 2), \phi = 2,\ R_1 = 1$; the phase boundary lines are ac and aE, or bE and bd.

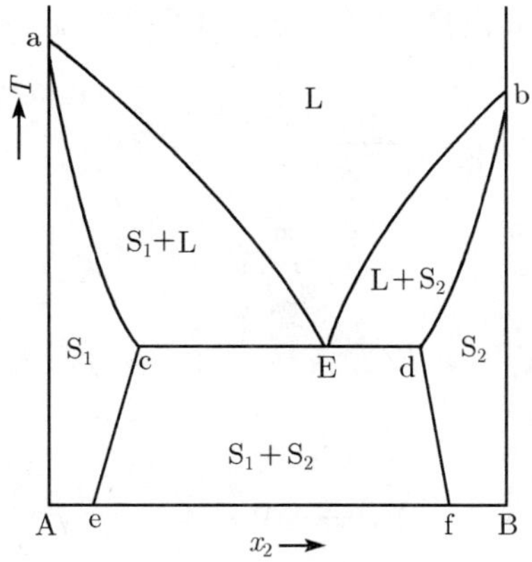

Fig. 10.1 A binary phase diagram at a given high pressure.

According to the phase equilibrium principle, at constant temperature and pressure, the chemical potentials for each component in the equilibrium phases are equal to one another. Therefore, when liquid phase L and solid solution phase S_j coexist in equilibrium, one has

$$\mu_{i\mathrm{L}}(T, p, x_{i_\mathrm{L}}) = \mu_{i\mathrm{S}_j}(T, p, x_{i\mathrm{S}_j}) \tag{10-3}$$

$\mu_{i\mathrm{L}}, \mu_{i\mathrm{S}_j}$ are the chemical potentials of the i-th component in phase L and S_j, respectively.

If the pure solid or liquid state of the i-th component is selected as the standard state, the chemical potential or the partial molar Gibbs free energy of the i-th component in the liquid or solid solution phase, $\mu_{i\mathrm{S}_j}(T, p, x_{i\mathrm{S}_j})$ or $\mu_{i\mathrm{L}}(T, p, x_{i\mathrm{L}})$, can be expressed as

$$\mu_{i\mathrm{L}}(T, p, x_{i\mathrm{L}}) = \mu^0_{i\mathrm{L}}(T, p_0) + RT \ln x_{i\mathrm{L}} \gamma_{i\mathrm{L}}(T, p_0, x_{i\mathrm{L}}) + \int_{p_0}^{p} \bar{V}_{i\mathrm{L}}(T, p, x_{i\mathrm{L}}) \mathrm{d}p \quad (i = 1, 2) \tag{10-4}$$

$$\mu_{i\mathrm{S}_j}(T, p, x_{i\mathrm{S}_j}) = \mu^0_{i\mathrm{S}}(T, p_0) + RT \ln x_{i\mathrm{S}_j} \gamma_{i\mathrm{S}_j}(T, p_0, x_{i\mathrm{S}_j}) + \int_{p_0}^{p} \bar{V}_{i\mathrm{S}_j}(T, p, x_{i\mathrm{S}_j}) \mathrm{d}p \quad (i = 1, 2) \tag{10-5}$$

where x_1, and γ_i are the mole fraction and activity coefficient of the i-th component, respectively; L denotes the liquid phase; and $S_j (j = 1, 2)$ the solid solution phase j: $\bar{V}_{i\mathrm{L}}$ and $\bar{V}_{i\mathrm{S}_j}$ are the partial molar volumes of the i-th component in phase L and phase S_j at a given temperature and pressure respectively; $\mu^0_{i\mathrm{L}}, \mu^0_{i\mathrm{S}}$ are the standard molar Gibbs free energy of the pure i-th component in phase L and phase S, respectively; p_0 and p are the atmospheric pressure and high pressure, respectively, and R is the gas constant.

Inserting eqs. (10-4) and (10-5) into eq. (10-3), it gives rise to

$$\begin{aligned}\frac{x_{i\mathrm{L}}\gamma_{i\mathrm{L}}(T,p_0,x_{i\mathrm{L}})}{x_{i\mathrm{S}_j}\gamma_{i\mathrm{S}_j}(T,p_0,x_{i\mathrm{S}_j})} =& \exp\left(-\frac{\mu^0_{i,\mathrm{L}}-\mu^0_{i,\mathrm{S}_j}}{RT}\right)\\ &\times \exp\left\{-\frac{1}{RT}\int_{p_0}^{p}[\bar{V}_{i\mathrm{L}}(T,p,x_{i\mathrm{L}})-\bar{V}_{i\mathrm{S}_j}(T,p,x_{i\mathrm{S}_j})]\mathrm{d}p\right\}\\ =&K_i = KT_i(T,p_0)\times VTp_i(T,p,x_{i\mathrm{L}},x_{i\mathrm{S}_j}) \quad (i=1,2)\end{aligned} \tag{10-6}$$

where

$$KT_i(T,p_0)=\exp\left(-\frac{\mu^0_{i\mathrm{L}}-\mu^0_{i\mathrm{S}}}{RT}\right) \tag{10-7}$$

$$\begin{aligned}&VTp_i(T,p,x_{i\mathrm{L}},x_{i\mathrm{S}_j})\\ &=\exp\left\{-\frac{1}{RT}\int_{p_0}^{p}[\bar{V}_{i\mathrm{L}}(T,p,x_{i\mathrm{L}})-\bar{V}_{i\mathrm{S}_j}(T,p,x_{i\mathrm{S}_j})]\mathrm{d}p\right\}\end{aligned} \tag{10-8}$$

K_i is divided into two parts: $KT_i(T,p_0)$ is the distribution coefficient between the liquid and solid states at temperature, T, and the atmospheric pressure, $p_0 = 0.1$ MPa, while VTp_i reflects the effect of pressure change on the phase equilibrium at temperature T.

By solving eq.(10-6), we obtain the compositions of the coexisting equilibrium phases at a given temperature and pressure.

By calculating a series of phase compositions at different temperatures and at a "given" high pressure, the phase diagram of an alloy system at the "given" high pressure can be constructed.

10.2 Calculation of the Standard Molar Gibbs Free Energy for the Pure Components

According to eq. (10-7)

$$KT_i(T,p_0)=\exp\left(-\frac{\mu^0_{i\mathrm{L}}-\mu^0_{i\mathrm{S}}}{RT}\right)$$

$$\begin{aligned}\mu^0_{i\mathrm{L}}-\mu^0_{i\mathrm{S}} =&\Delta\mu^0_{i(\mathrm{S}\to\mathrm{L})}=\Delta H^0_{i(\mathrm{S}\to\mathrm{L})}-T\Delta S^0_{i(\mathrm{S}\to\mathrm{L})}\\ =&\Delta H^0_{im(\mathrm{S}\to\mathrm{L})}+\int_{T_m}^{T}\Delta C_{p_i}\mathrm{d}T - T\left[\Delta S^0_{im(\mathrm{S}\to\mathrm{L})}+\int_{T_m}^{T}\frac{\Delta C_{p_i}}{T}\mathrm{d}T\right]\end{aligned} \tag{10-9}$$

Where $\Delta\mu^0_{i(\mathrm{S}\to\mathrm{L})}$ is the standard molar Gibbs free energy change for the i-th component, from pure solid to liquid phase; $\Delta H^0_{im(\mathrm{S}\to\mathrm{L})}$ and $\Delta S^0_{im(\mathrm{S}\to\mathrm{L})}$ are the standard molar enthalpy change and the standard molar entropy change of melting for the

i-th component; T_m(K) is the melting point of the i-th component, at $p_0 = 0.1$MPa, $\Delta C_{p_i} = C_{p_i\text{L}} - C_{p_i\text{S}}$

Assume that

$$\Delta C_{p_i} = \Delta a_i - \Delta b_i T \tag{10-10}$$

And, in substituting eq. (10-10) into eq. (10-9), we obtain

$$\Delta\mu^0_{i(\text{S}\to\text{L})} = \left(\Delta H^0_{im(\text{S}\to\text{L})} - \Delta a_i T_{im} - \frac{1}{2}\Delta b_i T^2_{im}\right) + \left(\Delta a_i + \Delta b_i T_{im} - \frac{\Delta H^0_{im(\text{S}\to\text{L})}}{T_{im}} + \Delta a_i \ln T_{im}\right) T - \frac{1}{2}\Delta b_i T^2 - \Delta a_i T \ln T$$

Let

$$\Delta\mu^0_{i(\text{S}\to\text{L})} = A'_i + B'_i T + C'_i T^2 + D'_i T \ln T \tag{10-11}$$

Then

$$KT_i(T, p_0) = \exp\left[-\frac{A'_i}{RT} - \frac{B'_i T}{RT} - \frac{C'_i T^2}{RT} - \frac{D'_i T \ln T}{RT}\right] = \exp\left(A_i + B_i T + \frac{C_i}{T} + D_i \ln T\right) \tag{10-12}$$

Where

$$A_i = -\frac{B'_i}{R}, \quad B_i = -\frac{C'_i}{R}$$

$$C_i = -\frac{A'_i}{R}, \quad D_i = -\frac{D'_i}{R}$$

From known values of the thermodynamic quantities; $T_m, \Delta H_m, \Delta S_m$ and ΔC_p [Húltgren *et al*, 1973; Barin *et al*, 1977; Brandes, 1983] for the pure components, the $KT_i(T, p_0)$ can then be calculated.

10.3 Calculation of Activity Coefficients $\gamma_i(T, p_0, x_i)$ of the i-th Component in the Equilibrium Phases

10.3.1 The activity coefficient $\gamma_i(T, p_0, x_i)$ of the i-th component in the liquid phase

The excess molar Gibbs free energy G^E_L, or the excess molar enthalpy H^E_L and excess molar entropy S^E_L of binary liquid alloys, at a given temperature T_i and at atmospheric pressure, may be found for a series of compositions in the literatures [Kubaschewski *et al.*, 1956; Hultgren *et al.*, 1973; Kubaschewski *et al.*, 1979]. From the discrete values of the excess molar quantities (for example, G^E), the analytical expression, $G^E = f(\chi_2)$, at temperature T_1 and at atmospheric pressure may be regressed through an equation of the form:

$$G^E = \sum_n a_n x_2^n \tag{10-13}$$

where α_n are adjustable parameters, $n = 0, 1, 2, \cdots$

From thermodynamic principles

$$G^E = H^E - T_1 S^E \tag{10-14}$$

If H^E and S^E are given, then G^E may be obtained. The excess partial molar quantities can be derived from the corresponding excess molar quantities:

$$\begin{aligned}
\mu_1^E &= G^E - x_2 \frac{\partial G^E}{\partial x_2} \\
\mu_2^E &= G^E + (1 - x_2) \frac{\partial G^E}{\partial x_2} \\
h_1^E &= H^E - x_2 \frac{\partial H^E}{\partial x_2} \\
h_2^E &= H^E + (1 - x_2) \frac{\partial H^E}{\partial x_2}
\end{aligned} \tag{10-15}$$

where μ_i^E and $h_i^E (i = 1, 2)$ are the excess, partial molar free enthalpy and the excess partial molar enthalpy for the i-th component in the liquid alloy, respectively, and their analytical expressions at temperature T_1 can be obtained from eq.(10-15).

In order to derive the corresponding expressions at any temperature T, the Gibbs-Helmholtz equation has to be used:

$$\frac{\partial \left(\dfrac{G^E}{T} \right)}{\partial T} = -\frac{H^E}{T^2} \tag{10-16}$$

Assuming H^E is independent of temperature, we get

$$\frac{G^E(T)}{T} - \frac{G^E(T_1)}{T_1} = H^E \left(\frac{1}{T} - \frac{1}{T_1} \right) \tag{10-17}$$

Similarly

$$\frac{\mu_i^E(T)}{T} - \frac{\mu_i^E(T_1)}{T_1} = h_i^E \left(\frac{1}{T} - \frac{1}{T_1} \right) \tag{10-18}$$

$$\mu_i^E(T) = \frac{T}{T_1} \mu_i^E(T_1) + h_i^E \left(1 - \frac{T}{T_1} \right) \tag{10-19}$$

Since μ_i^E is a function of temperature and composition, and

$$\gamma_{i\mathrm{L}} = \exp\left(\frac{\mu_i^E}{RT}\right) \tag{10-20}$$

$\gamma_{i\mathrm{L}}$ is a function of T and compositions, and usually one can write it in the from of $\gamma_{i\mathrm{L}}(T, p_0, x_{i\mathrm{L}})$.

$$\gamma_{i\mathrm{L}}(T, p_0, x_{i\mathrm{L}}) = \exp\left\{\frac{1}{R}\left[\frac{1}{T_1}\mu_{i\mathrm{L}}^E(T_1) + \left(\frac{1}{T} - \frac{1}{T_1}\right)h_{i\mathrm{L}}^E\right]\right\}, \quad (i = 1, 2) \tag{10-21}$$

If the values of excess molar quantities for the liquid solutions are not known, but the activity coefficients, $\gamma_{i\mathrm{S}_j}$, for the solid solutions are known, the activity coefficient $\gamma_{i\mathrm{L}}$ of the i-th component in the liquid solution can be generated by regression, with the known, experimental binary phase diagram of this system.

10.3.2 Activity coefficient $\gamma_{i\mathrm{S}}(T, p_0, x_{i\mathrm{S}})$ of the i-th component in the solid phase

If the excess molar quantities of the binary solid alloys are known, for a series of compositions at a given temperature T_1 and atmospheric pressure, then $\gamma_{i\mathrm{S}}(T, p_0, x_{i\mathrm{S}})$ can be treated in a similar way as for $\gamma_{i\mathrm{L}}(T, p_0, x_{i\mathrm{L}})$, and therefore its treatment is omitted here.

If the solubility of the solute, j, in the solid solutions is small, then the regular solution model can be applied:

$$RT \ln \gamma_{i\mathrm{S}_j}(T, p_0) = \alpha_{ij} x_{\mathrm{S}_j}^2, \quad (i = 1, 2; j = 1, 2) \tag{10-22}$$

The activity coefficient, $\gamma_{i\mathrm{S}_j}$, is generated by regression of the interaction parameter, α_{ij}, with the known, experimental binary phase diagram and the known values of $\mu_{i\mathrm{L}}^E$ or $\gamma_{i\mathrm{L}}$, for the equilibrium liquid solution.

10.4 Partial Molar Volumes

From eq. (10-4) to (10-6), it is clear that the volume term plays an important role in describing the effect of pressure on the partial molar Gibbs free energy and phase equilibrium at high pressure. It is a key problem needed to be solved in the calculation of high pressure phase diagrams.

10.4.1 Partial molar volume of the i-th component in the liquid phase, $\bar{V}_{i\mathrm{L}}(T, p, x_{i\mathrm{L}})$

$\bar{V}_{i\mathrm{L}}(T, p, x_{i\mathrm{L}})$ is expressed as

$$\bar{V}_{i\mathrm{L}}(T, p, x_{i\mathrm{L}}) = \bar{V}_{i\mathrm{L}}^0(T, p) + \bar{V}_{i\mathrm{L}}^E(T, p, x_{i\mathrm{L}}) \quad (i = 1, 2) \tag{10-23}$$

In eq. (10-23),

$$V_{i\mathrm{L}}^0(T,p) = V_{i\mathrm{L}}^0(T_m,p_0)\exp[\alpha_{i\mathrm{L}}(T-T_m)-\beta_{i\mathrm{L}}(p-p_0)] \tag{10-24}$$

The terms, $V_{i\mathrm{L}}^0(T,p)$ and $\bar{V}_{i\mathrm{L}}^E(T,p,x_{i\mathrm{L}})$, represent the standard molar volume and excess partial molar volume of the i-th component in the liquid phase under the given conditions, respectively. If the thermal expansion coefficient $\alpha_{i\mathrm{L}}$, the compressibility $\beta_{i\mathrm{L}}$ and the standard molar volume $V_{i\mathrm{L}}^0(T_m,p_0)$ of i-th component in the liquid state at the melting point T_m and the atmospheric pressure p_0(=0.1MPa) are known, $V_{i\mathrm{L}}^0(T,p)$ can be derived from eq.(10-24).

Using the discrete values of the molar volumes $V_\mathrm{L}(T,p_0,x_{i\mathrm{L}})$ the ratio of the molar volume changes of the liquid binary solutions at atmospheric pressure p_0 and a given temperature T_0 can be defined:

$$\Delta V_\mathrm{L}(T_0,p_0,x_{i\mathrm{L}}) = \frac{V_\mathrm{L}(T_0,p_0,x_{i\mathrm{L}})-\sum x_{i\mathrm{L}}V_{i\mathrm{L}}^0(T_0,p_0)}{\sum x_{i\mathrm{L}}V_{i\mathrm{L}}^0(T_0,p_0)} \quad (i=1,2) \tag{10-25}$$

Because the values of ΔV_L are usually not known over different temperature and pressure ranges, one has to assume that ΔV_L is a function of composition only and is independent of both temperature and pressure. Since there are molar volume terms in the denominator and numerator, the effects of temperature and pressure may be self canceling to some extent, therefore, the assumption may be a reasonable one. The excess molar volume of the liquid binary solution, at high temperatures/high pressures, may be derived:

$$V_\mathrm{L}^E(T,p,x_{i\mathrm{L}}) = \Delta V_\mathrm{L}(T_0,p_0,x_{i\mathrm{L}})\sum_i x_{i\mathrm{L}}V_{i\mathrm{L}}^0(T,p) \quad (i=1,2) \tag{10-26}$$

From eq. (10-26), it is clear that $V_\mathrm{L}^E(T,p,x_{i\mathrm{L}})$ is still a function of temperature, pressure and composition.

Using the known discrete values of $\Delta V_\mathrm{L}(T_0,p_0,x_{i\mathrm{L}})$, and by regression, one can obtain the polynomial expression or ΔV_L

$$\Delta V_\mathrm{L}(T_0,p_0,x_{i\mathrm{L}}) = \sum_K d_K x_{i\mathrm{L}}^K \tag{10-27}$$

where K is a positive integer, and d_K is the coefficient of the polynomial. So,

$$V_\mathrm{L}^E(T,p,x_{i\mathrm{L}}) = \left(\sum_K d_K x_{i\mathrm{L}}^K\right)\times\left\{\sum x_{i\mathrm{L}}V_{i\mathrm{L}}^0(T_m,p_0)\exp[\alpha_{i\mathrm{L}}(T-T_m)-\beta_{i\mathrm{L}}(p-p_0)]\right\} \tag{10-28}$$

For the binary system, the partial molar volume of the i-th component can be derived from

$$\bar{V}_{i\mathrm{L}}^{E}(T,p,x_{i\mathrm{L}}) = V_{\mathrm{L}}^{E} + (1-x_{i\mathrm{L}})\frac{\partial V_{\mathrm{L}}^{E}}{\partial x_{i\mathrm{L}}}, \quad (i=1,2) \tag{10-29}$$

By inserting eq. (10-29) into eq. (10-23), one obtains the partial molar volume, $\bar{V}_{i\mathrm{L}}(T,p,x_{i\mathrm{L}})$, of the i-th component in the liquid phase.

10.4.2 Partial molar volume of the *i*-th component in the solid phase $\bar{V}_{i\mathrm{S}}(T,p,x_{i\mathrm{S}_j})$

For the ideal condition, the lattice constant of the solid solution of the substitutional type, and of those components with similar crystal structures, obeys the Vegard's rule, *i.e.*

$$a = a_1x_1 + a_2x_2 \tag{10-30}$$

where, a and a_1, a_2 are the lattice constants of the solid solution and the two pure components respectively. Even for the system that does not obey Vegard's rule, the lattice constant $a_{\mathrm{S}_j}(T_0,p_0,x_{i\mathrm{S}_j})$, of terminal solid solutions of the binary alloy systems at atmospheric pressure and a given temperature, is approximately a linear function of the composition. Let $K_a(T_0,p_0)$ represent the slope of the straight line; and assume that the slope K_a is independent of temperature and pressure, and then it follows that

$$a_{\mathrm{S}_j}[T,p,(1-x_{i\mathrm{S}_j})] = a_{i\mathrm{S}}^{0}[1+K_a(T_0,p_0)(1-x_{i\mathrm{S}_j})] \tag{10-31}$$

$a_{i\mathrm{S}}^{0}$ is the solvent lattice constant for the solid solution, S_j. If the solid solution has a cubic structure, then the molar volume of the solid solution may be determined

$$V_{\mathrm{S}_j}[T,p,(1-x_{i\mathrm{S}_j})] = V_{i\mathrm{S}}^{0}(T,p)[1+K_a(T_0,p_0)(1-x_{i\mathrm{S}_j})]^3 \tag{10-32}$$

where

$$V_{i\mathrm{S}}^{0}(T,p) = V_{i\mathrm{S}}^{0}(T_m,p_0)\exp[\alpha_{i\mathrm{S}}(T-T_m) - \beta_{i\mathrm{S}}(p-p_0)] \quad (i=1,2)$$

$V_{i\mathrm{S}}^{0}(T,p)$ is the standard molar volume of the solvent component in the solid state at T and p, $V_{i\mathrm{S}}^{0}(T_m,p_0)$ is the standard molar volume of the i-th component in the solid state, at the melting point T_m and at atmospheric pressure. $\alpha_{i\mathrm{S}}, \beta_{i\mathrm{S}}$ are, respectively, the thermal expansion coefficient and the compressibility of the i-th component in the solid state.

For a solid solution with the tetragonal structure, there are two lattice constants, a and c, so

$$a_{\mathrm{S}_j}[T,p,(1-x_{i\mathrm{S}_j})] = a_{i\mathrm{S}}^{0}[1+K_a(T_0,p_0)(1-x_{i\mathrm{S}_j})] \tag{10-33}$$

$$c_{\mathrm{S}_j}[T,p,(1-x_{i\mathrm{S}_j})] = c_{i\mathrm{S}}^0[1+K_c(T_0,p_0)(1-x_{i\mathrm{S}_j})] \tag{10-34}$$

$$\begin{aligned} V_{\mathrm{S}_j}[T,p,(1-x_{i\mathrm{S}_j})] =& V_{i\mathrm{S}}^0(T,p)[1+K_a(T_0,p_0)(1-x_{i\mathrm{S}_j})]^2 \\ & \times [1+K_c(T_0,p_0)(1-x_{i\mathrm{S}_j})] \end{aligned} \tag{10-35}$$

For a solid solution with another structure, V_{S_j} must be treated in another way.

From the molar volume, the partial molar volume of the i-th component in the solid solution can be derived.

$$\bar{V}_{i\mathrm{S}_j} = V_{\mathrm{S}_j} + (1-x_{i\mathrm{S}_j})\frac{\partial V_{\mathrm{S}_j}}{\partial x_{i\mathrm{S}_j}} \quad (i=1,2) \tag{10-36}$$

10.5 Some Remarks on the Values of α and β

10.5.1 The coefficient of thermal expansion, α_{ij}

The coefficient of thermal expansion α_{ij} of the pure i-th component, existing in a given phase j, changes very little over a narrow temperature interval, thus it may be considered to be approximately constant. Its values, for different temperature intervals, may be found in the literature [Brandes, 1983].

The coefficients of thermal volume expansion, for some metals near their melting points, are listed in Table 10.1.

Table 10.1 Coefficients of thermal volume expansion for pure metals

Metal	T_{L}/K	$10^4\alpha_{\mathrm{L}}$/K^{-1}	T_{S}/K	$10^4\alpha_{\mathrm{S}}$/K^{-1}
Cd	594	1.5	500	1.152
Pb	600	1.2	600	1.032
Sn	505	1.0	500	0.825

10.5.2 Compressibility coefficients of pure components, β_{ij}

β_{ij} is considered to be constant in a narrow temperature interval, however, it must be considered as a function of temperature when the temperature change is large.

The values set out in Table 10.2 can be found in the literatures [Blair, 1978; Clark, 1966].

Table 10.2 Volume compressibility coefficients for pure components of the liquid and solid states

Metal	T_{L}/K	$10^6\beta_{i\mathrm{L}}$/bar^{-1}	T_{S}/K	$10^6\beta_{i\mathrm{S}}$/bar^{-1}
Cd	594	3.11	300	2.048
Pb	600	3.359	300	2.415
Sn	505	2.664	300	1.909

When calculating phase equilibrium near the melting point, the values of compressibility coefficients near the melting point have to be used, too. It is therefore better to obtain the value of $\beta_{i\mathrm{S}}$ at the melting temperature.

Above the Debye temperature, there is one approximate relationship between the coefficient of thermal expansion and the compressibility coefficient, at the same temperature [Akimoto *et al.*, 1982], for the metal:

$$\frac{\alpha(T)}{\beta(T)} = \text{Const.} \tag{10-37}$$

Since the Debye temperatures for Cd, Pb and Sn are all below 260K; according to the values found in the literature [Gray, 1963, 1972; Clark, 1966], and which are now listed in Table 10.3, and, by applying eq.(10-37), the compressibility coefficients for the pure solid metals near their melting temperatures, are obtained. The calculated compressibility coefficients are also listed in Table 10.3. From Tables 10.2 and 10.3, all of the compressibility coefficients for the pure liquid and solid metals, at or near the normal melting temperatures, are obtained (see Tables 10.2 and 10.3).

Table 10.3 Coefficients of pure solid metals at various temperatures

Metal	T/K	$10^6\alpha_S$/K^{-1}	$10^6\beta_S$/bar^{-1} (Literature)	T/K	$10^6\alpha_S$/K^{-1}	$10^6\beta_S$/bar^{-1} (Calculated)
Cd	300	31.5	2.048	500	38.4	2.497
Pb	300	28.8	2.415	600	34.4	2.890
Sn	300	22.2	1.909	500	27.5	2.365

10.6 Example-Calculation of the Cd-Pb Phase Diagram at High Pressure [Zhou *et al.*, 1990]

10.6.1 The treatment of thermodynamic quantities

10.6.1.1 The treatment of $\Delta\mu^0_{i(\mathrm{S\to L})}$ and KT_i

Since

$$\frac{x_{i\mathrm{L}}\gamma_{i\mathrm{L}}(T,p_0,x_{i\mathrm{L}})}{x_{i\mathrm{S}_j}x_{i\mathrm{S}_j}(T,p_0,x_{i\mathrm{S}_j})} = K_i \quad (i=1,2; j=1,2) \tag{10-6}$$

$$K_i = KT_i \times KTp_i = \exp\left(-\frac{\mu^0_{i\mathrm{L}}(T,p_0) - \mu^0_{i\mathrm{S}_j}(T,p_0)}{RT}\right)$$
$$\times \exp\left\{-\frac{1}{RT}\int_{p_0}^{p}[\bar{V}_{i\mathrm{L}}(T,p,x_{i\mathrm{L}}) - \bar{V}_{i\mathrm{S}_j}(T,p,x_{i\mathrm{S}_j})]\mathrm{d}p\right\}$$

$$\Delta\mu^0_{i,(\mathrm{S\to L})} = \Delta H^0_{im(\mathrm{S\to L})} + \int_{T_m}^{T}\Delta C_{p_i(\mathrm{S\to L})}\mathrm{d}T + T\left[\Delta S^0_{im(\mathrm{S\to L})} + \int_{T_{im}}^{T}\frac{\Delta C_{p(\mathrm{S\to L})}}{T}\mathrm{d}T\right] \tag{10-9}$$

$$\Delta C_{p_i(\mathrm{S\to L})} = \Delta a_i + \Delta b_i T \tag{10-10}$$

By substituting all the known thermodynamic quantities into eq.(10-28), we obtain

$$KT_{\mathrm{Cd}} = \exp\left(-4.4537 - 7.3119 \times 10^{-4}T - \frac{473.974}{T} + 0.8902 \ln T\right)$$

$$KT_{\mathrm{Pb}} = \exp\left(-5.5429 - 7.0961 \times 10^{-4}T - \frac{235.928}{T} + 0.9944 \ln T\right)$$

Table 10.4 Thermodynamic quantities of the pure components①

Metal	T_m/K	ΔH_m^0/J·mol^{-1}	ΔS_m^0/J·mol^{-1}·K^{-1}	ΔC_p/J·mol^{-1}·K^{-1}
Cd	594.18	6192.32	10.4265	$7.4015 - 12.1587 \times 10^{-3}T$
Pb	600.6	4799.05	7.9914	$8.2676 - 11.799 \times 10^{-3}T$
Sn	505.06	7029.12	13.916	$13.09510 - 27.36 \times 10^{-3}T$

① Hultgren *et al.*, 1977; Barin *et al.*, 1977; Brandes, 1983.

10.6.1.2 The activity coefficients of the components, $\gamma_{ij}(T, p_0, x_{ij})$

1. The activity coefficients of components in the liquid phase, $\gamma_{i\mathrm{L}}(T, p_0, x_{i\mathrm{L}})$

Z. Moser *et al.* [Moser *et al.*, 1975] obtained the expressions for the excess partial, free enthalpies and the excess partial enthalpies of the components at 760K for the Cd-Pb-Sn ternary system. From their expressions, it is now easy to derive the corresponding expressions for the Cd-Pb binary system ($x_2 = x_{\mathrm{Pb}}$).

$$\begin{aligned}
\mu^E_{\mathrm{Cd(760K)}} =& 17826.8x_{2\mathrm{L}}^2 - 30152.0x_{2\mathrm{L}}^3 + 33555.7x_{2\mathrm{L}}^4 - 13705.1x_{2\mathrm{L}}^5 \quad (\mathrm{J \cdot mol^{-1}}) \\
\mu^E_{\mathrm{Pd(760K)}} =& 10509.8 - 35653.52x_{2\mathrm{L}} + 63054.6x_{2\mathrm{L}}^2 - 74892.8x_{2\mathrm{L}}^3 \\
& + 50687.1x_{2\mathrm{L}}^4 - 13705.1x_{2\mathrm{L}}^4 \quad (\mathrm{J \cdot mol^{-1}}) \\
h^E_{\mathrm{Cd(760K)}} =& 24904.4x_{2\mathrm{L}}^2 - 29926.9x_{2\mathrm{L}}^3 + 15499.2x_{2\mathrm{L}}^4 \quad (\mathrm{J \cdot mol^{-1}}) \\
h^E_{\mathrm{Pd(760K)}} =& 15107.2 - 49808.8x_{2\mathrm{L}} + 69794.6x_{2\mathrm{L}}^2 \\
& - 50592.1x_{2\mathrm{L}}^3 + 15499.2x_{2\mathrm{L}}^4 \quad (\mathrm{J \cdot mol^{-1}})
\end{aligned}$$

From above equations, the following equation is obtained

$$RT \ln \gamma_{i,l} = \frac{T}{760}\mu^E_{i(760)} + \left(1 - \frac{T}{760}\right) h^E_i$$

Thus, we can now obtain the expressions for all of $\gamma_{i\mathrm{L}}(T, p_0, x_{i\mathrm{L}})$, for the components, Cd and Pb, in the liquid metals solution.

2. The activity coefficients of the components in the solid phases, $\gamma_{i\mathrm{S}_j}$

Based on thermodynamic principles, if all of the thermodynamic quantities of the pure components, and the binary phase diagram, are known, the $\gamma_{i\mathrm{S}_j}$ or the interaction parameters for the terminal solid solutions, can now be derived from the known value of $\gamma_{i\mathrm{L}}$ for the liquid solution.

For the Pb-rich, terminal solid solution, and since the solid solution region is very "narrow", the regular solution model may be used to represent the excess molar Gibbs free energy for this solid solution:

$$G_{12}^E = \alpha_{12} x_1 x_2 \tag{10-38}$$

By means of the regression, we obtain

$$\alpha_{12} = \alpha_{\mathrm{Cd-Pb}} = 14100\mathrm{J} \cdot \mathrm{mol}^{-1}$$

Since Pb does not dissolve appreciably in liquid Cd, the Cd-rich terminal solution may be considered to act as pure Cd.

10.6.1.3 The volume terms

1. The molar volumes for the liquid solutions

We now list the values of the thermodynamic parameters for Cd and Pb, in both the pure solid and liquid states [Brandes, 1983; Gorden, 1968; Marcus, 1977].

Table 10.5 Molar volumes of the pure metals

Metal	T_m/K	$V_\mathrm{L}^0(T_m, p_0)/\mathrm{cm}^3\cdot\mathrm{mol}^{-1}$	$V_\mathrm{S}^0(T_m, p_0)/\mathrm{cm}^3\cdot\mathrm{mol}^{-1}$
Cd(1)	594	14.02	13.4
Pb(2)	601	19.55	18.9

From the reported discrete values of ΔV_L for Cd-Pb liquid alloys at 350°C (T_0), and atmospheric pressure p_0, the expression for $\Delta V_\mathrm{L}(T_0)$ is thus obtained

$$\begin{aligned}\Delta V_\mathrm{L}(T_0) =& 0.03586 x_{2\mathrm{L}} - 0.04939 x_{2\mathrm{L}}^2 + 0.01854 x_{2\mathrm{L}}^3 \\ & - 0.006619 x_{2\mathrm{L}}^4 + 0.001932 x_{2\mathrm{L}}^5 - 0.0003148 x_{2\mathrm{L}}^6\end{aligned}$$

$$V_\mathrm{L}^E(T, p, x_{i\mathrm{L}}) = \Delta V_\mathrm{L}(T_0, p_0, x_{i\mathrm{L}}) \sum x_{i\mathrm{L}} V_{i\mathrm{L}}^0(T, p)$$

$$V_{i\mathrm{L}}^0(T, p) = V_{i\mathrm{L}}^0(T_m, p_0) \exp[\alpha_{i\mathrm{L}}(T - T_m) - \beta_{i\mathrm{L}}(p - p_0)]$$

From known values of $V_{i\mathrm{L}}^0(T_m, p_0)$, α_L and β_L($\alpha_\mathrm{L}, \beta_\mathrm{L}$ as listed in Tables 10.1 and 10.2), and the expression for $\Delta V_\mathrm{L}(T_0)$, the expression for $V_\mathrm{L}^E(T, p, x_{i\mathrm{L}})$ may be obtained.

Through the equations

$$\bar{V}_{i\mathrm{L}}^E = V_\mathrm{L}^E + (1 - x_{i\mathrm{L}}) \frac{\partial V_\mathrm{L}^E}{\partial x_{i\mathrm{L}}} \qquad (i = 1, 2) \tag{10-39}$$

$$\bar{V}_{i\mathrm{L}}(T, p, x_{i\mathrm{L}}) = V_{i\mathrm{L}}^0(T, p) + \bar{V}_{i\mathrm{L}}^E(T, p, x_{i\mathrm{L}}) \tag{10-40}$$

$\bar{V}_{i\mathrm{L}}^E$ may be calculated.

2. Partial molar volume of the i-th component in the solid phase, $\bar{V}_{i\mathrm{S}_j}(T, p, x_{i\mathrm{S}_j})$

According to the experimental values for the Cd-Pb system [Pearson, 1967], the lattice constant for the Pb-rich solid solution, S_2, is

$$a_{\mathrm{S}_2}(T, p, x_{1\mathrm{S}_2}) = a^0_{\mathrm{PbS}}(T, p)(1 - 0.0049726x_{1\mathrm{S}_2})$$

Since the solid solution is of the cubic structure type

$$V_{\mathrm{S}_2}(T, p, x_{1\mathrm{S}_2}) = V^0_{\mathrm{PbS}}(T, p)(1 - 0.49726x_{1\mathrm{S}_2})^3 \quad (10\text{-}41)$$

$$V^0_{\mathrm{PbS}}(T, p) = V^0_{\mathrm{PbS}}(T_m, p_0)\exp[\alpha_{\mathrm{PbS}}(T - T_m) - \beta_{\mathrm{PbS}}(p - p_0)]$$

The values of α_{S} and β_{S} for Pb are listed in Tables 10.1 and 10.2, and therefore, V_{S_2} can be obtained. $\bar{V}_{i\mathrm{S}_2}$, can then be calculated by

$$\bar{V}_{i\mathrm{S}_2} = V_{\mathrm{S}_2} + (1 - x_{i\mathrm{S}_2})\frac{\partial V_{\mathrm{S}_2}}{\partial x_{i\mathrm{S}_2}} \qquad (i = 1, 2) \quad (10\text{-}42)$$

The solid phase S_1 is pure Cd,

$$V_{\mathrm{S}_1} = V^0_{\mathrm{CdS}}(T, p) = V^0_{\mathrm{CdS}}(T_m, p_0)\exp[\alpha_{\mathrm{CdS}}(T - T_m) - \beta_{\mathrm{CdS}}(p - p_0)] \quad (10\text{-}43)$$

So

$$\bar{V}_{1\mathrm{S}_1} = V^0_{\mathrm{CdS}}(T, p) \quad (10\text{-}44)$$

All of the thermodynamic parameters have thus been determined, so, the equilibrium values for $x_{i\mathrm{L}}$ and $x_{i\mathrm{S}_j}$ $(i = 1, 2;\ j = 1, 2)$ at a series of temperatures and for a given high pressure, can be calculated, and thence the Cd-Pb phase diagram, adjusted to a given high pressure, is thereby obtained.

10.6.2 Calculated results and discussions

10.6.2.1 The effect of pressure on eutectic events

At atmospheric pressure, the Cd-Pb binary alloy system is a simple eutectic system [Massalski *et al.*, 1990], the eutectic point being located at 72 at% Pb and 248°C. Over the pressure range, 0 to 4GPa, this binary system remains as a simple eutectic one. [Clark *et al.*, 1987]

The dependence of the eutectic temperature on pressure is shown in Fig.10.2. The dashed line is that measured by Clark [Clark *et al.*, 1980], while the solid line is that calculated by us [Zhou *et al.*, 1988]. These results are in reasonable conformity with each other. As shown in Fig. 10.2, the eutectic temperature for this system rises "monotonously" with increasing pressure. This calculated result was verified by experiments. For Cd-Sn system at high pressures, there is similar phenomenon.

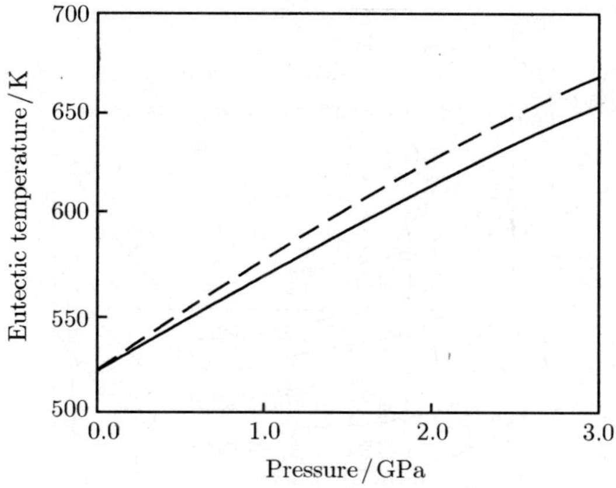

Fig. 10.2 The dependence of eutectic temperature on pressure for Cd-Pb system. Dashed line is from Clark [Clark *et al.*, 1980]. Solid line is our calculated result [Zhou *et al.*, 1988].

From Fig. 10.3, it may be seen that the actual eutectic composition shifts to decreasingly lower concentrations of lead, with the increasing pressure. This result is in agreement with the "revised" experimental results, presented by Clark *et al.* [Clark *et al.*, 1987]. Their original result(s) [Clark *et al.*, 1980] that the eutectic composition remains constant, may not be correct.

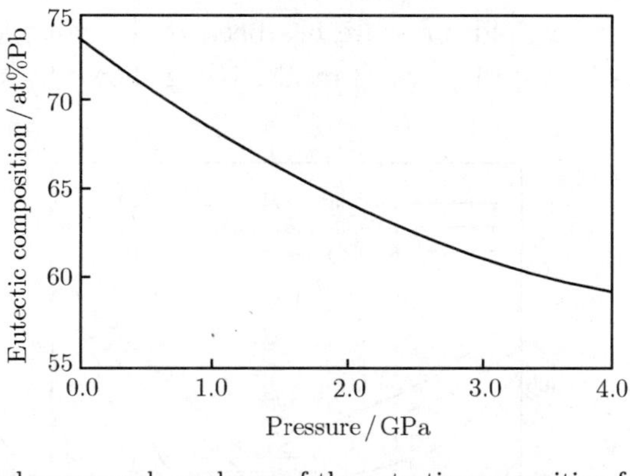

Fig. 10.3 Calculated pressure dependence of the eutectic composition for the Cd-Pb system [Zhou *et al.*, 1990].

10.6.2.2 Comparison of the calculated and experimental phase diagrams

Clark *et al.* determined the Cd-Pb binary phase diagrams under high pressure conditions [Clark *et al.*, 1980], and later, they calculated the theoretical phase diagram by the thermodynamic method. Based on the calculated results, the authors proposed experimental reinvestigation of the system, subsequently revising their own original published data.

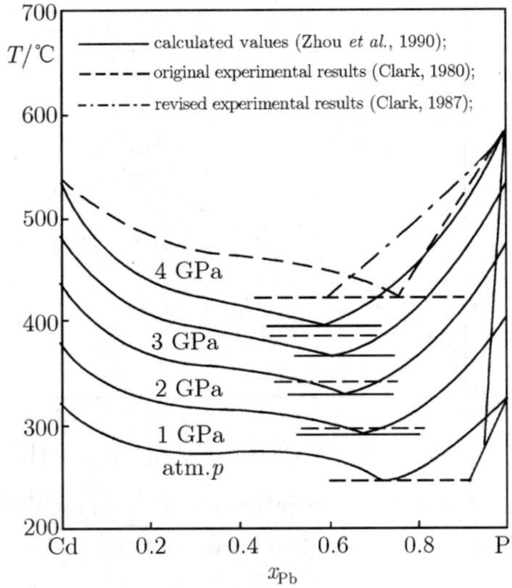

Fig. 10.4 Phase diagrams of the Cd-Pb system up to 4 Gpa.

The "revised" experimental and calculated results by Clark *et al.* agreed better with each other after revision. But, in Clark's calculations, it was assumed that the volume changes in the Cd and Pb at the melting point were independent of both pressure and temperature. This assumption is not considered to be acceptable.

The Cd-Pb system at high pressure has been recalculated with the use of reasonable assumptions by us, the revised results being shown by the solid lines in Fig 10.5.

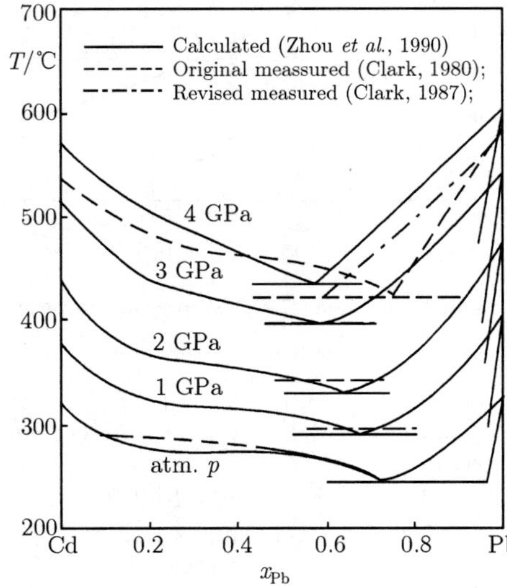

Fig. 10.5 The calculated effect of pressure on the liquidus temperatures in the Cd-Pb system, by Clark *et al.* [Clark *et al.*, 1987] and ours [Zhou *et al.*, 1990].

The original experiments by Clark *et al.* [Clark *et al.*, 1980] showed that the eutectic composition did not shift with pressure. The revised experiments [Clark, 1987] and Clark's recalculations [Clark, 1987] found this shift, *i.e.* the eutectic composition moves to a higher cadmium concentration.

Our calculated eutectic positions are 73.2 at% Pb, 249.3°C under atmospheric pressure, and 59.4 at%Pb, 399.7°C at 4GPa. These values now agree well with the revised experimental values of 72 at% Pb at normal pressure, and 60 at% Pb at 4 GPa [Clark, 1987], but they differ greatly from the original measured value of 72 at% Pb at 4 GPa [Clark, 1980].

Moreover, our calculated results indicate a pressure-induced change in the shape of the liquidus curve for the Cd-Pb system. Fig. 10.5 shows this variation graphically. The calculated variation in the liquidus shape could be useful for predicting and testing the experimental phase diagram.

(1) For the Cd-Pb system, the phase diagram at normal pressure and those at various higher pressures, are similar in form, all of them are of the simple eutectic type. Only the eutectic composition and the eutectic temperature change with the pressure to some extent, the liquidus curve shape also varies with the pressure.

(2) E. Yu. Tonkov [Tonkov, 1998] pointed out that there is strong correlation between the isobaric temperature-composition phase diagram at normal pressure, and those pitched at various higher pressures, thus, the isobaric phase diagram provides useful input information to the study of materials synthesis at high pressures.

Overall, our experimental results support the viewpoint advocated by Tonkov.

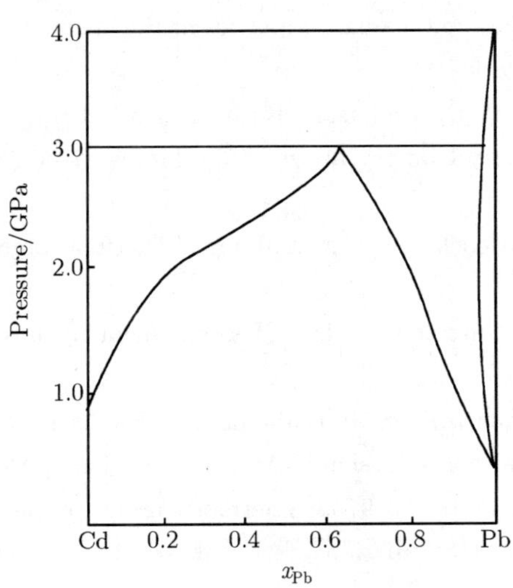

Fig. 10.6 Calculated *p*-*x* phase diagram of Cd-Pb system at 641.8K.

10.6.2.3 p-x phase diagram of the Cd-Pb system at a given temperature

We have also calculated a series of *p-x* phase diagrams of the Cd-Pb system at various temperatures. A typical result is shown in Fig. 10.6 [Zhou *et al.*, 1990]. It is, at the very least, an interesting phase diagram.

References-10

S. Blair. 1978. Predicting the compressibility of liquid metals. J. Inorg. Nucl. Chem., 40(6): 971-974

E. A. Brandes. 1998. Smithells metals reference book, 7th ed. London: Butterworth & Co., Ltd.

J. B. Clark, B. Metcalfe, R. A. Oaccy, P. W. Richter. 1980. High pressure study of Cd-Sn binary system. J. Less-Common Metals, 71: 33-45

J. B. Clark, P. W. Ricther. 1980. The determination of composition-temperature-pressure phase diagram of binary alloy systems. High Pressure Sci. Tech. Proc., 7th Int. AIRAPT Conference, 1: 363-371

J. B. Clark, M. E. Thomas, P. W. Ricther. 1987. Binary alloy system at high pressure. J. Less-Common Metals, 132: 181-194

S. P. Clark. 1966. Handbook of Physical Constants. New York: The Geological Soc. of Amer. Inc.

D. E. Gray. 1972. American Institute of Physics Handbook. 3rd ed. New York: McGraw-Hill

R. Hultgren, P. D. Desai, D. T. Hawkings, M. Gleiser, K. K. Kelley, D. D. Wagman. 1973. Selected Values of thermodynamic properties of the elements. Cleveland: Amer. Soc. for Metals, Metals Park

R. Hultgren, R. L. Orr, P. D. Anderson, K. K. Kelley. 1973. Selected values of thermodynamic properties of binary alloys. Cleveland: Amer. Soc. for Metals, Metals Park

O. Kubaschewski, C. B. Alcock. 1979. Metallurgical thermochemistry. 5th ed. New York: Pergamon Press

O. Kubaschewski, J. A. Catterall. 1956. Thermochemical data of alloys. New York: Pergamon Press

T. B. Massalski, H. Okamoto, P. R. Subramanian, L. Kacpzak. 1990. Binary alloy phase diagrams. 3 Vols, 2nd Ed. Cleveland: ASM International, Metals Park

Z. Moser, L. Zabdyr, A. Pelton. 1975. Thermodynamic properties of liquid Cd-Pb-Sn solution and analytical calculation of the phase diagram. Canadian Metallurgical Quarterly, 14(3): 257-264

Muyu Zhao, Ping Xiao, Hongye Kang. 1987. The principles of calculation of high pressure multicomponent phase diagrams. High Temperatures-High Pressures, 19: 513-518

Weiya Zhou, Zhongyi Shen, Yun Zhang, Muyu Zhao. 1988. The determination of high-pressure vertical sections of Cd-Pb-Sn ternary system. High Temperatures-High Pressures, 20: 561

Weiya Zhou, Lizhu Song, Fengqing Wu, Muyu Zhao. 1992. Optimization of thermodynamic properties and calculation of phase diagrams for the Cd-Sn system at high pressure. High Temperatures-High Pressures, 24: 511-518

Weiya Zhou, Lizhu Song, Muyu Zhao. 1990. Calculation of high-pressure phase diagrams of binary system. J. Less-Common Metals, 160: 237-245

Chapter 11

The Calculation of High-Pressure Ternary Phase Diagrams

11.1 The Characteristics of the Boundaries of the High-Pressure Ternary Phase Diagrams, and the Basic Equations for Their Calculation

The calculation of high-pressure, ternary phase diagrams is a more complicated process than that required for binary systems. Many investigators, especially geologists, have tried to calculate these phase diagrams theoretically. In geology, the calculated results on high-pressure phase equilibrium of multicomponent systems, usually of oxide systems are expressed, in most cases, in p-T and T-x_i diagrams. In our studies, we have tried to calculate the high-pressure, multicomponent phase diagrams for alloy systems. Additionally, the principles of our calculation method can be applied to other systems.

In order to calculate the boundaries of ternary phase diagrams at high pressures, the characteristics of boundaries between the NPRs of these phase diagrams will initially be discussed.

11.1.1 The characteristics of the boundaries between NPRs of high-pressure ternary phase diagrams

In the high-pressure ternary phase diagram, the number of components, $N = 3$, p =const, so the dimensions of the phase diagram $R = N + 1 = 4$, and thus it is a spatial phase diagram of four dimensions. In order to represent it within a two-dimensional plane, two of the variables have to become fixed. Usually, the pressure is initially fixed, and then the vertical section at a fixed composition of one component or, the horizontal section at a given temperature, can be depicted.

Since the pressure and the mole fraction of one component, or its pressure and temperature, are kept constant, the dimensions of the phase boundaries and the boundaries of the sections, $(R_1)_s$ and $(R_1')_s$ are two dimensions less than the dimensions of the phase boundaries, and the boundaries for the $(N + 1)$ dimensional spatial phase diagram, R_1 an R_1'.

$$(R_1)_s = R_1 - 2 = (N - \Phi + 2) - 2 = N - \Phi = 3 - \Phi \qquad (11\text{-}1)$$

$$(R_1')_s = R_1' - 2 \qquad (11\text{-}1')$$

If all of the phase boundaries and the boundaries in the sections satisfy the above two equations, these sections are titled "regular", otherwise, they are "irregular". For ternary systems at high pressures, there is one type of irregular phase boundaries or boundaries, which satisfy

$$(R_1)_s = R_1 - 1, \quad (R_1')_s = R_1' - 1$$

and have to be dealt with separately. However, most phase boundaries and the boundaries of the irregular sections still satisfy eq. (11-1) and eq. (11-1').

The characteristics of the boundaries for regular sections will now be discussed.

11.1.1.1 If $(R_1)_s = (R_1')_s$, this boundary is not only a boundary consisting of system points, it also acts as a phase boundary.

This kind of boundary will be known as the boundary of the first type, for example, lines fg, hi, bd, be, aj, ak, cl, cm in the isothermal section (Fig.11.1), and lines ab, bc in the vertical section (Fig.11.2). In both of these cases, the characteristics of the neighboring phase regions (NPRs) around these boundaries are $\Phi = 2, \phi_C = 1$, and

$$(R_1)_s = R_1 - 2 = (N - \Phi + 2) - 2 = (3 - 2 + 2) - 2 = 1 \qquad (11\text{-}2)$$

$$(R_1')_s = R_1' - 2 = (R_1 + \phi_C - 1) - 2 = (3 + 1 - 1) - 2 = 1 \qquad (11\text{-}2')$$

These lines are both the boundaries and the phase boundaries of the NPRs, and consist of sets of equilibrium phase points.

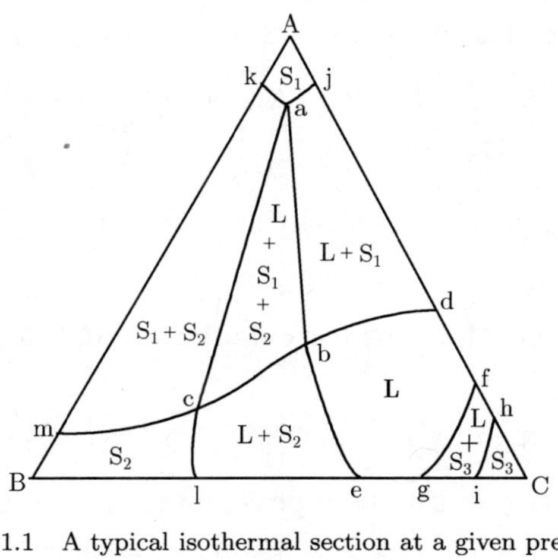

Fig. 11.1 A typical isothermal section at a given pressure.

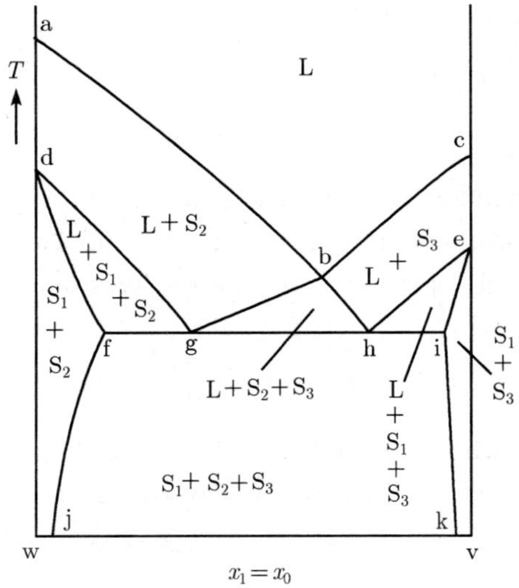

Fig. 11.2 A typical vertical section at a given composition.

11.1.1.2 If $(R_1)_s \neq (R_1')_s$ then these boundaries are boundaries only and are not phase boundaries.

These boundaries consist of sets of system points only and may be called the boundary of the second type; for example, lines ab, bc, and ca in Fig.11.1 and lines jf, fd, dg, gb, bh, he, ei and ik in Fig.11.2. In these cases, $\Phi = 3, \phi_C = 2$ and

$$(R_1)_\mathrm{s} = R_1 - 2 = (N - \Phi + 2) - 2 = (3 - 3 + 2) - 2 = 0 \tag{11-3}$$

$$(R_1')_\mathrm{s} = R_1' - 2 = (R_1 + \phi_C - 1) - 2 = (2 + 2 - 1) - 2 = 1 \tag{11-3$'$}$$

For lines ab, bc and ca, in Fig. 11.1, they are the tie-lines for the phase points. For lines jf, fd *etc*, in Fig.11.2 these will be discussed later.

For line fghi in Fig.11.2, $\Phi = 4, \phi_C = 2$, and

$$(R_1)_\mathrm{s} = R_1 - 2 = (N - \Phi + 2) - 2 = -1 \tag{11-4}$$

$$(R_1')_\mathrm{s} = R_1' - 2 = (R_1 + \phi_C) - 2 = 1 \tag{11-4$'$}$$

Therefore, lines fg, gh and hi act only as boundaries and they consist of sets of system points only.

11.1.2 The basic equations for the calculation of different kinds of boundaries

11.1.2.1 The calculation of phase boundaries (or the boundaries of the first type)

In the vertical section of a ternary phase diagram at a given elevated pressure p, only the boundary with $\Phi = 2$ belongs to the boundary of the first type. For example, lines ab and bc in Fig.11.2 are phase boundaries of the common phase L, of the two NPRs L/L+S_j ($j = 2, 3$). Let us first calculate the line ab (L/L+S_2). For a given temperature T and pressure p, when L and S_2 exist in equilibrium with each other, this gives rise to

$$\mu_{i,\mathrm{L}}(T,p,x_{i,\mathrm{L}}) = \mu_{i,\mathrm{S}_2}(T,p,x_{i,\mathrm{S}_2}) \quad (i=1,2,3) \tag{11-5}$$

$\mu_{i,\mathrm{L}}(T,p,x_{i,\mathrm{L}})$ is written as follows:

$$\begin{aligned}\mu_{i,\mathrm{L}}(T,p,x_{i,\mathrm{L}}) =& \mu^0_{i,\mathrm{L}}(T,p_0) + RT\ln x_{i,\mathrm{L}}\gamma_{i,\mathrm{L}}(T,p_0,x_{i,\mathrm{L}}) \\ &+ \int_{p_0}^{p} \bar{V}_{i,\mathrm{L}}(T,p_0,x_{i,\mathrm{L}})\mathrm{d}p\end{aligned} \tag{11-6}$$

and similarly

$$\begin{aligned}\mu_{i,\mathrm{S}_2}(T,p,x_{i,\mathrm{S}_2}) =& \mu^0_{i,\mathrm{S}}(T,p_0) + RT\ln x_{i,\mathrm{S}_2}\gamma_{i,\mathrm{S}_2}(T,p_0,x_{i,\mathrm{S}_2}) \\ &+ \int_{p_0}^{p} \bar{V}_{i,\mathrm{S}_2}(T,p_0,x_{i,\mathrm{S}_2})\mathrm{d}p\end{aligned} \tag{11-7}$$

Where $\mu^0_{i,\mathrm{L}}$ and $\mu^0_{i,\mathrm{S}}$ denote the standard chemical potentials of the i-th component in the pure liquid phase, L, and the pure solid phase, S, at T and p_0, respectively, $\gamma_{i,\mathrm{L}}(T,p_0,x_{i,\mathrm{L}})$ and $\gamma_{i,\mathrm{S}_2}(T,p_0,x_{i,\mathrm{S}_2})$ represent the activity coefficients of the i-th component in the liquid phase, L, and the solid phase, S_2, under the given conditions, respectively.

From eqs. (11-5). (11-6) and (11-7), we obtain

$$\begin{aligned}&RT\ln\frac{x_{i,\mathrm{L}}\gamma_{i,\mathrm{L}}(T,p_0,x_{i,\mathrm{L}})}{x_{i,\mathrm{S}_2}\gamma_{i,\mathrm{S}_2}(T,p_0,x_{i,\mathrm{S}_2})} \\ &=\mu^0_{i,\mathrm{S}} - \mu^0_{i,\mathrm{L}} + \int_{p_0}^{p}[\bar{V}_{i,\mathrm{S}_2}(T,p,x_{i,\mathrm{S}_2}) - \bar{V}_{i,\mathrm{L}}(T,p,x_{i,\mathrm{L}})]dp \\ &\frac{x_{i,\mathrm{L}}\gamma_{i,\mathrm{L}}(T,p_0,x_{i,\mathrm{L}})}{x_{i,\mathrm{S}_2}\gamma_{i,\mathrm{S}_2}(T,p_0,x_{i,\mathrm{S}_2})} = K_i = \exp\left(-\frac{\mu^0_{i,\mathrm{L}} - \mu^0_{i,\mathrm{S}}}{RT}\right) \\ &\times\exp\left\{\frac{1}{RT}\int_{p_0}^{p}[\bar{V}_{i,\mathrm{S}_2}(T,p,x_{i,\mathrm{S}_2}) - \bar{V}_{i,\mathrm{L}}(T,p,x_{i,\mathrm{L}})]dp\right\}\end{aligned} \tag{11-8}$$

Let

$$KT_i(T,p_0) = \exp\left(-\frac{\mu^0_{i,\mathrm{L}} - \mu^0_{i,\mathrm{S}}}{RT}\right) \tag{11-9}$$

$$VTp_i(T,p,x_{i,\mathrm{L}},x_{i,\mathrm{S}_2}) = \exp\left\{\frac{1}{RT}\int_{p_0}^{p}[\bar{V}_{i,\mathrm{S}_2}(T,p,x_{i,\mathrm{S}_2}) - \bar{V}_{i,\mathrm{L}}(T,p,x_{i,\mathrm{L}})]dp\right\} \tag{11-10}$$

$$KT_i(T,p_0)\times VTp_i(T,p,x_{i,\mathrm{L}},x_{i,\mathrm{S}_2}) = K_i \tag{11-11}$$

K_i is not a constant, it is a function of T, p and compositions, R is the gas constant. Since the phase points coincide with the system points on line ab, *i.e.* $x_{1,\text{L}} = x_1 = x_0$, $x_{2,\text{L}} = 1 - x_{3,\text{L}} - x_0$, only the mole fraction of one component in the liquid phase is an independent variable. In the solid solution phase, S_2, there exists $x_{1,\text{S}_2} = 1 - x_{2,\text{S}_2} - x_{3,\text{S}_2}$, therefore, for equilibrium between phases L and S_2, there are only three independent variables, selected as $x_{3,\text{L}}, x_{2,\text{S}_2}$ and x_{3,S_2}. Thus, one solves the three equations in eq. (11-8), the phase point compositions of the equilibrium phases (L and S_2) at given temperatures and pressures, are worked out. Following the calculation of a series of such phase point compositions at a series of temperatures and the same pressure, the phase boundary line, ab, may be depicted. The phase boundary line be is calculated in a similar fashion.

11.1.2.2 The calculation of the boundaries only (or the boundaries of the second type)

In Fig. 11.2, lines jf, fd, dg, gb, bh, he, ei and ik belong to the second type of boundaries. As an example, the line dg, between NPRs (L+S_2) and ($\text{L+S}_1\text{+S}_2$) is considered. On the boundary between NPRs (L+S_2)/($\text{L+S}_1\text{+S}_2$), there are two common phases L and S_2. When L, S_1 and S_2 phases coexist in equilibrium, one has

$$\frac{x_{i,\text{L}}\gamma_{i,\text{L}}(T, p_0, x_{i,\text{L}})}{x_{i,\text{S}_j}\gamma_{i,\text{S}_j}(T, p_0, x_{i,\text{S}_j})} = K_i \quad (i = 1, 2, 3; j = 1, 2) \tag{11-12}$$

Since the phase points do not coincide with the system points in these cases, $x_{1\text{L}}$ is a variable. We take, for example, $x_{1,\text{L}}$, $x_{2,\text{L}}$, x_{1,S_1}, x_{2,S_1}, x_{1,S_2} and x_{2,S_2} as the independent variables. One solves the six equations in eq. (11-12), phase equilibrium compositions, $x_{i,\text{L}}$ and x_{i,S_j} can be calculated.

According to the law of the centre of gravity, all of the components distribute almost completely over the common phases (L, S_2), when the system exists on the boundary line, dg. By the mass conservation law, the following equations will hold:

$$x_\text{L}x_{1,\text{L}} + (1 - x_\text{L})x_{1,\text{S}_2} = x_1 = x_0 \tag{11-13}$$

$$x_\text{L}x_{3,\text{L}} + (1 - x_L)x_{3,\text{S}_2} = x_3 \tag{11-14}$$

$$x_2 = 1 - x_0 - x_3 \tag{11-15}$$

$$x_\text{L} = \frac{N_\text{L}}{N} \tag{11-16}$$

x_L is the molar fraction of the liquid phase L, in the system, N_L and N are the mole number of liquid phase L, and the total mole number of the system, respectively. $(1 - x_\text{L})$ is the molar fraction of the solid phase, S_2, in the system. The phase compositions, $x_{i,\text{L}}, x_{i,\text{S}_2}$, are calculated via eqs. (11-12), x_i is the system point compositions, and can be calculated by eqs. (11-13), (11-14) and (11-15). After a series of system points at different temperatures are calculated, the boundary line, dg, can be calculated. The other lines jf, fd, gb, bh, he, ei and ik may all be calculated in a similar fashion. The points, f, g, h and i may be determined by the intersection of the boundary lines.

Thus, all points and lines, as shown in Fig. 11.2, can be calculated, and the whole T-x_i vertical section at a given pressure is depicted.

The p-x_i vertical section of a ternary system at a given temperature can be calculated in a similar way.

For the horizontal section shown in Fig. 11.1, the calculation is easier, since lines mc, cl, be, bd. gf, hi, ak and aj are phase boundary lines or the boundary lines of the first type. By calculating the boundaries of two-phase regions, these lines may be depicted. Points a, b and c are determined by the intersection of the corresponding phase lines.

In fact, for an N (more than three) component system, with the molar fractions of the $(N-2)$ components maintained constant, the T-x_i vertical section at a given pressure, or the p-x_i vertical section at a given temperature, can be calculated, while maintaining the molar fractions of $(N-3)$ components constant, the horizontal sections, at a given temperature and pressure, can be depicted. In calculating a series of T-x_i phase diagrams at various pressures, or a series of p-x_i phase diagrams at different temperatures, the p-T-x_i spatial phase diagram can thence be constructed.

11.2 The Treatment of Thermodynamic Parameters for Ternary Systems at High Pressure

From eq. (11-8) in section 11.1, it can be seen that the calculation of high-pressure phase diagrams for ternary systems requires the following thermodynamic parameters: $\mu^0_{i,\mathrm{L}}$, $\mu^0_{i,\mathrm{S}}$, $\gamma_{i,j}$ and $\bar{V}_{i,j}(j = \mathrm{L}, \mathrm{S}_2)$. Previously, in Chapter 10, the treatment for these parameters of binary systems has been discussed. $\mu^0_{i,\mathrm{S}}(T, p_0), \mu^0_{i,\mathrm{L}}(T, p_0)$ can be calculated from the thermodynamic parameters for the pure substance, this has been fully discussed in Chapter 10 and is therefore omitted here. $\gamma_{i,j}$, $\bar{V}_{i,j}$ are related to the ternary systems, we will discuss them in this section.

Much less data is known of the thermodynamic properties for ternary systems than that for binary systems. Thus, it is a difficult job to assemble the thermodynamic properties data for the ternary systems. To obtain the data, one usually applies one of the following two methods.

1. If there are discrete values for the thermodynamic properties of a given ternary system, one can regress them through an analytical equation or an equation based on some physical model.

2. One can evaluate the thermodynamic quantities for the ternary system from those of the corresponding binary systems. The second method is applied more frequently, it is therefore now described in more detail.

The thermodynamic properties for the ternary system are evaluated by multiplying those for the corresponding binary systems by some weighting factors and then making a summation of them. There are two types of methods available for choosing the weighting factors.

(1) Symmetrical methods: when the three components of the ternary system are similar in all characteristics, all of the thermodynamic properties of the three binary systems are multiplied by the weighting factors of the same form. These methods include:

a) Kohler's method [Kohler, 1960]

$$G_m^E = \sum (x_1 + x_2) G_{12}^E \left(\frac{x_1}{x_1 + x_2}, \frac{x_2}{x_1 + x_2} \right)$$

and

b) Colinet's method [Colinet, 1967]

$$G_m^E = \sum \left[\frac{\frac{x_2}{2}}{1 - x_1} G_{12}^E (x_1, 1 - x_1) + \frac{\frac{x_1}{2}}{1 - x_2} G_{12}^E (1 - x_2, x_2) \right]$$

c) Muggianu's method [Muggianu, 1975]

$$G_m^E = \sum \frac{x_1 x_2}{\omega_{12} \omega_{21}} G_{12}^E (\omega_{12}, \omega_{21})$$

$$\omega_{12} = \frac{1 + x_1 - x_2}{2}$$

$$\omega_{21} = \frac{1 + x_2 - x_1}{2}$$

$$\omega_{12} + \omega_{21} = 1$$

the summation is the summing up of the values for the three binary systems, G_m^E is the excess molar thermodynamic property for the ternary system, G_{12}^E, G_{23}^E, and G_{31}^E are those for the three binary systems.

(2) Asymmetrical methods: if the weighting factors of the different binary systems are different, these methods are called asymmetrical. For example, if the ternary system's second and third components have similar characteristics, but the first is different, this system is described as asymmetrical and can thus be treated by different asymmetrical methods, for example:

a) Toop's method [Toop, 1965]

$$\begin{aligned} G_m^E =& \frac{x_2}{1-x_1} G_{12}^E(x_1, 1-x_1) + \frac{x_3}{1-x_1} G_{13}^E(x_1, 1-x_1) \\ &+ (x_2+x_3)^2 G_{23}^E \left(\frac{x_2}{x_2+x_3}, \frac{x_3}{x_2+x_3} \right) \end{aligned}$$

or

b) Hillert's method [Hillert, 1980]

$$G_m^E = \frac{x_2}{1-x_1} G_{12}^E(x_1, 1-x_1) + \frac{x_3}{1-x_1} G_{13}^E(x_1, 1-x_1) + \frac{x_2 x_3}{\omega_{23}\omega_{32}} G_{23}^E(\omega_{23}, \omega_{32})$$

$$\omega_{23} = \frac{1+x_2-x_3}{2}$$

$$\omega_{32} = \frac{1+x_3-x_2}{2}$$

$$\omega_{23} + \omega_{32} = 1$$

2 and 3 represent two similar components and 1 represents the other component.

K.C. Chou worked out a new general model for predicting thermodynamic properties of a multicomponent system from binaries [Chou, 1997]. That model is more complicated and therefore it is not mentioned further here.

Since

$$\mu_{i,j}^E(T, p_0, x_{i,j}) = RT \ln \gamma_{i,j}(T, p_0, x_{i,j})$$

$$\mu_{i,j}(T, p_0, x_{i,j}) = \mu_i^0(T, p_0) + RT \ln x_{i,j}\gamma_{i,j}(T, p_0, x_{i,j})$$

The treatment of $\gamma_{i,j}(T, p_0, x_{i,j})$ and $\mu_{i,j}^E(T, p_0, x_{i,j})$ for the ternary system are the same as the treatment for the phase diagram at atmospheric pressure. There are a lot of works dealing with this problem, and therefore we will discuss only the treatment in the example (see subsection 11.4).

We have discussed the molar volume, the excess molar volume, the partial molar volume and partial excess molar volume for binary systems. If the values of the excess molar volumes of the three binary systems are known and no compound is formed in the ternary systems, the value of the excess molar volume V_m^E for a ternary system may be evaluated from those for binary systems. If the system is an asymmetric one, Hillert's asymmetric method may be used, *i.e.*

$$V_m^E = \frac{x_2}{1-x_1} V_{12}^E(x_1, 1-x_1) + \frac{x_3}{1-x_1} V_{13}^E(x_1, 1-x_1) + \frac{x_2 x_3}{\omega_{23}\omega_{32}} V_{23}^E(\omega_{23}, \omega_{32})$$

$$\omega_{23} = \frac{1+x_2-x_3}{2}$$

$$\omega_{32} = \frac{1+x_3-x_2}{2}$$

$$\omega_{23} + \omega_{32} = 1$$

V_{12}^E, V_{13}^E and V_{23}^E are the excess molar volumes for the three binary systems, V_m^E is the excess molar volume for the ternary system.

Since

$$\bar{V}_i^E = V_m^E + \frac{\partial V_m^E}{\partial x_i} - \sum_{j=1}^{3} x_j \frac{\partial V_m^E}{\partial x_j}, \quad (i = 1,2,3)$$

$$\bar{V}_i = V_i^0 + \bar{V}_i^E, \quad (i = 1,2,3) \tag{11-17}$$

Partial molar volume of the i-th component $(i = 1,2,3)$ in the ternary system $\bar{V}_i(T, p_0, \chi_i)$ can be evaluated from the values of V_{ij}^E for the three binary systems.

11.3 Verification of the Estimation Method for the Excess Molar Volume by Experiment

Molar volumes play an important role in the calculation of multicomponent phase diagrams at high pressures. There is few experimental data for the molar volumes of ternary alloy solution phases, so we have to estimate the values of molar volumes for ternary phases from the data for binary phases. The validity of this estimation method has to be tested experimentally. Thus, we have determined the molar volumes of ternary solid phases and investigated systematically the variations of the molar volumes of these phases with composition. The lead-based α-phase solid solutions in the Pb-Sn-Cd and Pb-Sn-Bi ternary systems are taken as examples [Liu *et al.*, 1990].

Homogeneous, single-phase alloy samples were prepared from accurately weighed amounts of metals of 99.999wt% purity. The lattice parameters of the samples were determined by X-ray diffraction. The crystal structure of the lead-based α-phase solid solution is of the f.c.c. type, so the molar volume, V_x is

$$V_x = \frac{N_0}{N} v_x = \frac{N_0}{N} a_x^3 \tag{11-18}$$

where the unit cell volume is $v_x = a_x^3$, the number of atoms per unit cell N is 4 for the f.c.c. structure and Avgadro's number $N_0 = 6.023 \times 10^{23}\text{mol}^{-1}$, α_x(cm) and V_x (cm^3) are the lattice parameter and molar volume of the solid solution phase, respectively.

$$V_x = V^0 + V_x^E = \sum x_i V_i^0 + V_x^E, \quad (i = 1,2,3) \tag{11-19}$$

$$V_x^E = V_x - \sum x_i V_i^0 \tag{11-20}$$

V_x is an experimental value determined by x-ray diffraction, V_x^E is obtained through eq. (11-20).

The excess molar volume, V_h^E of the Pb-Sn-Cd or Pb-Sn-Bi solid solution phase, is calculated from the $V_{i,j}^E$ for the binary solution phases of Pb-Sn, Pb-Bi, Pb-Cd, Sn-Cd, or Sn-Bi binary systems by the Hillert's asymmetric method. The values of V_x^E (experimental) and V_h^E (calculated by Hillert's method) are compared in Tables 11.1 and 11.2.

Table 11.1 The compositions, molar volumes and excess molar volumes of the Pb-Sn-Cd system ($T = 20.0°C$)

x_{Pb}	x_{Sn}	$V_x/cm^3 \cdot mol^{-1}$	$V_x^E/cm^3 \cdot mol^{-1}$	$V_h^E/cm^3 \cdot mol^{-1}$
0.9910	0.0000	18.2387	0.0209	
0.9890	0.0000	18.2276	0.0255	
0.9500	0.0460	18.1657	0.0176	0.0181
0.9600	0.0360	18.1854	0.0168	0.0165
0.9700	0.0260	18.1970	0.0155	0.0150
0.9800	0.0160	18.2127	0.0136	0.0134
0.9900	0.0060	18.2305	0.0111	0.0119
0.9500	0.0410	18.1607	0.0299	0.0308
0.9600	0.0310	18.1701	0.0296	0.0293
0.9800	0.0110	18.2134	0.0253	0.0262
0.9900	0.0010	18.2208	0.0213	0.0248
0.9400	0.0510	18.1411	0.0289	0.0323
0.9300	0.0607	18.1130	0.0273	0.0346
0.9600	0.0267	18.1781	0.0400	0.0403
0.9800	0.0133	18.2202	0.0200	0.0203

Table 11.2 Compositions, molar volumes and excess molar volumes of the Pb-Sn-Bi system ($R = 20.0°C$)

x_{Pb}	x_{Sn}	$V_x/cm^3 \cdot mol^{-1}$	$V_x^E/cm^3 \cdot mol^{-1}$	$V_h^E/cm^3 \cdot mol^{-1}$
0.9500	0.0250	18.2352	–0.0399	–0.0389
0.9000	0.0333	18.2766	–0.1127	–0.1085
0.8500	0.0188	18.3803	–0.2305	–0.2218
0.9000	0.0125	18.3372	–0.1545	–0.1484
0.9500	0.0063	18.3033	–0.0805	–0.0744
0.9300	0.0175	18.2861	–0.0912	–0.0874
0.9500	0.0438	18.1733	–0.0039	–0.0036
0.9750	0.0125	18.2425	–0.0212	–0.0195
0.9500	0.0450	18.1866	–0.0017	–0.0013
0.9500	0.0350	18.2225	–0.0201	–0.0200
0.9500	0.0250	18.2451	–0.0399	–0.0389
0.9500	0.0150	18.2806	–0.0610	–0.0578
0.9850	0.0075	18.2565	–0.0131	–0.0117
0.9650	0.0175	18.2495	–0.0288	–0.0273
0.9400	0.0300	18.2456	–0.0473	–0.0465
0.9300	0.0350	18.2513	–0.0548	–0.0542
0.9650	0.0044	18.2882	–0.0575	–0.0521
0.9200	0.0400	18.2344	–0.0627	–0.0618
0.9200	0.0100	18.3311	–0.1252	–0.1188
0.8800	0.0150	18.3659	–0.1842	–0.1778
0.9000	0.0063	18.3639	–0.1673	–0.1604

From Tables 11.1 and 11.2, a comparison between V_x^E and V_h^E indicates that the differences between them occur only in the 3rd and 4th decimal places for most samples. This means that the calculated values V_h^E are quite consistent with the experimental data V_x^E. Thus, our method for the estimation of excess molar volumes for ternary systems is reliable.

11.4 The Calculation of High-Pressure Phase Diagrams of Cd-Pb-Sn and Cd-Sn-Zn Systems

Here, only the calculation of the Cd-Pb-Sn system is discussed in detail.

The basic equations for $L/(L+S_2)$ phase equilibrium of the ternary system at high pressure are

$$\begin{aligned}&\frac{x_{i,\mathrm{L}}\gamma_{i,\mathrm{L}}(T,p_0,x_{i,\mathrm{L}})}{x_{i,\mathrm{S}_2}\gamma_{i,\mathrm{S}_2}(T,p_0,x_{i,\mathrm{S}_2})}\\&=\exp\left(-\frac{\mu_{i,\mathrm{L}}^0-\mu_{i,\mathrm{S}}^0}{RT}\right)\times\exp\left\{\frac{1}{RT}\int_{p_0}^{p}[\bar{V}_{i,\mathrm{S}_2}(T,p,x_{i,\mathrm{S}_2})-\bar{V}_{i,\mathrm{L}}(T,p,x_{i,\mathrm{L}})]\mathrm{d}p\right\}\\&=KT_i(T,p_0)\times VTp_i(T,p,x_{i,\mathrm{L}},x_{i,\mathrm{S}_2})=K_i\quad(i=1,2,3)\end{aligned}$$

11.4.1 Calculation of $KT_i(T,p_0)=\exp\left(-\frac{\mu_{i,\mathrm{L}}^0-\mu_{i,\mathrm{S}}^0}{RT}\right)$

The following equations have been discussed in Chapter 10.

$$\begin{aligned}\mu_{i,\mathrm{L}}^0-\mu_{i,\mathrm{S}}^0=&\Delta H_{i,m(\mathrm{S}\to\mathrm{L})}^0+\int_{T_m}^{T}\Delta C_{p,i(\mathrm{S}\to\mathrm{L})}dT\\&+T\left[\Delta S_{i,m(\mathrm{S}\to\mathrm{L})}^0+\int_{T_m}^{T}\frac{\Delta C_{p,i(\mathrm{S}\to\mathrm{L})}}{T}dT\right]\end{aligned}\qquad(11\text{-}21)$$

$$\Delta C_{p,i(\mathrm{S}\to\mathrm{L})}=\Delta a_i+\Delta b_i T\qquad(11\text{-}22)$$

$$KT_i=\exp\left(-\frac{\mu_{i,\mathrm{L}}^0-\mu_{i,\mathrm{S}}^0}{RT}\right)=\exp\left(A+BT+\frac{C}{T}+D\ln T\right)$$

From the known values (these values are the values at the melting point) of the thermodynamic properties (T_m, ΔH_m, ΔS_m) [Hultgren *et al.*, 1973] and ΔC_p [Barin, 1977; Brandes, 1983] of the pure elements: Cd, Pb and Sn (see Table 11.3) we obtain

Table 11.3 Thermodynamic data of pure elements

element	T_m/K	$\Delta H_m/\mathrm{J\cdot mol^{-1}}$	$\Delta S_m/\mathrm{J\cdot mol^{-1}\cdot K^{-1}}$	$\Delta C_p/\mathrm{J\cdot mol^{-1}\cdot K^{-1}}$
Cd	594.18	6192.32	10.4265	$7.4015\text{-}12.1587\times10^{-3}T$
Pb	600.6	4799.05	7.9914	$8.2676\text{-}11.799\times10^{-3}T$
Sn	505.06	7029.12	13.916	$13.09510\text{-}27.36\times10^{-3}T$

the coefficients A, B, C and D, in the expressions of the functions, $KT_i(T, p_0)$, see Table 11.4.

Table 11.4 Coefficients of the expression of KT_i

element	A	B	C	D
Cd	–4.4537	-7.3119×10^{-4}	–473.974	0.8902
Pb	–5.5429	-7.0961×10^{-4}	–235.928	0.9944
Sn	–8.0436	-1.6453×10^{-3}	–469.603	1.5751

11.4.2 The activity coefficients $\gamma_{i,j}(T, p_0, x_{i,j})$ of the i-th component in the equilibrium phases

11.4.2.1 The activity coefficient $\gamma_{i,j}(T, p_0, x_{i,j})$ (i=1, 2, 3) of the i-th component in the liquid phase

The expressions of the excess partial molar Gibbs free energy, μ_i^E and the partial molar enthalpy of mixing, Δh_i at 760K for the Cd-Pb-Sn ternary system, were calculated from the experimental emf data by Z. Moser *et al.* [Moser *et al.*, 1975]. Let $x_{i,\mathrm{L}}$ be the molar fraction of the i-th component in the liquid phase [i=1(Cd), 2(Pb), 3(Sn)], $y = 1 - x_{i,\mathrm{L}}$ and $t = \dfrac{x_{3,\mathrm{L}}}{x_{2,\mathrm{L}} + x_{3,\mathrm{L}}}$. The unit of g_i^E and Δh is J·mol^{-1}.

$$
\begin{aligned}
\mu^E_{\mathrm{Cd}(760\mathrm{K})} =&(17826.8 - 20562.7t + 10678.4t^2 - 2293.7t^3)y^2\\
&+ (-30152.0 + 25586.0t - 902.5t^2)y^3\\
&+ (33555.7 - 27908.1t)y^4 + (13705.1 + 11864.2t)y^5\\
\mu^E_{\mathrm{Pb}(760\mathrm{K})} =&5305.3t^{1.9} + (-35653.5 + 20562.7t - 2293.7t^3)(y - 1)\\
&+ (63054.6 - 46148.7t + 11129.9t^2 - 2293.7t^3)(y^2 - 1)\\
&+ (-74892.8 + 53494.1t - 902.5t^2)(y^3 - 1)\\
&+ (50687.1 - 39772.3t)(y^4 - 1) + (-13705.1 + 11864.2t)(y^5 - 1)\\
\mu^E_{\mathrm{Sn}(760\mathrm{K})} =&5305.3(t^{1.9} - 2.111t^{0.9} + 1.111)\\
&+ (-15090.9 - 794.1t + 6881.0t^2 - 2293.7t^3)(y - 1)\\
&+ (50261.6 - 45246.2t + 11129.9t^2 - 2293.7t^3)(y^2 - 1)\\
&+ (-66590.1 + 53494.1t - 902.5t^2)(y^3 - 1)\\
&+ (47721.0 - 39772.3t)(y^4 - 1) + (13705.1 + 11864.2t)(y^5 - 1)\\
\Delta h_{\mathrm{Cd}} =&(24904.4 - 33680.4t + 18159.8t^2)y^2\\
&+ (-29926.9 + 56108.3t - 22755.5t^2)y^3\\
&+ (15499.2 - 37143.0t + 14275.0t^2)y^4\\
\Delta h_{\mathrm{Pb}} =&5305.3t^{1.9} + (-49808.8 + 33680.4t)(y - 1)
\end{aligned}
$$

$$
\begin{aligned}
&+ (69796.6 - 89788.6t + 29537.4t^2)(y^2 - 1)\\
&+ (-55092.1 + 93251.3t - 32272.0t^2)(y^3 - 1)\\
&+ (15499.2 - 37143.0t + 14275.0t^2)(y^4 - 1)\\
\Delta h_{\mathrm{Sn}} =& 5305.3(t^{1.9} - 2.111t^{0.9} + 1.111)\\
&+ (-16128.5 - 2639.3t)(y - 1)\\
&+ (41740.4 - 67033.1t + 29537.4t^2)(y^2 - 1)\\
&+ (-38210.8 + 83734.4t - 32272.0t^2)(y^3 - 1)\\
&+ (15499.2 - 37143.0t + 14275.0t^2)(y^4 - 1)
\end{aligned}
$$

Applying the Gibbs-Helmholtz equation and assuming that Δh_i is independent of temperature T, we obtain:

$$RT \ln \gamma_{i\mathrm{L}}(T, p_0, x_{i\mathrm{L}}) = \frac{T}{760}\mu^E_{i\mathrm{L}(760\mathrm{K})} + \left(1 - \frac{T}{760}\right)\Delta h_i$$

11.4.2.2 The activity coefficient γ_{i,S_j} of the i-th component in solid phase S_j

Since the values of $\gamma_{i,\mathrm{L}}[i = 1(\mathrm{Cd}), 2(\mathrm{Pb}), 3(\mathrm{Sn})]$ have been calculated, the interaction parameters of binary solid phases can be regressed from the data of experimental phase diagrams of Cd-Pb, Cd-Sn binary systems and the thermodynamic properties of the three pure components.

For the Pb-rich solid solution in the Cd-Pb system, the Sn-rich solid solution in the Cd-Sn system and the Sn-rich solid solution in the Pb-Sn system, since the solubility of the solute in the solid phase are small, the regular solution model can be used to represent the excess molar Gibbs free energy.

$$G^E_{\mathrm{AB}} = \alpha_{\mathrm{AB}} x_{\mathrm{A,S}_j} x_{\mathrm{B,S}_j}$$

Where α_{AB} is the interaction parameter for the A-B binary solid solution S_j.

For the Pb-rich solid solution in the Pb-Sn system, and since the solubility of Sn in the solid solution is large, the sub-regular solution model is applied:

$$G^E_{\mathrm{Pb-Sn}} = x_{\mathrm{Pb,S_2}} x_{\mathrm{Sn,S_2}}[q_0 + q_1(x_{\mathrm{Pb,S_2}} - x_{\mathrm{Sn,S_2}}) + q_2(x_{\mathrm{Pb,S_2}} - x_{\mathrm{Sn,S_2}})^2]$$

q_1, q_2 and q_0 are the adjustable coefficients.

Since the solubility of Pb and Sn in the Cd solid solution is very small, the Cd-rich solid phases are considered as composed of pure solid Cd.

By regression, the interaction parameters for the binary solid phases are as follows: for the Sn-rich solid solution,

$$\alpha_{\mathrm{Sn-Cd}} = 11500\ \mathrm{J{\cdot}mol^{-1}}$$

$$\alpha_{\text{Sn-Pb}} = 14000 \text{ J}\cdot\text{mol}^{-1}$$

For the Pb-rich solid solution,

$$\begin{aligned}\alpha_{\text{Pb-Cd}} =& 14100 \text{ J}\cdot\text{mol}^{-1}\\ \alpha_{\text{Pb-Sn}} =& 8981.96 - 5150.76(x_{\text{Pb,S}_2} - x_{\text{Sn,S}_2})\\ &+ 2601.6(x_{\text{Pb,S}_2} - x_{\text{Sn,S}_2})^2 \text{ J}\cdot\text{mol}^{-1}\end{aligned}$$

By applying Hillert's asymmetric method (see eq. (11-13)) and using the following equations for ternary systems:

$$\mu_i^E = G^E + \frac{\partial G^E}{\partial x_i} - \sum_{k=1}^{3} x_k \frac{\partial G^E}{\partial x_k} \tag{11-23}$$

$$\mu_i^E = RT \ln \gamma_{i\text{S}_j} \tag{11-24}$$

The activity coefficient of the i-th component in the Cd-Pb-Sn ternary system is gotten.

For the Pb-rich solid solution S_2:

$$\begin{aligned}\gamma_{\text{Cd,S}_2} =& \exp\{(RT)^{-1}[\alpha_{\text{Pb-Cd}} x_{\text{Pb,S}_2}^2 + \alpha_{\text{Sn-Cd}} x_{\text{Sn,S}_2}^2\\ &+ (\alpha_{\text{Pb-Cd}} + \alpha_{\text{Sn-Cd}} - \alpha_{\text{Pb-Sn}}) x_{\text{Pb,S}_2} x_{\text{Sn,S}_2}\\ &+ x_{\text{Pb,S}_2} x_{\text{Sn,S}_2} (x_{\text{Sn,S}_2} - x_{\text{Pb,S}_2}) Q]\}\\ \gamma_{\text{Pb,S}_2} =& \exp\{(RT)^{-1}[\alpha_{\text{Pb-Cd}} x_{\text{Cd,S}_2}^2 + \alpha_{\text{Pb-Sn}} x_{\text{Sn,S}_2}^2\\ &+ (\alpha_{\text{pb-Cd}} + \alpha_{\text{Pb-Sn}} - \alpha_{\text{Sn-Cd}}) x_{\text{Cd,S}_2} x_{\text{Sn,S}_2}\\ &+ x_{\text{Pb,S}_2} x_{\text{Sn,S}_2} (x_{\text{Sn,S}_2} - x_{\text{Pb,S}_2} + 1) Q]\}\\ \gamma_{\text{Sn,S}_2} =& \exp\{(RT)^{-1}[\alpha_{\text{Sn-Cd}} x_{\text{Cd,S}_2}^2 + \alpha_{\text{Pb-Sn}} x_{\text{Pb,S}_2}^2\\ &+ (\alpha_{\text{Sn-Cd}} + \alpha_{\text{Pb-Sn}} - \alpha_{\text{Pb-Cd}}) x_{\text{Cd,S}_2} x_{\text{Pb,S}_2}\\ &+ x_{\text{Pb,S}_2} x_{\text{Sn,S}_2} (x_{\text{Sn,S}_2} - x_{\text{Pb,S}_2} - 1) Q]\}\end{aligned}$$

$$Q = \frac{\partial \alpha_{\text{Pb-Sn}}}{\partial x_{\text{Pb,S}_2}}.$$

While for the Sn-rich solid solution S_3:

$$\begin{aligned}\gamma_{\text{Cd,S}_3} =& \exp\{(RT)^{-1}[\alpha_{\text{Pb-Cd}} x_{\text{Pb,S}_3}^2 + \alpha_{\text{Sn-Cd}} x_{\text{Sn,S}_3}^2\\ &+ (\alpha_{\text{Pb-Cd}} + \alpha_{\text{Sn-Cd}} - \alpha_{\text{Pb-Sn}}) x_{\text{Pb,S}_3} x_{\text{Sn,S}_3}]\}\\ \gamma_{\text{Pb,S}_3} =& \exp\{(RT)^{-1}[\alpha_{\text{Pb-Cd}} x_{\text{Cd,S}_3}^2 + \alpha_{\text{Pb-Sn}} x_{\text{Sn,S}_3}^2\\ &+ (\alpha_{\text{Pb-Cd}} + \alpha_{\text{Pb-Sn}} - \alpha_{\text{Sn-Cd}}) x_{\text{Cd,S}_3} x_{\text{Sn,S}_3}]\}\\ \gamma_{\text{Sn,S}_3} =& \exp\{(RT)^{-1}[\alpha_{\text{Sn-Cd}} x_{\text{Cd,S}_3}^2 + \alpha_{\text{Pb-Sn}} x_{\text{Pb,S}_3}^2\\ &+ (\alpha_{\text{Sn-Cd}} + \alpha_{\text{Pb-Sn}} - \alpha_{\text{Pb-Cd}}) x_{\text{Cd,S}_3} x_{\text{Pb,S}_3}]\}\end{aligned}$$

11.4.3 The partial molar volumes for the Cd-Pb-Sn ternary systems

11.4.3.1 The partial molar volume of the i-th component in the liquid phase for the ternary system

In the preceding Chapter 10, the partial molar volumes for binary liquid phases have been discussed.

$$\bar{V}_{i\mathrm{L}}(T,p,x_{i,\mathrm{L}}) = V_{i\mathrm{L}}^{0}(T,p) + \bar{V}_{i\mathrm{L}}^{E}(T,p,x_{i\mathrm{L}}) \tag{11-25}$$

$$V_{i\mathrm{L}}^{0}(T,p) = V_{i\mathrm{L}}^{0}(T_m,p_0)\exp[\alpha_{i\mathrm{L}}(T-T_m) - \beta_{i\mathrm{L}}(p-p_0)] \tag{11-26}$$

Assume (see subsection 10.6.1):

$$\begin{aligned}\Delta V_T(T,p,x_{i\mathrm{L}}) =& \Delta V_T(T_0,p_0,x_{i\mathrm{L}}) \\ =& \frac{V_L(T_0,p_0,x_{i,\mathrm{L}}) - \sum\limits_i x_{i\mathrm{L}}V_{i\mathrm{L}}^{0}(T_0,p_0)}{\sum\limits_i x_{i\mathrm{L}}V_{i\mathrm{L}}^{0}(T_0,p_0)} \\ =& \sum_j d_j x_i^j \qquad (i=1,2)\end{aligned} \tag{11-27}$$

Then

$$\begin{aligned}V_{\mathrm{L}}^{E}(T,p,x_{i,\mathrm{L}}) =& \Delta V_T(T_0,p_0,x_{i,\mathrm{L}})\sum_i x_{i,\mathrm{L}}V_{i,\mathrm{L}}^{0}(T,p) \\ =& \left(\sum_j d_j x_{i\mathrm{L}}^j\right)\left\{\sum_i x_{i,\mathrm{L}}V_{i\mathrm{L}}^{0}(T_m,p_0)\exp[\alpha_{i\mathrm{L}}(T-T_m)-\beta_{i\mathrm{L}}(p-p_0)]\right\} \\ & (i=1,2)\end{aligned} \tag{11-28}$$

All of the symbols have been mentioned. The values of atomic mass, M_i [Hultgren, 1973], the density $D_{i,\mathrm{L}}(T_m, p_0)$ [Brandes, 1983] or molar volume $V_{i,\mathrm{L}}^{0}(T_m,p_0)$ [Gordon, 1968; Marcus, 1977] of the i-th pure liquid metal at atmospheric pressure, p_0 and melting point, T_m are listed in Table 11.5.

Table 11.5 Molar volume of the pure liquid metal

Metal	M/g·mol^{-1}	T_m/K	$D_\mathrm{L}(T_m,p_0)$/g·cm^{-3}	$V_\mathrm{L}^0(T_m,p_0)$/cm^3·mol^{-1}
Cd(1)	112.40	594	8.02	14.02
Pb(2)	207.19	601	10.68	19.55
Sn(3)	118.69	505	7.00	16.95

The values of $\alpha_{i\mathrm{L}}$ and $\beta_{i\mathrm{L}}$ for liquid metals Cd, Pb and Sn have been mentioned in subsection 10.6 of Chapter 10.

From the experimental values of molar volumes of Cd-Pb liquid alloys at atmospheric pressure p_0, and 350°C [Crawley, 1973] and the discrete values of ΔV_T for Cd-Sn liquid alloys at atmospheric pressure and 575K [Kubaschewski *et al.*, 1956], the coefficient d_j in eq.(11-27) may be regressed, and these are listed in Table 11.6.

Table 11.6 Coefficient d_j in eq. (11-27)

d_j	Cd-Pb(x)	Cd(x)-Sn
d_1	0.03586	0.14529
d_2	–0.04939	–0.35859
d_3	0.01854	–0.31347
d_4	–0.006619	3.27272
d_5	0.001932	–6.57769
d_6	–0.0003148	5.61795
d_7		–1.78621

According to the reference [Kubaschewski *et al.*, 1956], the value of ΔV_T for Pb-Sn system is very small. So, $V_{\rm L}^E$ for this system can be neglected.

After the expressions of $V_{i,j}^E$ for the three binary systems are obtained, the excess molar volume for the Cd-Pb-Sn system, V_m^E, can be derived by Hillert's method:

$$V_m^E = \frac{x_2}{1-x_1} V_{12}^E(x_1, 1-x_1) + \frac{x_3}{1-x_1} V_{13}^E(x_1, 1-x_1) + \frac{x_2 x_3}{\omega_{23}\omega_{32}} V_{23}^E(\omega_{23}, \omega_{32}) \quad (11\text{-}29)$$

$$\omega_{23} = \frac{1 + x_2 - x_3}{2}$$

$$\omega_{32} = \frac{1 + x_3 - x_2}{2}$$

V_m^E, the excess molar volume for the Cd-Pb-Sn ternary system: V_{12}^E, V_{13}^E and V_{23}^E represent the excess molar volumes for the Cd-Pb, Cd-Sn and Pb-Sn binary systems respectively.

The partial excess molar volume $\bar{V}_i^E$ for the i-th component in the Cd-Pb-Sn system may be deduced by means of:

$$\bar{V}_i^E = V_m^E + \frac{\partial V_m^E}{\partial x_i} - \sum_{j=1}^{3} x_j \frac{\partial V_m^E}{\partial x_j} \quad (11\text{-}30)$$

Eqs.(11-29) and (11-30) are valid for both the liquid and solid ternary phases of the Cd-Pb-Sn system.

Substituting eqs.(11-26) and (11-30) into eq. (11-25), the expression $\bar{V}_{i\rm L}(T, p, x_{i\rm L})$ for the partial molar volume of the i-th component in the ternary liquid phase is obtained.

11.4.3.2 The partial molar volume $\bar{V}_{i\mathrm{S}}(T,p,x_{i\mathrm{S}})$ of the i-th component in the solid phase for the ternary system.

Because of the lack of data on the molar volumes of solid phases in the Cd-Pb-Sn system, these data were evaluated from those data for the binary system.

The Pb-rich solid solutions of the Pb-Cd and Pb-Sn systems are of the f.c.c. structure; their molar volumes (cm^3) are represented as:

$$V_{\mathrm{Pb-Cd,S_2}}(T,p,x_{\mathrm{Cd,S_2}}) = V^0_{\mathrm{Pb,S}}(T,p)(1-0.049726x_{\mathrm{Cd,S_2}})^3$$

$$V_{\mathrm{Pb-Sn,S_2}}(T,p,x_{\mathrm{Sn,S_2}}) = V^0_{\mathrm{Pb,S}}(T,p)(1-0.0288x_{\mathrm{Sn,S_2}})^3$$

The structures of Sn-rich, solid solutions of Sn-Cd and Sn-Pb systems are of tetragonal, the molar volumes (cm^3) are:

$$V_{\mathrm{Sn-Cd,S_3}}(T,p,x_{\mathrm{Cd,S_3}}) = V^0_{\mathrm{Sn,S}}(T,p)(1-0.0378x_{\mathrm{Cd,S_3}})^2.(1-0.0221x_{\mathrm{Cd,S_3}})$$

$$V_{\mathrm{Sn-Pb,S_3}}(T,p,x_{\mathrm{Cd,S_3}}) = V^0_{\mathrm{Sn,S}}(T,p)(1+0.0732x_{\mathrm{Pb,S_3}})^2.(1+0.0643x_{\mathrm{Pb,S_3}})$$

$$V^0_{i\mathrm{S}}(T,p) = V^0_{i\mathrm{S}}(T_m,p_0)\exp[\alpha_{i,\mathrm{S}}(T-T_m)-\beta_{i,\mathrm{S}}(p-p_0)] \quad (i=1,2,3)$$

The values of $\alpha_{i\mathrm{S}}$ and $\beta_{i\mathrm{S}}$ [i=1(Cd), 2(Pb), 3(Sn)] have been discussed in subsection 10.6 of Chapter 10. The values $V^0_{i\mathrm{S}}(T_m,p_0)$ [Gordon, 1968] are listed in Table 11.7.

Table 11.7 Molar volume of pure solid metals at their normal melting temperatures

Metal	Cd	Pb	Sn
$V^0_{\mathrm{S}}(T_m,p_0)/\mathrm{cm}^3\cdot\mathrm{mol}^{-1}$	13.4	18.9	16.5

From the above quantities or expressions, the $V^E_{ij}(T,p)(i,j=1,2,3;i\neq j)$ for the binary solid solutions can be calculated; $V^E(T,p)$ for the ternary solid solutions S_j ($j=2,3$; S_1 is pure Cadmium) is calculated, using Hillert's equation (11-29), while $\bar{V}^E_{i,\mathrm{S}_j}(T,p,x_{i\mathrm{S}_j})$ is obtained with eq.(11-30). Substituting the obtained expressions into

$$\bar{V}_{i\mathrm{S}_j}(T,p,x_{i\mathrm{S}_j}) = V^0_{i\mathrm{S}}(T,p)+\bar{V}^E_{i\mathrm{S}_j}(T,p,x_{i\mathrm{S}_j})$$

the expression for the partial molar volume $\bar{V}_{i\mathrm{S}_j}$ is obtained.

Now, all values or expressions of the thermodynamic properties in eq. (11-8) have been calculated. By means of the principles presented in subsection 11.1, we can now calculate both the boundaries of the first and second types. Therefore, the high-pressure vertical and horizontal sections of the high-pressurephase diagrams of the Cd-Pb-Sn system can be obtained.

The vertical sections of the ternary system at high pressure are also similar to those at atmospheric pressure in the form, which has been mentioned in section 10.6 of Chapter 10.

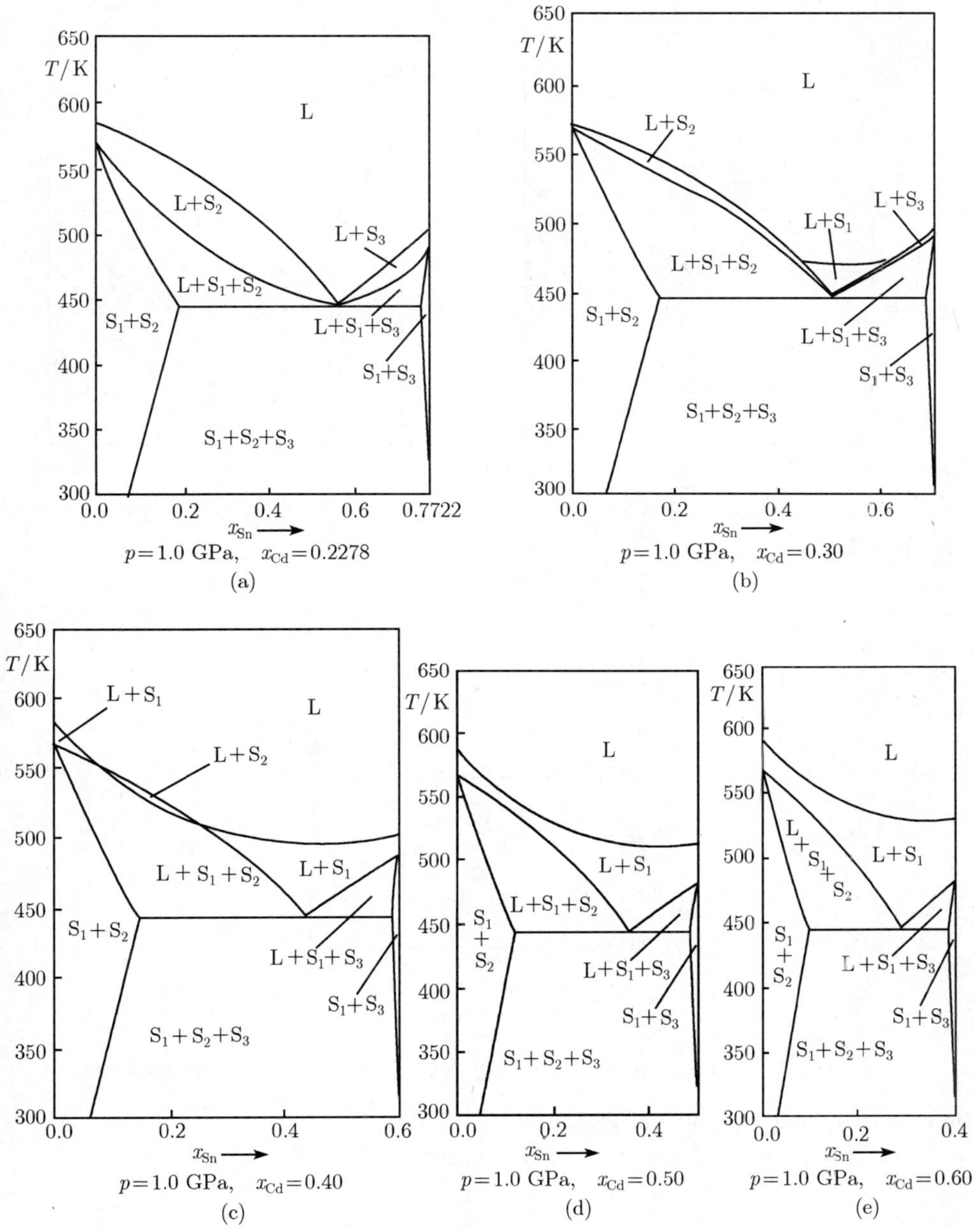

Fig. 11.3 Vertical sections of the Cd-Pb-Sn system at p = 1.0 GPa.

In comparing the vertical sections of the ternary system at the same composition, it can be seen that the increase of pressure results in an increase of the melting temperatures of the solid alloys, and in the ternary eutectic temperature of the system.

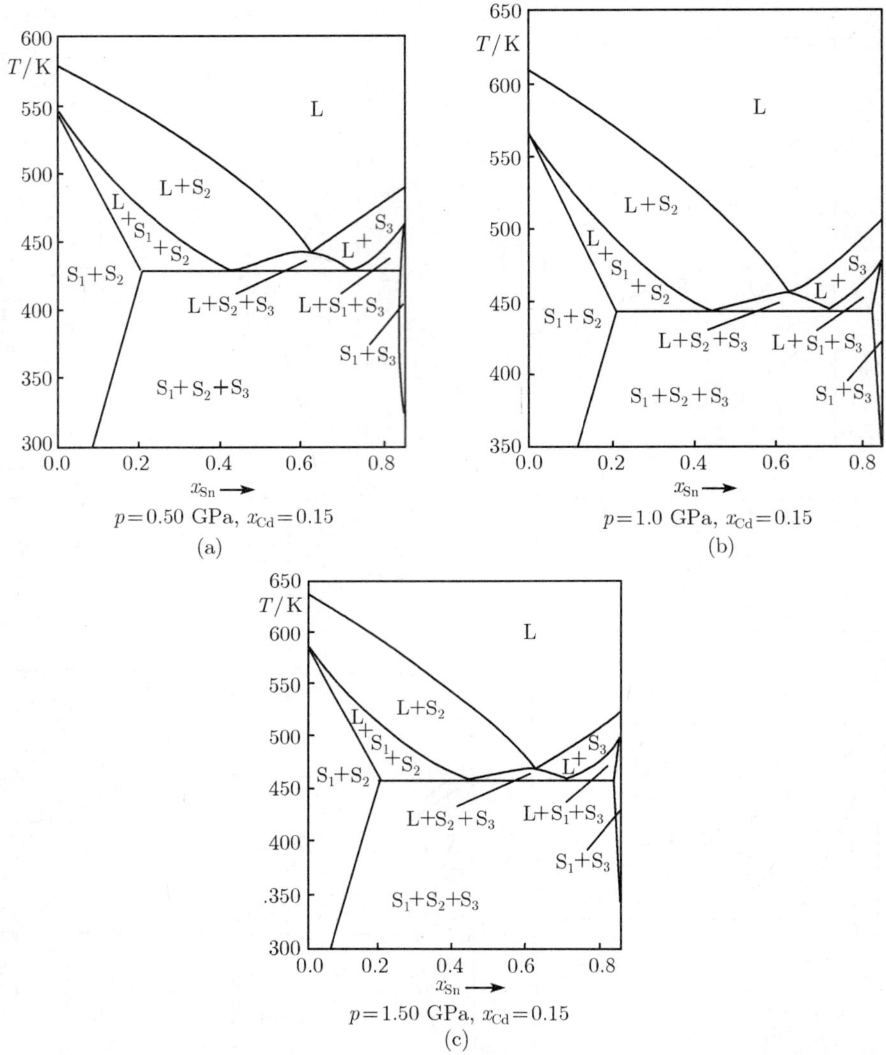

Fig. 11.4 Vertical sections of Cd-Pb-Sn system $x_{\mathrm{Cd}} = 0.15$, at different pressures.

Since for the multicomponent system,

$$\frac{dT}{dp} = \frac{\Delta \bar{V}}{\Delta \bar{S}}$$

$\Delta \bar{V}$ and $\Delta \bar{S}$ are the change in molar volume and the molar entropy of the alloy, from the solid state to the liquid state at equilibrium, respectively. For most alloys, $\Delta \bar{V} > 0$ and $\Delta \bar{S} > 0$, so $\dfrac{dT}{dp} > 0$.

From Fig.11.5 (a)~(e), it may be seen that temperature increases, the phase region L becomes larger. These phenomena are similar to the phase diagrams at atmospheric pressure.

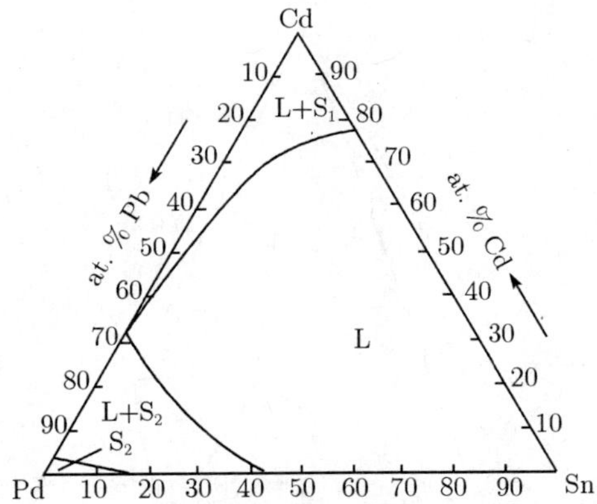

$p = 1.0$ GPa $T = 567.1$ K
(a)

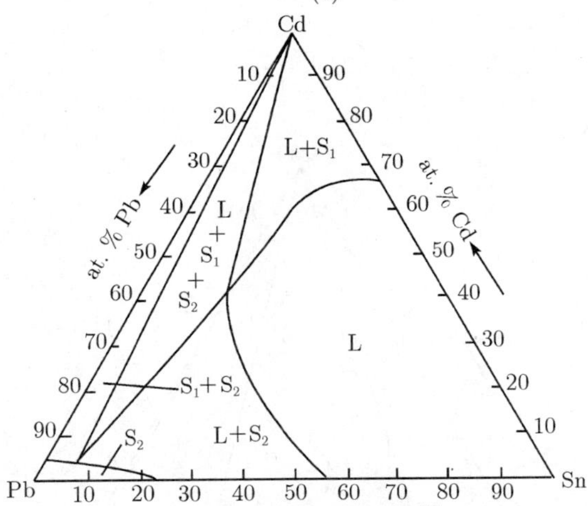

p=1.0 GPa T=540 K
(b)

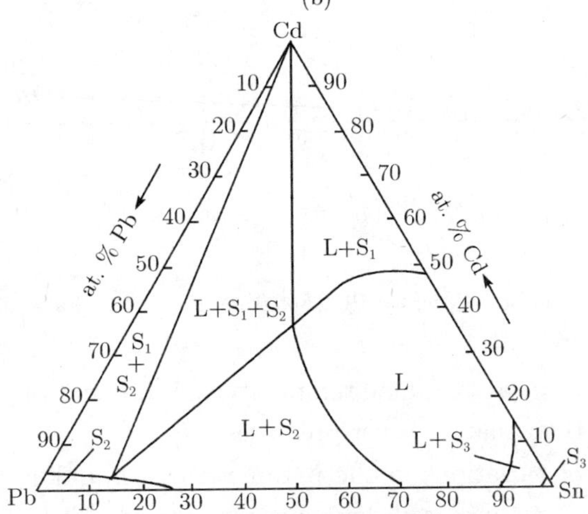

$p = 1.0$ GPa $T = 510$ K
(c)

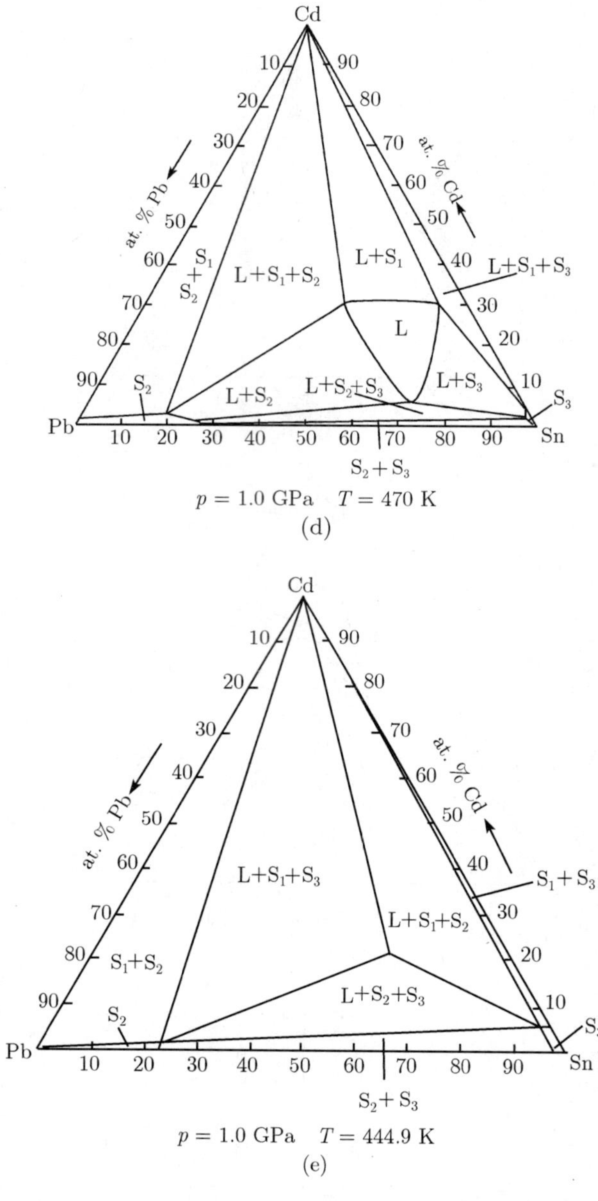

Fig. 11.5 Horizontal sections of the Cd-Pb-Sn system at p = 1.0GPa at different temperatures.

It may be seen that, at the same temperature, the liquid phase region is smaller at higher pressure than that at lower pressures.

The influences of variations in the parameters T, p and x_i, made to the high-pressure phase diagrams in detail, have been discussed. The authors think that it constitutes a useful contribution to the science of high pressure phase diagrams.

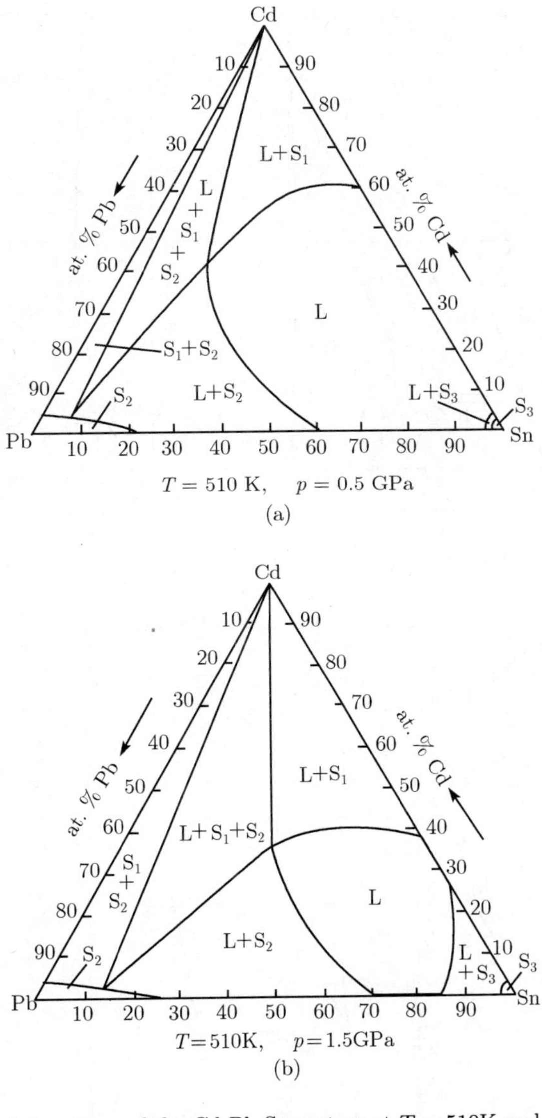

Fig. 11.6 Horizontal sections of the Cd-Pb-Sn system at $T = 510$K and different pressures.

These p-x_i phase diagrams are interesting, but less useful.

A series of vertical sections and horizontal sections for the Cd-Sn-Zn system at high pressures have also been calculated (Zhao *et al.*, 1987; Xiao *et al.*, 1989; Song *et al.*, 1991).

All of the conclusions drawn from the research of high-pressure phase diagrams of the Cd-Pb-Sn system are similar to those of the Cd-Sn-Zn system. While it is important, the Cd-Sn-Zn system research "in detail" is not discussed here.

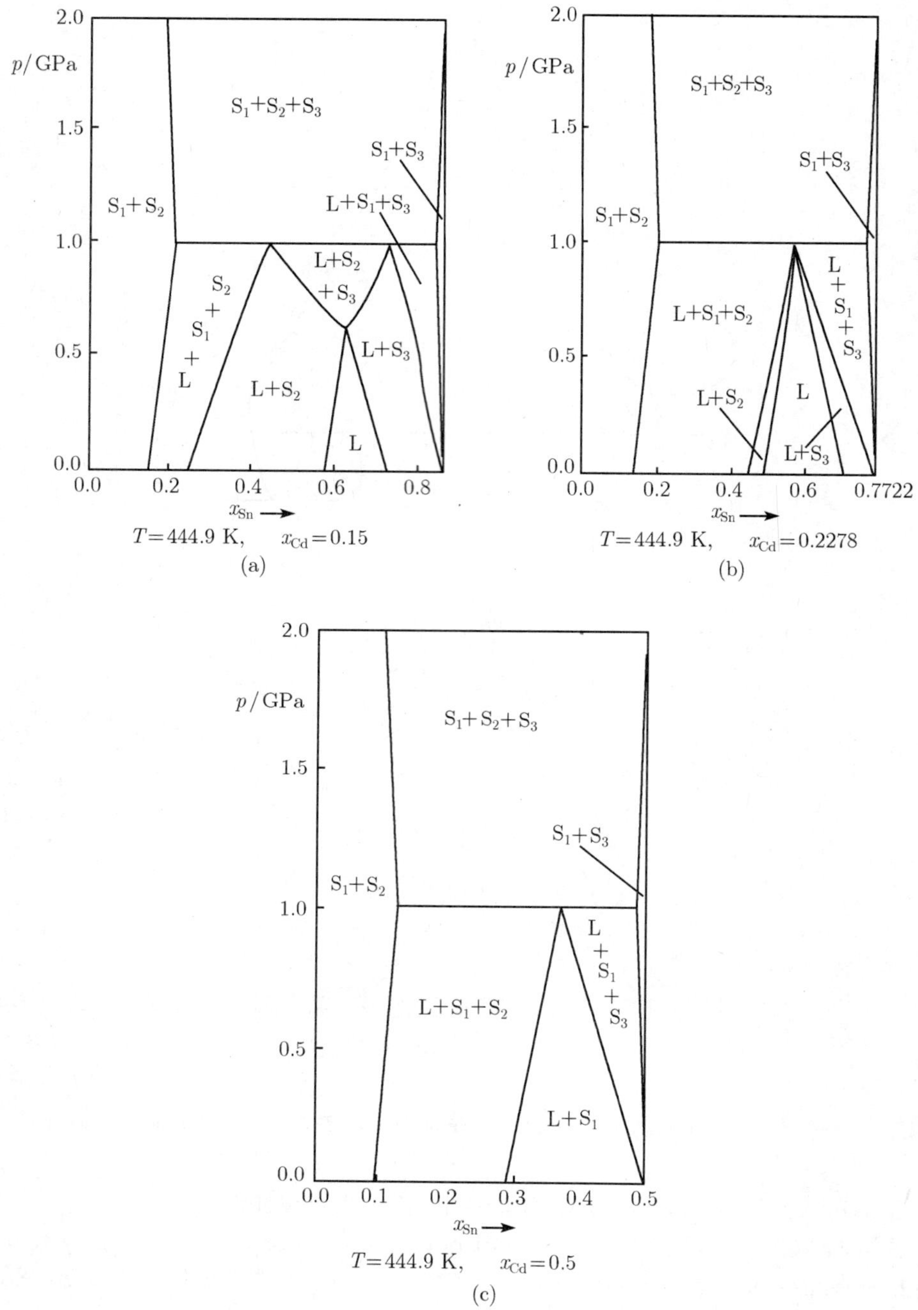

Fig. 11.7(a-c) p-x_{Sn} vertical sections of the Cd-Pb-Sn system at $T = 444.9\mathrm{K}$ with different x_{Cd}.

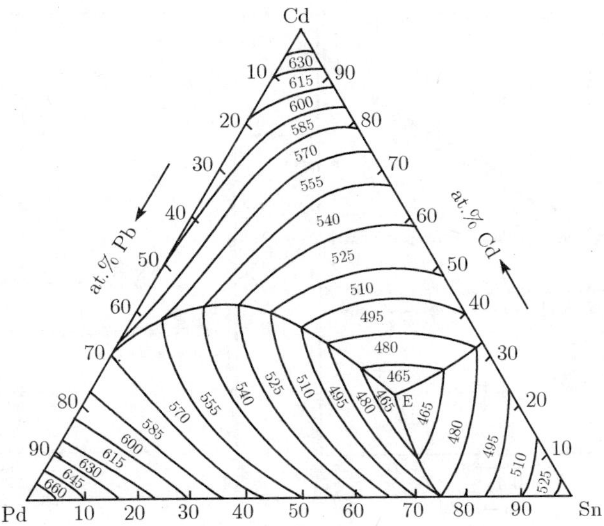

Fig. 11.8 The liquid projection for Cd-Pb-Sn system at $p = 1.0$ GPa.

11.5 Verification of Calculated High-Pressure Ternary Phase Diagrams through Experimental Determination

Since, several approximate assumptions have been proposed during the calculation procedure, the validity of the calculated high-pressure ternary phase diagrams needs to be verified. For this reason, the vertical sections of the Cd-Pb-Sn and Cd-Sn-Zn ternary systems have been determined by improved high-pressure DTA (HPDTA) [Zhou *et al.*, 1990; Song *et al.*, 1992].

Metals (Cd, Pb, Sn and Zn) of high purity (99.999 wt.%) were used. The homogeneous alloy samples were prepared with care. The results of chemical analysis of some alloys, with random sampling, agreed well with the nominal compositions. HPDTA was performed in a piston-cylinder high-pressure apparatus. The pressure medium was pyrophyllite. In our experiment, the sample capsule, which was made of a thin NiSi sheet, was used as one arm of a point thermocouple in contact with the alloy sample. This sample assembly method improved the sensitivity of the determination. Phase transitions were detected by HPDTA with $\phi = 0.3$mm NiCr-NiSi thermocouples.

All experiments performed revealed that the experimentally determined and the calculated results coincided well with each other. The comparisons of the calculated and determined results for the Cd-Pb-Sn system are shown in the following figures [Zhou, 1990]. Due to the lack of thermodynamic data, line 1 in the figures has not been calculated.

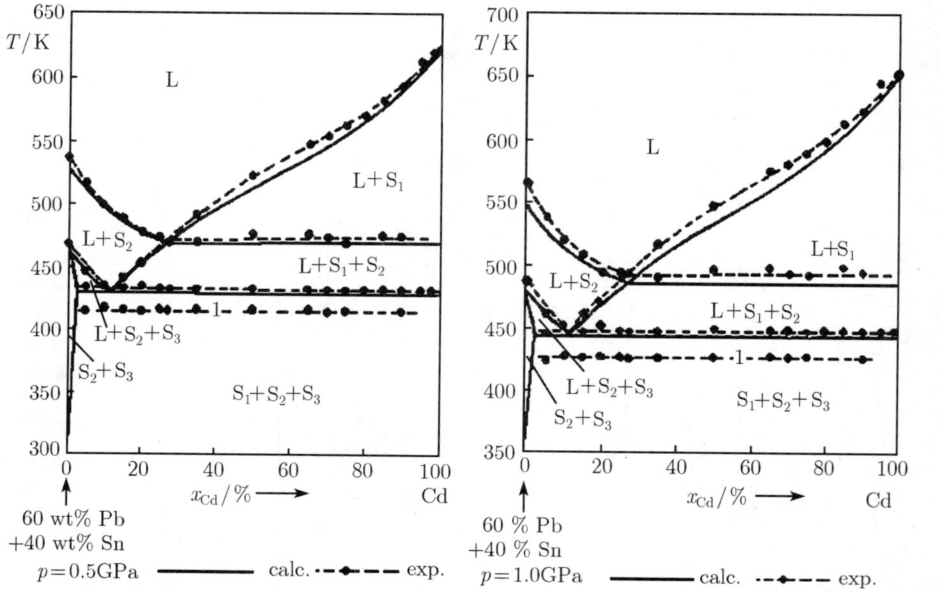

(a) Cd-(60wt%Pb+40wt%Sn) (b) Cd-(60wt%Pb-40wt%Sn)

Fig. 11.9 Vertical sections at different pressures.

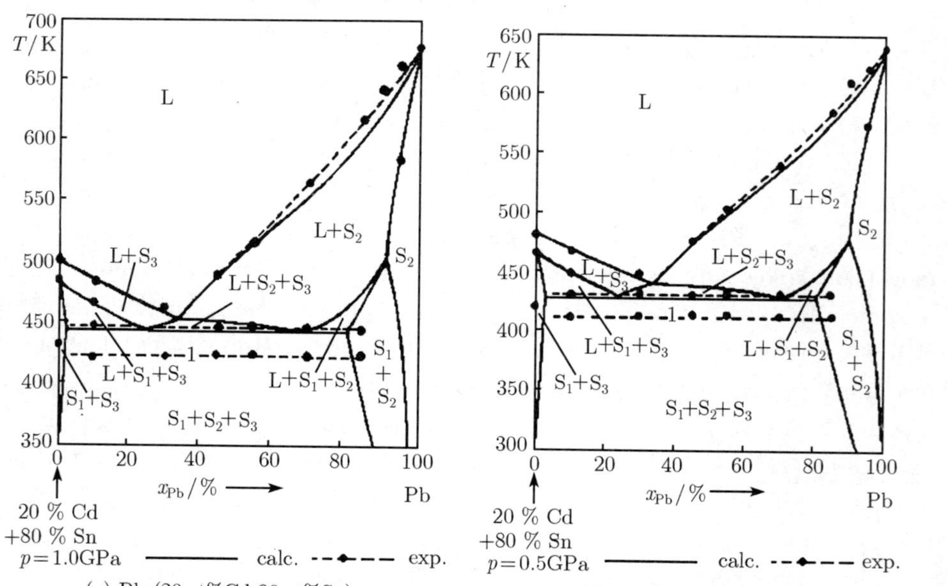

(a) Pb-(20wt%Cd-80wt%Sn) (b) Pb-(20wt%Cd-80wt%Sn)

Fig. 11.10 Vertical sections of another composition of the system at different pressures.

Another example is the comparison of the calculated and experimentally determined high-pressure phase diagram for the Cd-Sn-Zn system. The calculated and the experimentally determined liquidus data also agree well with each other [Song *et al.*, 1992; Song *et al.*, 1993].

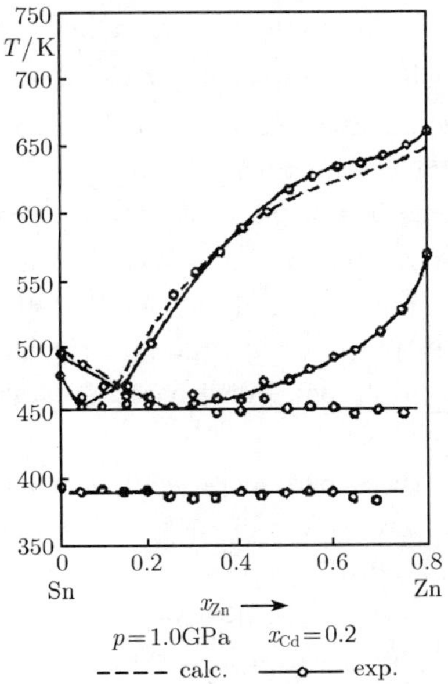

Fig. 11.11 High-pressure vertical section of the Cd-Sn-Zn system at $x_{Cd} = 0.2, p = 1.0$GPa.

All other calculated high-pressure phase diagrams of the Cd-Pb-Sn and Cd-Sn-Zn systems have been compared with the experimentally determined phase diagrams, the results are also satisfactory. But they are not presented here for saving of space.

11.6 The Comparison between the Methods of Experimental Determination and Thermodynamic Calculation of High Pressure Phase Diagrams [Song *et al.*, 1993]

By comparison with the experimental determination, the thermodynamic calculation is easier. However, there are some "troubles" associated with it. The main ones are as follows.

(1) The lack of thermodynamic data.

It is well known that much thermodynamic data is needed in the support of the thermodynamics calculations for a high-pressure, multicomponent phase diagram. The data related to high pressure conditions are difficult to obtain. It may be that it is not so difficult to get all of the data for some individual components, but it is very difficult to get all of this data for all of the components in the chosen, multicomponent system.

(2) Not all of the thermodynamic data obtained for these studies are accurate enough, especially that data used in the calculation of high pressure, multicomponent phase diagrams. Some of the data can only be obtained from one reference, *i.e.*comparison data cannot be found for use in the particular study.

(3) Calculation results have to be checked by experiment.

Though the phase diagram under extreme conditions can be constructed by thermodynamic calculation; when there are no experimental data for cross-checking, then the calculated results should be accepted with caution, even if they may be correct.

The experimental determination is the basic method to construct the high-pressure, multicomponent phase diagram. The HPDAT method and other methods have been used for this purpose but experimental determination of these phase diagrams is still not extensively performed because many problems tend to be encountered. They are as follows.

(1) The complexity of the experimental equipment is the major difficulty. For the HPDTA, a large pressure generator, a set of the DTA apparatus and many consumable materials are needed.

(2) The experimental workload is also very large. If HPDTA experiments for a ternary, high-pressure phase diagram, are designed as for DTA experiments at atmospheric pressure, then at least 100 samples and five pressure conditions are needed. Taking into consideration the low measurement success rate and the necessary repeat tests, the workload will be greatly increased. Furthermore, the high pressure condensed phase has to be characterized by an in situ diffraction method with X-ray or synchrotron radiation and these techniques are not readily accessible to most researchers.

(3) The accuracy of the measured data is not as good as is desired, since there are many factors that influence the accuracy of the data. For the Cd-Sn-Zn system with a low melting point, a high pressure phase diagram, determined experimentally with the aid of HPDTA, are accurate to within ± 4K only. This error range corresponds to about 0.3 GPa in the Cd-Sn-Zn system, when converted to a pressure difference, and it thus approximates the designed pressure interval in the experiment. Thus, if the designed pressure interval is made smaller, the temperature change, produced by a pressure change in the experiment, is masked by the measurement errors and this makes the reliability level of the measurement lower.

To sum up these considerations, there are some definite advantages and limitations to the study of high-pressure phase diagrams, either by thermodynamic calculations or by experimental determination only. Our quoted work on Cd-Pb-Sn and Cd-Sn-Zn high-pressure phase diagram shows that there is good coincidence between the calculated and the experimentally determined results. This finding means that our calculation method is generally satisfactory and that the calculated results are reliable. Thus, we consider that it is an effective way to combine the thermodynamic calculation and experimental determination methods for the construction of high pressure multicomponent phase diagrams, *i.e.* by calculating the data theoretically at first and then verifying the calculation results by experimental methods. This kind of direct experimental measurement verification is estimated to be required for about one-fifth of the total workload for determining the phase diagrams without the aid of theoretical calculations. For the calculation of high-pressure, multicomponent phase diagrams, many thermodynamic properties, especially those related to the pressure effects have to be determined and collected. Finally, we can say that the proposed experimental methodology is a straightforward way to promote the development of research on high pressure, multicomponent phase diagrams, by combining the theoretical calculation component(s) with the method of direct experimental measurement.

References-11

E. A. Brandes. 1998. Smithells metals reference book. 7th ed. London: Butterworth-Heinemann

K. C. Chou. 1987. A new solution model for predicting ternary thermodynamic properties. CALPHAD, 11(3): 293-300

K. C. Chou, Y. A. Chang. 1989. A study of geometrical model. Ber. Bunsenges Phys. Chem., 94: 735-741

K. C. Chou, S. K. Wei. 1995. A general solution model for predicting ternary thermodynamic properties. CALPHAD, 19(3): 315-325

K. C. Chou, S. K. Wei. 1997. A new generation solution model for predicting thermodynamic properties of a multicomponent system from binaries. Metall. Mater. Trans. B, 28 B: 439-445

C. Colinet. 1967. D. E. S., Fac. Des Sci., Univ. Grenoble, France

A. F. Crawley. 1972. Densities and viscosities of some liquid alloys of Zinc and Cadnium. Metal. Trans., 3(4): 971

M. Hillert. 1980. Emperical methods of predicting and representating thermodynamic properties. CALPHAD, 4(1): 1-13

F. Kohler. 1960. Zur berechnung der thermodynamischen daten eines ternaren systems aus den zugehorigen systems. Monat fur Chemie, 91: 738

O. Kubaschewski, J. A. Catterall. 1956. Thermochemical data of alloys. New York: Pergamon Press

Hengli Liu, Lizhu Song, Muyu Zhao. 1990. A study of molar volumes of ternary alloy solid solutions. J. Less-Common Metals, 166: 271-281

Hengli Liu, Lizhu Song, Muyu Zhao. 1990. Excess molar volumes of lead-based α-phase solid solution in (Pb+Bi+In) at 298.15K. J. Chem. Thermodynamics, 22: 821

Z. Moser, L. Zabdyr, A. Pelton. 1975. Thermodynamic properties of liquid Cd-Pb-Sn solution and analytical calculation of the phase diagram. Canadian Metallurgical Quarterly, 14(3): 257-264

Y. M. Muggianu. 1975. J. Chimie Physique, 72: 83

Lizhu Song, Hua Yang, Ping Xiao, Muyu Zhao. 1993. Phase diagrams of ternary alloy system at high pressure. J. Alloys and Compounds, 196: 229-234

Lizhu Song, Hua Yang, Muyu Zhao. 1992. Determination of the phase diagrams of the Cd-Sn(0.2)-Zn ternary system at high pressure. J. Alloys and Compounds, 187: 137

E. Yu. Tonkov. 1998. Compound and alloy under high pressure: A handbook. NY: CRC Press

G. W. Toop. 1965. Trans. Met. Soc., AIME, 233: 850-854

Ping Xiao, Lizhu Song, Hongye Kang, Muyu Zhao. 1988. The calculation of P-T-X_i phase diagrams of Cd-Sn, Cd-Zn and Sn-Zn binary systems. J. Less-Common Metals, 144: 1-13

Ping Xiao, Muyu Zhao. 1989. The calculation of P-T-$X_i$high pressure phase diagram of Cd-Sn-Zn ternary system. High Temperatures-High Pressures, 21(4): 441-445

Muyu Zhao, Ping Xiao, Hongye Kang. 1987. The principles of calculation of high pressure multicomponent phase diagrams. High Temperatures-High Pressures, 19: 513-518

Weiya Zhou, Zhongyi Shen, Yun Zhang, Muyu Zhao. 1988. Effects of pressure on the eutectic or eutectoid temperatures of Cd-Pb, Cd-Sn, Pb-Sn and Cd-Pb-Sn system. J. Less-Common Metals, 143: 59

Weiya Zhou, Zhongyi Shen, Yun Zhang, Muyu Zhao. 1988. The determination of high-pressure vertical sections of Cd-Pb-Sn ternary system. High Temperatures-High Pressures, 20: 561

Summary of Part Three

Having worked out a systematic boundary theory of multi-component $p-T-x_i$ phase diagrams, we reached the key to high-pressure phase diagrams. Indeed, the high-pressure phase diagrams are similar, in many respects, to the phase diagrams at normal pressures. This has been concluded by E.Yu. Tonkov [Tonkov, 1998], and the phase diagrams at normal pressure are generally used as a good starting-point to study the material properties and synthesis under high pressures.

Based on the principle of the boundary theory, we have developed the theoretical method to calculate the high-pressure phase diagram. A lot of binary and ternary alloy high-pressure phase diagrams have been calculated and determined, and the calculated diagrams tally with the experimental ones.

For Cd-Pb, Cd-Sn binary solid-liquid phase diagrams, our calculated and experimental results show that the eutectic temperatures for these systems rise monotonously with increasing pressures. For Cd-Pb system, with the increasing pressures, the %Cd of eutectic compositions is increasing, as the melting point of Cd at normal pressure is higher than those of Pb. Our calculated results of Cd-Pb high-pressure phase diagrams indicate a pressure-induced change in the shape of liquidus curves.

For most of the binary phase diagrams, the eutectic temperature will rise with increasing pressure. This has been well observed by many authors, and is also well recorded in our experiments. Our calculations also predict a "pressure-induced" change in the shape of liquidus curve. If these interesting phenomena should be universal, they could be helpful for the geological research and the materials synthesis work.

Our preliminary work in high-pressure phase diagram calculation is very promising. Combining the theoretical calculation and experimental measurement techniques, will definitely promote the progress in the high-pressure phase diagrams' research.

References of This Book

C. W. Bale, A. D. Pelton, M. Regand. 1997. The measurement and analytical computation of thermochemical properties in a quaternary system, Cd-Sn-Bi-Zn. Z. Metalkde. Bd. 68(H.1): 69-74.

I. Barin. 1989. Termochemical Data of Pure Substances. Part I and II. Weinheim: VCH

I. Barin, O. Knacke, O. Kubaschewski. 1977. Thermochemical properties of inorganic substances. Supplement. Berlin: Springer-Verlag

S. Blair. 1978. Predicting the compressibility of liquid metals. J. Inorg. Nucl. Chem., 40(6): 971-974

E. A. Brandes. 1998. Smithells metals reference book. 7th ed. London: Butterworth-Heinemann

S. R. Brinkley. 1946. Note on the Conditions of equilibrium for systems of many constituents. J. Chem. Phys., 14: 563, 564, 686

Arthur H. Brownlow. 1979. Geochemisty. Englewood Cliffs: Prentice-Hall, Inc.

K. C. Chou. 1987. A new solution model for predicting ternary thermodynamic properties. CALPHAD, 11(3): 293-300

K. C. Chou, Y. A. Chang. 1989. A study of geometrical model. Ber. Bunsenges Phys. Chem., 94: 735-741

K. C. Chou, S. K. Wei. 1995. A general solution model for predicting ternary thermodynamic properties. CALPHAD, 19(3), 315-325

K. C. Chou, S. K. Wei. 1997. A new generation solution model for predicting thermodynamic properties of a multicomponent system from binaries. Metall. Mater. Trans. B, 28 B(June): 439-445

J. B. Clark, B. Metcalfe, R. A. Oaccy, P. W. Richter. 1980. High pressure study of Cd-Sn binary system. J. Less-Common Metals, 71: 33-45

J. B. Clark, P. W. Richer. 1980. The determination of composition-temperature-pressure phase diagram of binary alloy systems. High Pressure Sci. Tech. Proc., 7th Int. AIRAPT Conference, 1: 363-371

J. B. Clark, M. E. Thomas, P. W. Ricther. 1987. Binary alloy system at high pressure. J. Less-Common Metals, 132: 181-194

S. P. Clark. 1966. Handbook of physical constants. New York: The Geological Soc. of Amer. Inc.

C. Colinet, D. E. S., 1967. Fac. Des Sci., Univ. Grenoble, France

A. F. Crawley. 1972. Densities and viscosities of some liquid alloys of Zinc and Cadnium. Metal. Trans., 3(4): 971

Ying Fu. 1963. Introduction to Chemical Thermodynamics. Beijing: Science Press (in Chinese)

J. W. Gibbs. 1950. The Collected works of J. W. Gibbs. Vol. 1. New Haven: Yale University Press

P. Gordon. 1968. Principles of Phase Diagrams in Materials Systems. New York: McGraw-Hill

D. E. Gray. 1972. American Institute of Physics Handbook. Amer. Inst. of Physics. 3rd ed. New York: McGraw-Hill

H Gupta, J. E Morral, H Nowotny. 1986. Constructing multicomponent phase diagrams by overlapping ZPF lines. Scripta Metallurgica, 20: 889-894

M. Hillert. 1980. Emperical methods of predicting and representating thermodynamic properties. CALPHAD, 4(1): 1-13

M. Hillert. 1985. Principles of phase diagrams. International Metals Rev., 30(2): 45

M. Hillert. 1988. Constructing multicomponent phase diagrams using ZPF lines and Schreinemakers' rule. Scripta Metallurgica, 22: 1085

M. Hillert. 1993. Gibbs' phase rule applied to phase diagrams and transformations. J. Phase Equilibrium, 14: 418

M. Hillert. 2007. Phase Equilibria, Phase Diagrams and Phase Transformations, Their Thermodynamic Basis. 2nd ed. Cambridge: Cambridge University Press

R. Hultgren, P. D. Desai, D. T. Hawkings, M. Gleiser, K. K. Kelley, D. D. Wagman. 1973. Selected Values of Thermodynamic Properties of the Elements. Amer. Soc. for Metals, Metals Park, Cleveland, Ohio

R. Hultgren, R. L. Orr, P. D. Anderson, K. K. Kelley. 1973. Selected Values of Thermodynamic Properties of Binary Alloys. Amer. Soc. for Metals, Metals Park, Cleveland, Ohio

F. Kohler. 1960. Zur berechnung der thermodynamischen daten eines ternaren systems aus den zugehorigen systems. Monat fur Chemie, 91: 738

O. Kubaschewski, C. B. Alcock. 1979. Metallurgical Thermochemistry. 5th ed. New York: Pergamon Press

O. Kubaschewski, J. A. Catterall. 1956. Thermochemical data of alloys. New York: Pergamon Press

Hengli Liu, Lizhu Song, Muyu Zhao. 1990. A study of molar volumes of ternary alloy solid solutions. J. Less-Common Metals, 166: 271-281

Hengli Liu, Lizhu Song, Muyu Zhao. 1990. Excess molar volumes of lead-based α-phase solid solution in (Pb+Bi+In) at 298.15K. J. Chem. Thermodynamics, 22: 821

T. B. Massalski, H. Okamoto, P. R. Subramanian, L. Kacpzak. 1990. Binary Alloy Phase Diagrams. 3 Vols. 2nd Ed. ASM International, Metals Park, Cleveland, Ohio

Z. Moser, L. Zabdyr, A. Pelton. 1975. Thermodynamic properties of liquid Cd-Pb-Sn solution and analytical calculation of the phase diagram. Canadian Metallurgical Quarterly, 14(3): 257-264

Y. M. Muggianu. 1975. J. Chimie Physique, 72: 83

L. S. Palatnik, A. I. Landau. 1964. Phase Equilibria in Multicomponent Phase Diagrams. New York: Holt Rinehart and Winston, Inc

D. Perkner, I. M. Berstein. 1977. Handbook of Stainless Steels. New York: McGraw-Hill Inc.

A. Prince. 1966. Alloy phase equilibria. New York: Elsevier

F. N. Rhines. 1956. Phase diagram in metallurgy. New York: McGraw-Hill

F. A. H. Schreinemakers, Proc. K. Akad. 1915. Wetenschappen (Section of Sciences), 18: 116

G. I. Shiflet *et al.* 1979. CALPHAD, 3(2): 129

Lizhu Song, Hua Yang, Ping Xiao, Muyu Zhao. 1992. Phase diagrams of ternary alloy system at high pressure. J. Alloys and Compounds, 196, 229-234

Lizhu Song, Hua Yang, Muyu Zhao. 1992. Determination of the phase diagrams of the Cd-Sn(0.2)-Zn ternary system at high pressure. J. Alloys and Compounds, 187: 137

Lizhu Song, Hua Yang, Ping Xiao and Muyu Zhao. 1993. Phase diagrams of ternary alloy system at high pressure. J. Alloys and Compounds, 196: 229-234

E. Yu. Tonkov. 1998. Compound and alloy under high pressure: A handbook. New York: CRC Press

G. W. Toop. 1965. Trans. Met. Soc., AIME, 233: 850-854

Ping Xiao, Lizhu Song, Hongye Kang, Muyu Zhao. 1988. The calculation of P-T-X_i phase diagrams of Cd-Sn, Cd-Zn and Sn-Zn binary systems. J. Less-Common Metals, 144: 1-13

Ping Xiao, Muyu Zhao. 1989. The calculation of p-T-x_i high pressure phase diagram of Cd-Sn-Zn ternary system. High Temp.-High Pressures, 21(4): 441-445

F. Van Zeggeren, S. H. Storey. 1970. The computation of chemical equilibria. Chapter 2 The foundations of chemical equilibrium computation. Cambridge: Cambridge University Press

M. W. Zemansky. 1968. Heat and Thermodynamics. 5th ed. New York McGraw-Hill Inc.

Muyu Zhao. 1983. The application of theorem of corresponding relation and its corollaries for p-T-x_i multicomponent phase diagrams. Scientia Sinica, Ser. B, 26(3): 274

Muyu Zhao. 1983. The theorem of corresponding relation between neighboring phaese regions and their boundaries in phase diagrams. CALPHAD, 7(3): 185-199

Muyu Zhao, Xiaobao Fan. 1985. The relation between the dimensions of the boundary and phase boundary in isobaric phase diagrams. Scientia Sinica, Ser. B, 28(5): 458

Muyu Zhao. 1985. The relation between the dimensions of the boundary and phase boundary of the p-T-x_i multicomponent phase diagram, Scientia Sinica, Ser. B, 28(6): 655

Muyu Zhao, Zezhong Fu, Baokun Xu. 1986. Method of the direct calculation of vertical sections in isobaric phase diagrams. High Temperature Science, 22(2): 15-22

Muyu Zhao, Baokun Xu, Xiaobao Fan, Zezhong Fu. 1986. Progress in the theorem of the corresponding relation in isobaric phase diagrams and its application. High Temperature Science, 22(2): 1-14

Muyu Zhao, Ping Xiao, Hongye Kang. 1987. The principles of calculation of high pressure multicomponent phase diagrams. High Temperatures-High Pressures, 19: 513-518

Muyu Zhao. 1992. The boundary theory of isobaric phase diagrams // Tang Youqi. Advances of Sciences of China, Chemistry. Beijing: Science Press, 4: 147-162

Muyu Zhao, Zichen Wang, Liangzhi Xiao. 1992. The determination of the number of independent components by Brinkley's method. J. Chem. Education, 69(7): 539

Weiya Zhou, Zhongyi Shen, Yun Zhang, Muyu Zhao. 1988. Effects of pressure on the eutectic or eutectoid temperatures of Cd-Pb, Cd-Sn, Pb-Sn and Cd-Pb-Sn system. J. Less-Common Metals, 143: 59

Weiya Zhou, Zhongyi Shen, Yun Zhang, Muyu Zhao. 1988. The determination of high-pressure vertical sections of Cd-Pb-Sn ternary system. High Temperatures-High Pressures, 20: 561

Weiya Zhou, Lizhu Song, Muyu Zhao. 1990. Calculation of high-pressure phase diagrams of binary system. J. Less-Common Metals, 160: 237-245

Weiya Zhou, Lizhu Song, Fengqing Wu, Muyu Zhao. 1992. Optimization of thermodynamic properties and calculation of phase diagrams for the Cd-Sn system at high pressure. High Temperatures-High Pressures, 24: 511-518

Important Symbols

C number of the independent components

C heat capacity

K the coefficient of distribution

M total molar number of the entire system

M number of elements in the system

M_i the mole number of i-th component in the system

N number of components in the system

NPRs neighboring phase regions

PR phase region

R dimensions of the isobaric phase diagram

R_1 dimensions of the phase boundary

R_1' dimensions of the boundary

$(R_1)_i$ dimensions of the phase boundary in an isopleth section

$(R_1')_i$ dimensions of the boundary in an isopleth section

S entropy of the system

T temperature

TCR theorem of corresponding relationship

U internal energy of the system

V volume of the system

V_m^E excess molar volume

$\bar{V}_i^E$ partial excess molar volume

$\bar{V}_{i\mathrm{L}}(T, p, x_{i\mathrm{L}})$ partial molar volume

Z number of other independent constraining conditions in the system

a activity

m_j mole number of the j-th phase of the system

m_{ij} mole number of i-th component in the j-th phase

p pressure

p_j pressure of the j-th phase of the system

r number of independent equilibrium chemical conditions

r^* number of independent chemical reactions inhibited by some restrictions
s_j entropy of the j-th phase of the system
t_j temperature of the j-th phase of the system
u_j internal energy of the j-th phase of the system
v_j volume of the j-th phase of the system
x_i mole fraction of i-th component of the system
x_{ij} mole fraction of i-th component in the j-th phase
Φ total number of all different phases in NPRs
α the thermal expansion coefficient
$\alpha, \beta, \gamma \cdots$ the symbols used to identify different phases
β the compressibility
γ activity coefficient
γ_{i,S_j} activity coefficient of i-th component in the S_j-th solid phase
μ chemical potential
$\mu_{i,j}$ chemical potential of i-th component in the j-th phase
$\mu_{i,\mathrm{L}}^0$ chemical potential of pure i-th component in the liquid state
$\mu_{i,\mathrm{S}}^0$ chemical potential of pure i-th component in the solid state
μ_i^E excess partial molar Gibbs free energy
ϕ number of phases existing in the system
ϕ_1 number of phases in 1st NPR
ϕ_2 number of phases in 2nd NPR
ϕ_C number of common phases existing in NPRs
$\phi_{\max}$ the maximum number of phases existing in any phase regions

Index

Annex

A quiet life of "pursuing the truth"

– Introduction of Josiah Willard Gibbs

MUYU ZHAO, LIANGZHI XIAO, XIAOBAO FAN

Josiah Willard Gibbs was born on February 11th 1839 at New Haven, Connecticut. He died at the age of 64 years, in the same city, on April 28th, 1903.

The ancestor of the long established Gibbs' family, he emigrated from England to Boston in 1658. This move led to the establishment of a distinguished and learned family, continuing over a long period. J.W, Gibbs' mother was a daughter of a Yale graduate in literature. Among her ancestors were at least two graduates from the Yale College; one of them became the first Dean of the then, New Jersey College. On his fathers' side of the family, there were 5 generations of ancestors who had graduated from Harvard University, and his father who graduated from Yale. From 1824 to 1861, Gibbs' father was the professor of "Sacred Literature" at the Yale College. He was renowned to his contemporaries for his wide and deep knowledge acquisition. He had published many books. His modest life style, and the rigorous mode in which he "approached" his work, had greatly influenced the formation of Gibbs' personality in his early growth and development years.

Gibbs was the fourth child, and the only boy born, into his family. He matriculated at Yale College in 1854, winning prizes in both Latin and Mathematics. Graduating in 1858, he continued his studies there and was awarded the Ph.D. degree of Yale in 1863. After that, he was appointed to the post of tutor in Yale College. During his three years of tutorial sessions, he taught Latin during the first two years, and natural philosophy (Physics) in the third year. In return, he received the love and esteem of his students. He finished his sessions as tutor, and then he went aboard, together with his three elder sisters. They were in Paris from the winter of 1866 to the beginning of 1867, he then moved to Berlin in the same year, where he attended the Magnus *et al* classes. In 1868, he went to another German city, Heidelberg. Gibbs returned to New Haven in 1869. Two years later, he was appointed as Yale's Professor of Mathematical Physics. He held this position until his death in April, 1903. At that time, he "passed away",due to the consequence of 5 days of serious illness.

Gibbs' lifetime contribution to the sciences is enormous, particularly within the fields of thermodynamics and statistical mechanics. In 1873, when he was already 34 years old, he published his first paper on the topic of the geometric representation of thermodynamic properties of a fluid. In the same year, there was another paper on a method of geometrical representation of the thermodynamic properties of substances by means of surfaces. He became fully engaged in the study of thermodynamics over the following several years. The vintage Gibbs paper, *On the Equilibrium of Heterogeneous Substances* was published in 1876 and further 1878, separately. This work is now deemed to be an event of the "first importance" in the history of chemistry, and one that laid the solid foundation for the subject of chemical thermodynamics. Suppose that Gibbs had not had any other publications to his name and endeavors, then this paper alone would have been preeminent enough to render him a position among the ranks of the greatest scientists that rise from time to time in the history of the science. Le Chatelier himself, commented that Gibbs, through his own greatness, had founded a new Department of Chemical Science which was then rapidly becoming comparable in importance to that Institution, created by Lavoisier. Le Chatelier also had translated the first part of *On the Equilibrium of Heterogeneous Substances* and published this version, in Paris, in 1899. Even earlier, Ostwald had translated the three papers above into German and had them published in Leipzig. Ostwald appreciated Gibbs' work very highly in saying that Gibbs had given 100 years to the advance of Physical Chemistry, from the initial form to substantial content.

Gibbs' work also received special attention in the Netherlands. Van der Waals was among the first persons who first applied Gibbs' theory. He also introduced Gibbs' work to his personal student, Roozeboom. The later scientist carried out much research work on the phase rule, and enthusiastically introduced Gibbs' theory, particularly the phase rule, to all interested persons.

Another important lasting contribution of Gibbs' work was his contributions in the area of Statistical Mechanics. In 1902, one year before his death, he published his famous treatise *Elementary Principles in Statistical Mechanics*, in which he developed the Boltzmann's and Maxwell's theories into the theory of "ensembles", thus putting the subject of statistical mechanics on a firm foundation.

Gibbs also generated many publications in vector analysis that constitutes the basis of this branch of mathematics. Moreover, he was also involved in studies of astronomy, the electromagnetic theory of light, Fourier's series, *etc.*

With the elapse of time, the influence of Gibbs' work on the development of science has become more and more significant.

The many contributions of Gibbs had been well recognized before his death. In 1881, American Academy of Arts and Sciences in Boston awarded him the Rumford Medal. In 1901, Gibbs was awarded the Copley Medal of the Royal Society of the United Kingdom, illustrating the worldwide recognition of his work among contemporary theoreticians. He was also the member, or the communications member, of The National Academy of Sciences, American Academy of Arts and Sciences, American Physical Society, The Royal Society in London, The Russian Academy of Sciences, Royal Netherlands Academy of Sciences, French Institute, Göttingen Royal Society, Bavarian Academy of Sciences and Humanities, and the Physical Society of London. He also held Honorary Degrees from four prestigious Institutes such as Princeton University.

However, all of these acts of recognition were, to an extent, a type of superficial acknowledgement. The real value of many of Gibbs' works, including his opus *On the Equilibrium of Heterogeneous Substances*, had not been generally known for a number of years. This delay was due largely to the fact that its complex mathematical expressions and the rigorous deductive process, make it somewhat difficult reading for many, especially for the "experimental chemists", who were then, at least, "poor in mathematics", such that even the simple parts of Gibbs' papers appeared to be too esoteric for them. Not a great many colleagues could fully understand Gibbs' theory. This is why many important conclusions, expounded in Gibbs' paper, have been re-discovered by other renowned scholars, in later years. For example, the Gibbs-Helmholtz equation in 1882, Gibbs-Duhem equation in 1886, and the osmotic pressure rule by Van't Hoff in 1887, to just name a few.

In Germany, though there was Ostwald's translation, it did not produce a "big echo". For a long time, it was Nernst's work that governed the direction of chemistry in Germany.

The same situation existed in the United States, nobody in New Haven, and their peers elsewhere in the US, really understood Gibbs. One of his colleagues at Yale admitted that in the Connecticut Academy there is no one who understands Gibbs' thermodynamics, he said, "We acknowledge and recognize Gibbs' contribution, completely in the blind." At that particular time, it was Lewis' theory that prevailed in the States.

This may be the reason why Gibbs didn't receive much salary in his first 10 years of the professorship career at Yale. It was 1920, some 17 years after his death, that he was, for the first time, nominated as a candidate for the Hall of Fame of Great Americans, in New York. However, he received only 9 votes from the eligible 100 voting persons. After another 30 years had passed, Gibbs' bust was finally placed in this hall in 1950. Even today, with the exception of those engaged in natural sciences, many educated Americans are still unfamiliar with this name. It prompts "deep thought" that we could find today, thousands of papers on Gibbs' theories and applications in "Chemical Abstracts", but we find very few mentions of his biography. This is because of his tranquil characteristics and his quiet life. He made no effort to attract followers, nor to endeavor to communicate to a wider audience.

All of his life was that of a quiet and simple character. Once, in his childhood, he became infected with scarlet fever. This significantly impaired his long term health, he was always somewhat weak in much of his life. Thanks to his careful self-attention and to the adoption of a regulated life style, his weakness did not influence his researches. He did not have much involvement in social activities, because of his poor health and of his retiring nature. He appeared to be a stranger, even in his home town. Except for the three years in Europe, he lived nearly all of his time in New Haven, in his surviving sister's household, that was the shared inherence from their father.

Gibbs was of noble morality and feeling. His modesty, shown in his scientific research, was sincere, and without any pretence. He never doubted the rightness of his theory, never under-estimated its importance, but he never flaunted his work. He trusted that any other researcher would arrive at the same conclusion if they could pay attention to the same subject. He belongs to those rare persons who pursue no applause from their contemporaries but only the "truth of science". He contented himself by solving those problems that "haunted" his brain. He began thinking of the next problem immediately after solving the previous one. He did not care if others could or could not understand what he had done. In his papers, he rarely cited others references to explain his own points.

There is an anecdote in one of his biographies. In his early paper on the representation of the thermodynamic properties of substances, by means of their surfaces, there is one section about the three-phase equilibrium of water, where he provided only dull and dry concepts, without making any effort to crash the "fence of understanding" of his readers. The famous physician, Maxwell, had, by chance, read this paper somewhere and much appreciated the importance of it. Maxwell spent much time using his own hands to prepare a plaster cast model illustrating the thermodynamic surface of water (*i.e.*the three-dimensional, phase diagram of water) and sent it to Gibbs. It was a pity that Maxwell died too early, at only 48 years of age, in 1879. He had not made any particular comments on Gibbs' work; otherwise the fate of Gibbs's theory may well have been drastically different. The model, as presented by Maxwell, helped very much in the explanation of Gibbs' points. However, Gibbs never mentioned its originality in class. One student once asked where is the model from? Gibbs answered, with his unique modesty, "from a friend". The student actually knew well the real story but still pushed for the answer to, "and who is the friend?" "A friend in England", was Gibbs' insipid answer.

Gibbs was very serious and earnest in his teachings. Bearing in mind the importance of his scientific research; he never ignored any trivial matters in school. He was always warm towards his students, helped them in all possible ways with his precious time and vigor. Compared with other colleagues, he was more compulsive to lead students going to the field of natural philosophy. His lectures were carefully prepared, as were his treatise, only that he put in more proper and concise examples. All those who attended his seminars, were deeply impressed.

Gibbs was both genial and kindly in his intercourse with his fellow-men. A pious Christian gentleman, his mind was so tranquil and calm that he was always immune to fidgety and agony. His noble and simple characteristics were comparable with his brilliant achievements in science.

Gibbs was highly gifted, his mind being so sharp and insightful, especially his feelings on the subject of physics science. In terms of the scope of his studies in natural philosophy, there are not many who are able to surpass Gibbs.

The peculiar style of his life and work made, both him and his publications, unknown for a long time. He worked hard for all of his life, but did not get much by way of material benefits. Nevertheless, it is just because of his low profile, his thought process became so profound and rigorous, that he made abundant time and vigor to solve, one after another, the many challenges in the sciences. He left us with an enormous spiritual fortune, adding incomparable values to the science. Because of this, Gibbs became one of the few of our greatest giants in science, and continues to be admired all around the world, today.

(End)